Amateur Radio Astronomy

2nd edition

John Fielding, ZS5JF

Radio Society of Great Britain

Published by the Radio Society of Great Britain, 3 Abbey Court, Priory Business Park, Bedford MK44 3WH UK

First edition published 2006
Reprinted 2006, 2008 & 2010

Second edition 2011
Reprinted 2013
Digitally Reprinted 2016 onwards

ISBN 9781-9050-8667-2

Publisher's note
The opinions expressed in this book are those of the author and not necessarily those of the RSGB. While the information presented is believed to be correct, the author, publisher and their agents cannot accept responsibility for consequences arising from any inaccuracies or omissions.

Production: Mark Allgar M1MPA
Cover design: Kim Meyern
Editing, typography and design: Mike Dennison, G3XDV, Emdee Publishing

Printed in Great Britain by 4Edge Ltd of Hockley, Essex

Any amendments to this book can be found at the supporting website:

http://rsgb.org/main/publications-archives/books-extra/

Any corrections and points of clarification that have not been incorporated in this printing of the book can be found here along with any supporting material that may have become available

Contents

Foreword

The writing of this book took approximately three years of my spare time. The research period stretches back 10 years or more and is still ongoing. I was persuaded to write such a book because there is not an equivalent one, dealing with radio astronomy from the radio amateur's perspective. There are others, but these focus on the amateur astronomer, those people who already have an interest in the observation of the galaxies via optical means.

Let me first of all dispel any idea that I am an astronomer. Nothing could be further from the truth, I have never claimed to be. I simply have a strong desire to understand the radio frequency engineering aspects of what make radio telescopes work and how to improve the engineering side. My professional career stretches back over 30 years in the radio frequency engineering design and development field. During that time I have been a radio amateur, first licensed in 1972, although I passed the UK Radio Amateurs Examination in 1969.

During my period of working for various companies, I have found that being a 'ham' has given me a better insight into some of the engineering tasks I have had to face. My approach has always been based on the KISS principle (Keep It Simple - Stupid), and that over-engineering does not make a poor design into a good one. Many of my former colleagues failed to grasp the necessity of making the fewest components do the maximum amount of work. I have worked on some very complex design and development problems, often with a limited timescale and budget, and have always managed to get through it to the satisfaction of my employers and customers.

The other pitfall into which some design engineers fall is using components that cost more than is necessary. In the defence industry, where I spent most of the 30 years, this is often unavoidable because of the specifications that have to be met, both electrically and environmentally. However, if you can substitute lower-cost components, with an equivalent specification, you can save a huge amount of money on high-volume production runs. Some of my former colleagues didn't have any idea of the cost of certain components; they simply drew components from the stores because they were there. I proved on several occasions that, by changing some components to industrial or automotive grade, a significant cost-saving could be achieved. I suppose part of this is due to my Scottish ancestry!

Being a radio amateur in this type of environment is a sort of busman's holiday, but I have achieved deep satisfaction from my constructional work and experimenting in my shack. Being not only electronically-minded but also somewhat skilled in the mechanical field is a double blessing. I can usually visualise in my head what the finished product will look like and how it will all fit together, even before I have started designing. I also have a fairly well-equipped workshop where I can make most of the mechanical components needed for my constructional projects.

Inevitably, as a book of this sort evolves, certain changes will occur in the structure or presentation as new developments occur or other facts come to light. One of the many problems is being able to quote the names of component manufacturers and part numbers. The last five to 10 years have seen a complete upheaval in the traditional electronics field. Many of the household names have gone, often swallowed up in a take-over by another conglomerate. For example, RCA, who made RF transistors and other semiconductors were bought out and the name changed to Harris. No sooner had this happened than another name change occurred to Intersil. This seems to be a common feature today, the names you relied on to supply data and samples for development are suddenly missing.

Another curse of the industry is the sudden discontinuation of a device. The microprocessor manufacturers seem to do this quite regularly, but it also applies to the RF semiconductor industry. On a number of occasions, I have had a product just about ready to start production when it is found that some key device is on a 'last-buy' schedule. My reason for mentioning this unhappy state of affairs is that, throughout the book, I have given examples of suitable part numbers and manufacturers names. If, after the book is published, some of these parts become obsolete, I have no control over that fact. I have endeavoured to quote, to the best of my knowledge, correct part numbers and current manufacturers' names as at the time of writing.

Usually, when a part goes out of production, the manufacturer will recommend a direct- or near-replacement. Unfortunately, the sort of components that amateur constructors use (devices with leads) are getting scarcer, as the general trend is towards surface-mount technology and many of the older devices are now only available as SMD types. Electrically they are the same, but much smaller and more difficult to use breadboard-style. For a one-off item for the shack, a breadboard type of construction is usually quite adequate; as long as the circuit performs the way it should, there is no need to spend money on printed circuit boards unless you intend to mass-produce the item. If you are like me, of 'mature years', you will sympathise with the constructor with poor eyesight, handling minute components under a magnifying glass!

Another factor driving the semiconductor industry is the mass-market. In days gone by, this was nearly always the defence industry. With the gradual downturn of this field, the semiconductor manufacturers have made many of the older devices obsolete because of economic factors. Today, the mass market is the cellular telephone industry. Hence, you will find a dearth of RF devices for the traditional 450MHz equipment, but a vast variety of 900MHz devices for GSM handsets. This is good and bad for the amateur constructor. Many of the 900MHz parts will work quite well at 432MHz and 1296MHz. With the GSM handset market expanding into the 1.8GHz and 2.4GHz regions, this is a blessing for amateurs active at these frequencies.

The presentation of information is not easy for the target market. Some amateurs might be practising engineers in a specialised field, others might be what most of the general public regard as 'hams' and work in a job with no contact with technology, but use amateur radio as a way to unwind from the day's stresses. Because of this, the danger is to give either too little or too much detail. Giving too little detail is worse than too much; the reader is left with more questions. I have tried to avoid this by the use of shaded panels. Often I can recount an amusing incident connected with the topic, or give some historical background to the way the technology evolved. A book does not need to be dull and heavy going; some humour lifts the reader after a deeply technical portion.

History is a powerful tool for the design engineer. Many times I have met newly-graduated junior engineers, excited about a new idea they have come up with. Upon listening to their idea you realise it isn't new at all - we did it that way 20 years ago! Without some historical background in a topic you can follow a dead-end path until you realise the idea will never work. I have been fortunate to have shared my working time with many older engineers, who not only taught me things I didn't know, but gave me some valuable insight into the history of a topic. Consequently, the first few chapters cover the historical course of radio astronomy from its beginning, and I add extra historical details when I believe it will aid the reader to understand the subject better.

There is an old saying 'there is nothing new under the sun'. This fact crops up time and again. In 1903, a German engineer by the name of Christian Hulsmeyer proposed the use of radio waves to detect the movement of ships; he built a crude version, took out a British patent and demonstrated it, no one was interested. In 1922 Marconi proposed the same idea again - no one listened. Only after the ionospheric sounders (built to try to understand how the ionospheric layers affect radio waves in 1925) showed a return echo, was the first radar 'invented'. Later in 1937, with the obvious threat of World War II looming, the British defence industry rushed to develop radar for military purposes. It was all available in 1903 but no one took any notice. There are many people who believe that Sir Robert Watson-Watt was the father of radar, this is simply untrue. Watson-Watt simply used known technology to design the early British 'Chain Home' system during the run up to World War II. He had been asked by the Tizard Committee to develop a 'death-ray' transmitter to burn up German aircraft. When he explained this was impossible with the available technology he countered the request by pointing out that with the available technology it would be better to use this for more elaborate direction-finding equipment. He had spent many years developing equipment to track thunder storms. So the birth of radar began quite late in the British scientific circles.

I cannot finish this foreword without giving acknowledgement to some people or organisations that have given me invaluable assistance in compiling this work I have relied on data from a great number of textbooks, magazine articles and other amateur publications to collect the necessary information. Wherever possible, I have tried to acknowledge the source. I should like to personally thank the following:

Chris Leah - for his assistance with the chapter on radar and the loan of several text books; Stuart MacPherson, ZR5SD, Director of Electronics, Durban University of Technology (DUT) - for reviewing the technical portions; Dr Gary Hoile - for his suggestions on the sections covering power amplifiers; David Joubert - for suggestions covering the signal processing aspects; Sir Bernard Lovell - for inspiring me to become interested in radio astronomy and for providing some historical data on the early Jodrell Bank equipment; the University of Manchester, Jodrell Bank and the Lovell Radio Telescope - for assistance with historical pictures. Derek Barton - for identifying the radar system used by Lovell; the UK Ministry of Defence for supplying technical details of the GL2 radar system from its archives; Lew Paterson of RAF Cranwell for further historical information on the early radar development and for correcting some factual items on the GL2 radar system; Dr Graham Elford of Adelaide University, Australia, for supplying details of modern meteor-detection radar and the meteor trail topic.

I would also like to express my sincere gratitude to the specialists at the University of Manchester, Jodrell Bank Radio Observatory, especially Tim Ikin and his team who afforded me numerous hours of their limited time to explain difficult details in layman's terms, and to Janet Eaton - Sir Bernard Lovell's secretary - who assisted with my search through the archived artefacts. During this search, some very rare photographs were uncovered that have not seen the light of day for over 50 years. Some of these are reproduced in Chapter 1. During my visits, I was also privileged to be shown the new development work being done on the very low-noise front-end units that use liquid helium cooling and operate on frequencies up to 44GHz. This radio telescope was launched 14 May 2009 to explore the L2 region in deep space, a project sponsored by the Max Planck Institute in Bonn, Germany and the European Space Agency (ESA). It operates between 30GHz and 857GHz.

For the latest revision I need to include several other people who have made a contribution to the updated book. Dr Michael Gaylard and Dr Justin Jonas of Hart RAO, South Africa, for information on the SKA system. Dr David Johnson and Anthon Luc Human of Durban University of Technology, Mechanical Engineering Faculty, for the detailed design of the mechanical portions of the new Indlebe Enkulu radio telescope. Dr Brian Austin, G0GSF (ex ZS6BKW) for the information about Sir Oliver Lodge. Jim Sky of Radio-Sky Publishing for providing the automated version of *Radio-Eyes* for telescope positioning. Mark Allgar and Mike Dennison for professional assistance in publishing this book, my first attempt at a written work.

Finally, but by no means least, my dear wife Penny, for encouraging me in the long period I took to write it all down.

I dedicate this book in memory of all those 'amateurs' who played a small but vital part in the science of Radio Astronomy.

John Fielding, ZS5JF
Monteseel
South Africa
2010

1

A Brief History of Radio Astronomy

In this chapter:

- [ ] Pioneers
- [ ] The war years
- [ ] German wartime radar
- [ ] The birth of the big telescope
- [ ] Lunar radar - moonbounce or EME
- [ ] Parkes radio telescope

T his is a fascinating period in the development of the science and, as will be seen, although some of the results confirmed earlier optical observations, many experiments gave conflicting answers and, in many cases, opened up further areas of investigation, some of which are still on-going. Many amateur radio operators figured in the early period and with their aptitude for problem-solving and constructing complex equipment, the science advanced rapidly.

PIONEERS

Sir Oliver Lodge

Sir Oliver Joseph Lodge was one of the great pioneers in radio communication history, but very few people today have even heard of him. Lodge's discoveries in radio and electricity were revolutionary. They turned what was inconceivable in Victorian times into part of everyday life. His ideas have since been incorporated into millions of pieces of equipment working all over the world. Yet Lodge was more than a brilliant scientist. He was a professor of physics at 30, at the time an unheard of achievement in Britain, and later the first principal of Birmingham University College, an author of many books, a lecturer who attracted huge audiences, and a much-appreciated broadcaster.

In 1877 he was awarded the Doctor of Science degree (D Sc now called Ph D) and employed as a lecturer for several years. Lodge became assistant professor of applied mathematics at University College, London in 1879 and was appointed to the chair of physics. In 1881 he was appointed Professor of Physics at the newly formed Liverpool University College, setting a precedent, as he was just

Note: Several of the dimensions quoted in this book are in imperial measurements, as originally presented in the various publications

30 years old. He wrote his first book, *Elementary Mechanics*, at 26. Many years later, Lodge wrote in his autobiography: "At an early age I decided that my main business was with the imponderables, the things that work secretly and have to be apprehended mentally." He spent 19 years as professor of experimental physics at the new Liverpool University College before his academic career reached its peak in 1900 when he was appointed the first principal of Birmingham University College.

Whilst at Liverpool, apart from his academic duties, he was busy experimenting with the transmission of radio waves along wire conductors. This was demonstrated in 1888. His great friend and scientific rival Heindrich Hertz in Germany worked on the transmission of radio waves through the ether. Lodge developed a new detector for radio waves, which he called a 'coherer'. This was based on the earlier experiments made by Edöard Branley in France. Lodge's version improved the detector, which consisted of finely ground metallic particles in a glass tube with electrodes, by the addition of a mechanical trembler that shook the particles after each reception of radio waves to stop them from sticking together (cohering). The new coherer exhibited a varying resistance when acted on by radio waves. This detector when used with a voltaic cell and a mirror galvanometer caused a spot of light to be moved on a projection screen. Lodge took out a world wide patent for his version of the coherer.

In 1894 at a meeting of the British Association for the Advancement of Science in Oxford, Lodge demonstrated in front of a packed lecture room the reception of Hertzian waves. This used the new coherer connected to an inker (as used for Morse telegraphy using wires) that produced marks on a piece of paper. This was the first recorded reception of wireless telegraphy anywhere in the world. This was almost exactly one year before Marconi performed the same demonstration in Italy. As well as the coherer, Lodge obtained patents in 1897 for the use of inductors and capacitors to adjust the frequency of wireless transmitters and receivers.

Fig 1.1: Renowned physicist and RSGB Past President, Sir Oliver Lodge

When Marconi arrived in England in February 1896 and demonstrated his wireless apparatus, Lodge saw that it infringed on his patents and he sued Marconi. The result of this protracted legal battle was that Lodge eventually won the patent case and Marconi was liable for large damage payments. In order to appease Lodge the young Italian appointed Lodge as the official scientific advisor to the now prosperous Marconi Company. Marconi applied for and was granted a patent for wireless telegraphy on 2 June 1896 not being aware of Lodge's prior application for this new mode of communication.

It was to take until 1942 for Marconi's patent to be declared null and void by a court in the USA, after both he and Lodge were dead.

Lodge also experimented with what today we know as radio astronomy, although the science was only recognised later. In Liverpool he set up an experiment to receive signals from the Sun. His contemporaries believed he was quite mad to consider such a possibility. He devised an ingenious method where his coherer was mounted behind a blackboard to exclude the light rays but allowing the longer radio waves to pass through. (Lodge had noted that the coherer was susceptible to strong sunlight falling on it and this predates the invention of photo-electric cells by almost 50 years. Lodge did not pursue this line of research and others some time later discovered the same effect). Lodge was later to write of his experiment:

"I did not succeed in this, for a sensitive coherer in an outside shed unprotected by the thick walls of a substantial building cannot be quiet for long. I found the spot of light liable to frequent weak and occasionally violent excursions, and I could not trace any of these to the influence of the Sun. There were evidently too many terrestrial sources of disturbance in a city like Liverpool to make the experiment feasible" (The spot of light refers to Lodge's mirror galvanometer).

He was only proven to be correct in 1942. Lodge had correctly calculated from Maxwell's equations that the Sun must be a strong source of electromagnetic radiation. Unfortunately his coherer and mirror galvanometer were not sensitive enough to detect the radio waves from the Sun and Liverpool city centre was a very noisy electrical environment, causing erratic measurements, so his experiment was deemed to be a failure.

One of the early beliefs amongst scientists working on Hertzian waves was the mysterious 'ether' that was assumed to be responsible for the transmissions. Lodge although at the time a believer in this unseen matter devised an experiment to prove its existence. His experiment however proved it was a figment of the imagination, and led to the dropping of this concept. Hertz in Germany later confirmed Lodge's findings about the ether.

Lodge also studied the electromagnetic waves caused by lightning discharges and how the waves propagate over long distances. He postulated that there was some invisible layer high above the Earth that allowed these "crashes" to be reflected and heard over a wide area. This was proven several years later by others and given the name 'ionosphere' by Robert (Watson) Watt. It is largely due to Lodge's research that Marconi had the idea that radio waves could travel across large distances, culminating in his transatlantic radio experiments.

Note: Prior to February 1942 when the knighthood was bestowed on him, Watson-Watt was named Robert Alexander Watt. Upon becoming Sir Robert he added the hyphenated Watson-Watt.

Guglielmo Marconi

Although Marconi is not considered by many people to have made any significant input to astronomical science, this is not so. Due to his pioneering work in demonstrating that trans-Atlantic radio communications was possible, the scientific world at the time then had to explain how it was possible.

Up until 1901, when Marconi and his colleagues succeeded in sending radio signals across the Atlantic from Poldhu in Cornwall to Newfoundland, the belief was that radio waves, like light waves, only travelled in straight lines. After his

Fig 1.2: Guglielmo Marconi

success, the scientific world was left with the problem of how this had occurred, and fairly soon it became apparent that the radio waves were being bent or refracted by the upper atmosphere. This refraction was deduced to be due to the effect of the Sun's ultra-violet radiation releasing free electrons in the rarefied upper atmosphere, the ionosphere, to behave like a radio 'mirror', allowing radio waves to be returned to earth at great distances from the source.

From the 1920s to the present day, the science of the refracting mechanism in the ionosphere has been studied using ionospheric sounding apparatus, both from the surface of the earth and from sounding balloons and rockets. The early result from these studies was that radio waves were unable to penetrate the ionosphere and hence were prevented from passing into space. This theory was turned on its head a few years later!

Marconi developed a practical microwave link to join the Italian telephone network to the summer residence of the Pope and, in 1922, proposed the use of radio waves to detect objects, many believe this to be the first attempt at radar. Although Marconi did not find much favour for his idea, this was taken up by others and pursued to its conclusion. In an address to the American Institute of Radio Engineers (IRE) in 1922 Marconi stated:

"As was first shown by Hertz, electric waves can be completely reflected by conducting bodies. In some of my tests, I have noticed the effects of reflection and detection of these waves by metallic objects miles away.

"It seems to me that it should be possible to design apparatus by means of which a ship could radiate or project a divergent beam of these rays in any desired direction; which rays, if coming across a metallic object, such as another steamer or ship, would be reflected back to a receiver screened from the local transmitter on the sending ship, and thereby, immediately reveal the presence and bearing of the other ship in fog or thick weather."

Marconi had obviously not heard of Christian Hulsmeyer or his patent of 1903 where he not only proposed the idea but also built a working system and demonstrated it.

In the light of Marconi's address, two scientists at the American Naval Research Laboratory (NRL) determined that Marconi's concept was possible and, later that same year (1922), detected a wooden ship at a range of five miles using a wavelength of 5m using a separate transmitter and receiver with a CW wave. In 1925, the first use of pulsed radio waves was used to measure the height of the ionospheric layers, radar had been born. (RADAR is the acronym for Radio Detection and Ranging.)

Karl G Jansky - USA

Between 1930 and 1932, Karl Jansky, an engineer working for the Bell Telephone Corporation Laboratory, (BTL) in Belmar, New Jersey was investigating the problem of interference to long-distance HF ship-to-shore radio links. This took the form of bursts of noise or a hissing sound and was seemingly of a random nature.

In order to study this interference, Jansky constructed a large multi-loop Bruce antenna array supported on a framework of wood and mounted this on old Ford Model T wheels to allow it to be rotated and pointed in various directions. This became known as Jansky's 'merry-go-round'. It was set up in a potato field in New Jersey. The antenna and receiver worked on a frequency of 20.5MHz (14.6m).

Jansky discovered that the noise emanated from two different sources, lightning-induced noise (at any one time there are an estimated 1,800 different lightning storms in existence), and also a noise that appeared when the antenna was pointed in a particular direction at the same time every day, but Jansky could not immediately correlate this to any known source. Further careful observations showed the rather startling fact that the time between successive peaks was not 24 hours but was 23 hours and 57 minutes, which is the time taken for the earth to complete one revolution, the sidereal day. (In actual fact, a sidereal day is 23hr 56m 4s).

Jansky correctly deduced in 1932 that the source must be extra-terrestrial and suggested a source in the Milky Way, Sagittarius, which meant that the source was about 25,000 light years distant. In view of the impossibility of curing the interference, Jansky was removed from the project; the one credit to him was

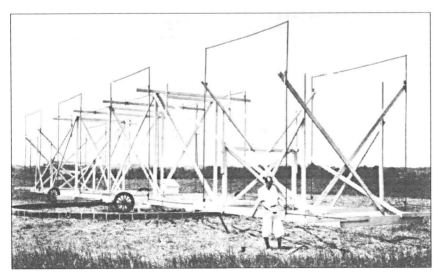

Fig 1.3: Karl Jansky and his 'Merry-Go-Round' antenna

the naming of the radio flux unit, the jansky (Jy). His paper was published in 1933 [1]. Jansky's work brought to the attention of scientists that a 'radio-window' existed in the earth's ionosphere, similar to the window through which light from distant stars was also able to reach the earth's surface. This was an extremely important discovery, and from this the science of radio astronomy advanced rapidly in later years.

Karl Jansky was the son of a brilliant scientist and he, in turn, became like his father. After his work on the ionospheric disturbances was concluded, Jansky was retained by Bell Telephone Laboratories (BTL) as an expert on interference matters and provided valuable assistance during the war years to the American Armed forces, receiving an Army-Navy citation for his work in direction finding to detect enemy transmitters. Jansky tried to persuade BTL to build a 100ft radio telescope to study the sky noises further; this was rejected, the reason given being that this was felt to be domain of academic bodies and not a commercial enterprise. He died at the relatively early age of 44 in 1950. He had been a sickly person all his life and had been rejected by the Army due to his health.

Grote Reber - USA

Reber, who was a radio engineer in a factory by day and a radio amateur, W9GFZ, in his spare time, read the paper that Jansky had published about his findings. Jansky's paper surprisingly did not attract much interest from the astronomical fraternity but, as it was first published in a journal for electrical and radio engineers (IRE) this is probably the reason, as astronomers did not know of its existence for several years. Reber had become an amateur at the early age of 15 and had built his transmitter and receiver and earned the Worked All Continents Award (WAC) on radiotelegraphy in a short space of time. He was looking for something equally challenging and, having read Jansky's paper, felt this was the next project for him. Reber is quoted as saying "In my estimation, it was obvious Jansky had made

a fundamental and very important discovery. Furthermore, he had exploited it to the limit of his equipment's facilities. If greater progress were to be made, it would be necessary to construct new and different equipment, especially designed to measure the cosmic static."

Reber was immediately spurred into action. He decided that a parabolic reflector antenna was the best approach, and drew up the design of a suitable piece of equipment. However, when he obtained quotes from contractors to build the dish antenna, it came to more than he earned in a year, hence he set to and built the large parabolic antenna

Fig 1.4: Grote Reber's parabolic antenna in his back yard at Wheaton, Illinois, USA

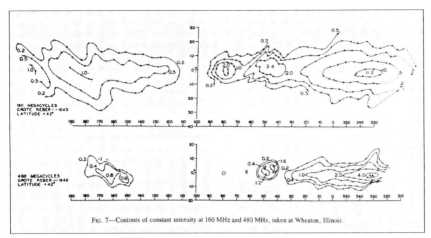

Fig 1.5: Sky Noise plots made by Reber in 1943 at 160 and 440MHz

FIG. 7—Contours of constant intensity at 160 MHz and 480 MHz, taken at Wheaton, Illinois.

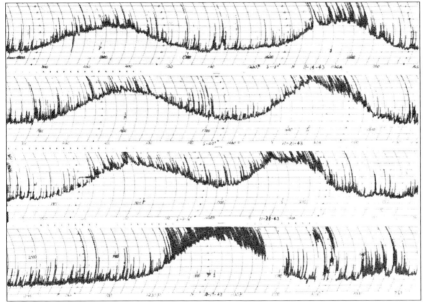

Fig 1.6: Reber's original chart recorder plots of sky noise. The 'spikes' on the traces were caused by automobile igni-tion interference

31.5ft in diameter (~10m) in his back yard at Wheaton, near Chicago, Illinois, by himself. The reflecting surface was made from 45 pieces of 26-gauge gal-vanised sheet iron screwed onto 72 radial wooden rafters cut to a parabolic shape. Reber single-handedly made all the timber and sheet iron pieces and, apart from some labour to excavate and cast the concrete foundation, built the entire structure in the space of four months, completing it in September 1937. The total construction cost was $1300, which was about three times the cost of a new car at that time.

Reber wrote that upon completion: "The mirror emitted snapping, popping and banging sounds every morning and evening due to unequal expansion in the reflector skin. When parked in the vertical position, great volumes of water poured through the central hole during a rainstorm. This caused rumours amongst the neighbours that the machine was for collecting water and for con-trolling the weather."

Fig 1.7: Grote Reber standing next to his preserved antenna shortly before his death. In this picture, the dish has been adapted to be rotatable on a turntable mount, so making it a true Az-El mount

Reber made extensive observations on a wavelength of 9cm (~3.3GHz) and later 33cm (~900MHz) without any success. Finally, after changing to a frequency of 160MHz, Reber detected strong noise sources.

The data collected showed several sources of extra-terrestrial noise and confirmed the findings of Jansky of the Sagittarius source. A crude map of noise sources in the sky was painstakingly built up over a long period, the first of many that were to be made in later years. Reber published his findings in 1938, the first paper on the subject to appear in an astronomical journal [2]. Reber, unlike Jansky, had the foresight to publish his findings in an astronomical journal; if he had not done so, it may well have been many years before its significance was noted.

Fig 1.8: Grote Reber with his radio telescope receiver

Reber had earlier attempted (unsuccessfully) to obtain radar echoes from the Moon using the amateur 144MHz band. It was to take nearly 10 years before a successful moon echo was achieved by professionals and nearly 15 years before an amateur group succeeded in 1953.

The American National Radio Astronomy Observatory (NRAO) Research Centre at West Virginia, employed Reber from 1950 as a consultant. Reber's antenna is preserved and is still occasionally operational, residing near the entrance to the NRAO at Green Bank, West Virginia, USA. Although Reber failed to detect radio noise at 9 and 33cm, it is now known that it does exist, and he failed because his equipment was not sensitive enough. His dish is unusual as it can only be moved in one axis, a so-called 'meridian-mount', often used for optical telescopes. Today large parabolic (dish) antennas normally have two-axis rotation, in azimuth and elevation, the AZ-El mount. To observe a particular point in the sky, the dish was altered to the required elevation angle and then Reber had to wait until the portion of sky fell into the antenna beam by the earth's rotation.

Reber must have been extremely dedicated. As well as working at a radio factory during the day he would arrive home from work in the evening, eat his evening meal and then sleep for a few hours, observe from about midnight until 6am, eat breakfast and then drive 30 miles to his work place in Chicago. He had to do this because he found that in the early evening the man made noise was too high and it only abated after about 10pm. He continued this for several years building up detailed sky noise maps piece by piece.

In later years, Reber emigrated from the USA having donated his original dish and equipment to the NRAO and he spent the rest of his life in Tasmania building and operating radio telescopes for the Australian CSIRO (Council for Scientific and Industrial Research Organisation).

Grote Reber died in Tasmania on 20 December 2002, two days before his 91st birthday. The callsign W9GFZ is now used by the amateur radio club station at the National Radio Astronomy Observatory at Socorro, New Mexico.

THE WAR YEARS

During the wartime period of 1939 to 1945, very little work was published on radio astronomy, mainly because the majority of the scientists who studied this were working on top-secret defence projects. The one exception was in occupied Holland where a clandestine group based in Leiden in 1943 managed to perform some useful work. Later it transpired that several events, which at the time were presumed to be due to electrical interference or enemy counter-measures (jamming), turned out to have great astronomical significance.

One such event took place on 27 February 1942 and, at the time, it was suspected that the interference was another type of German jamming. (By a remarkable coincidence this occurred on the day after the successful raid by British paratroopers on the German radar installation at Bruneval, France, where a Würzburg radar was dismantled and brought back to England.) The Germans from 1941 had been making more and more attempts to knock out the allied radar by high-power jammers. The escape of the German warships *Scharnhorst* and *Gneisenau* on 12 February 1942 from the French port of Brest was made possible by heavy enemy jamming from the French coast and this caused a drastic reappraisal of the allied radar systems. Because of this a large number of 'J-Watch' radar systems (Jerry Watch - Jerry or Gerry being the nickname the allies gave to the Germans) were set up on cliffs overlooking the British coastline to probe for German activity and jamming. These radars all operated within the 4m to 8m spectrum (35 to 75MHz).

Investigation later confirmed the source of the jamming was the Sun generating large bursts of noise due to solar flares and sunspots. James Stanley Hey, a civilian scientist attached to the British Army Operational Radar Group (AORG), was given the task of finding out what was causing the radars to be blinded by the high noise levels. After studying the various reports of the interference, Hey noted that in all the reports the radar systems pointed at an azimuth and elevation that was towards or very near to the Sun. Upon checking with the Royal Observatory at Greenwich, it was confirmed that a major solar sunspot was occurring and this, Hey deduced, accounted for the large interfering signals. This was an unknown effect at the time and, although it allayed fears, it was of grave concern as it showed a severe weakness in the low-frequency VHF radars used by the British. Several eminent British scientists were consulted on the matter and they discounted the Sun as a possible source, feeling that it was unlikely to be the cause. This information was kept as a closely guarded secret amongst a very small number of people and only after the war ended was Hey able to publish details in a scientific paper. The 'jamming' was usually worst at dawn as the majority of the British coastal J-Watch radar systems spent most of their time pointed at the European landmass, which is to the east, where the Sun rises. German bombing attacks at that time usually occurred at sunrise, as the technique of night bombing by the Germans had been largely unsuccessful because their radio navigation beam systems had been knocked out by allied countermeasures or bombing.

A separate study made in America at the same time at Bell Telephone Labs by Southworth reached the same conclusion as Hey and confirmed the Sun as the noise source. This, like Jansky's earlier discovery, made the scientific world reassess the solar flare and sun spot situation. Due to the security restrictions of wartime, neither of these reports was published until after the war in 1946.

In 1938, a radio amateur, D W Heightman (G6DH), had almost put his finger on the solar noise problem, but was ridiculed by the scientific experts. He wrote "At such times (when fade-outs occur) the writer has often observed the reception of a peculiar radiation, mostly on frequencies over 20Mc/s (20MHz) which, on the receiver, takes the form of a smooth though loud hissing sound. This is presumably caused by the arrival of charged particles from the Sun on the aerial". Two Japanese scientists in 1939 came within a hairsbreadth of the same conclusion, but attributed the noise to some disturbance in the ionosphere.

Another case of suspected enemy jamming involved the detection of sporadic meteor echoes that at first were thought to be the result of radar echoes from German V-2 missiles (Vergeltungswaffen zwei - vengeance weapon 2), known by the Germans as the A4. Many false alarms occurred with the radar used to detect the V-2 missiles but it was later confirmed by allied secret agents that no rockets had been launched at the times in question.

The radar used for the detection of the V-1 was a modified anti-aircraft gun-laying radar operating on 55 to 75MHz. The original radar sets used dipole arrays but Hey and his team modified these to gain extra range for the V-1

Fig 1.9: The German V-1 'Flying Bomb'

threat, and they used four-element Yagi antennas pointed close to the horizon. When the V-2 threat appeared the same system was quickly adapted by Hey by the simple matter of tilting the Yagi beam upward to an elevation of 60 degrees.

Fig 1.10: The German V-2 missile

The German Army developed the V-2 whereas the V-1 was developed by the German Air Force, the rivalry and secrecy between the two armed forces being quite intense. The V-1 missile was a cheap weapon to make, estimates at the time indicated the cost was around £100 whereas the V-2 was estimated to cost £10,000. Each carried a warhead of approximately one ton. The V-1 threat was known about by the British military intelligence by the interception of coded German signals some six

V-1 was the German pilotless plane, known as the 'flying-bomb', 'buzz-bomb' or 'doodle-bug', weighing 2,500kg and carrying one ton of high explosive. The bombardment of London and the south-east of England began in June 1944 and ended with the capture of the last of the launching sites by the Allies in March 1945. In total, 9,521 were launched at London of which 4,621 were shot down either by radar-controlled anti-aircraft fire or by fighter aircraft capable of catching them. By August 1944, only 20% of V-1s launched were finding their target, largely due to the radar detection. The V-1 flew at 500km/h at an altitude of between 500 and 2000m. In total, some 30,000 were manufactured using Polish slave labour, the bulk of which were destroyed by allied bombing raids.

V-2 was a 12.8-ton ballistic missile carrying 0.85 ton of high explosive over a range of 180 to 210 miles, and could attain an altitude of 60 miles. The attacks on London began on 9 September 1944, soon after the allied D-Day landings, and ended with the capture of the last of the launching sites on 27 March 1945.

In total 1,115 V-2 missiles fell on London and southern England, killing 2,754 people and injuring another 6,523. Casualties from the V-1 missiles caused over 6,000 deaths and 18,000 injuries. The V-2 missile fell from a great height and attained a velocity of 3,500mph (5,700km/h) five times the speed of sound before impact. Fast fighters could sometimes intercept the V-1 missiles as they flew at sub-sonic speeds at low altitude; there was no effective way to intercept the V-2. The only thing that could be done was to sound the air-raid warning when a missile was detected by the radar, so giving a few minutes for people to scurry to air-raid shelters.

The V-2 missile was, in reality, a relatively ineffectual weapon. Although the British general public regarded it with horror, the hard fact is that only some 900 tons of high explosives where successfully delivered to the target over a period of about four months. The large target spread of missiles over London and south-east parts of Britain showed the inefficiency of the inertial guidance system. The American and British Air Forces at the time were delivering with pin-point accuracy to within a 0.5km an average of 5,000 tons of high explosives on each raid into the industrial centres of Germany. These raids occurred up to four nights a week at the peak. The mass bombing raid on the city of Cologne dropped nearly 8,000 tons in one raid.

The Belgian population felt the effect much more than the British - of the approximately 2,900 V-2 missiles launched, about 1,100 were aimed at London and the surrounding areas, and about 1,600 at Antwerp; about 200 failed on launch and were destroyed by the onboard remote controlled explosive charges.

months before any were launched. Four hundred launching sites were planned along the French and Belgian coastlines, many of these being destroyed by allied bombing before they could be put into service. Other causes of delays in bringing the V-1 into active service were due to accurate bombing of the assembly and supply sites by the American and British Air Forces, problems with the navigation system and production facilities problems. In fact, the V-2 was intended to be in service long before the V-1, but considerable technical difficulties caused the long delay and the bombing of launching and production sites by the allied air forces delayed matters still further. When the allied forces made the D-Day landings in France in August 1944, Hitler was forced to order the V-2 into service, although it was still a long way from being perfected. The V-1, although a crude mass-produced weapon, was amazingly effective and caused many more deaths and injuries than the more elaborate V-2 missile.

Wernher von Braun, the German scientist leading the V-2 development team is said to have commented upon the first successful launch of a V-2 when it landed

It is recorded that the Germans were puzzled by the large masts being erected along the south and east coasts of England for the Chain Home system prior to the outbreak of the war. Because this operated at a low frequency of about 30MHz, exploratory flights by Lufthansa civil aircraft and Zeppelin dirigibles failed to detect radar signals because the Germans expected them to be in the VHF or UHF spectrum.

On the first probing flight by a Zeppelin, the Chain Home transmitters were, in fact, not operational due to a fault; on a later flight of the LZ130, the Graf Zeppelin, in August 1939, the Germans detected a peculiar buzzing noise on VHF, but could not find the carrier frequency. What they heard were the signals and the harmonics of the Chain Home HF transmitters, which did not use harmonic filtering, so the levels of the harmonics were quite high. As the German aircraft did not carry HF receivers, they assumed this was due to some fault with their VHF receivers or that it was caused by arcing of the electricity high-voltage overhead lines.

The Chain Home stations' transmitters were locked to the public mains supply of 50Hz and produced either 12.5, 25 or 50 pulses per second. The Germans only tumbled to the fact that the Chain Home stations operated at such low frequencies much later during the war.

Fig 1.11: Official RAF photograph of the LZ130 Graf Zeppelin dirigible intercepted over Aberdeen on 3 August 1939 (just prior to the outbreak of war), while on an ELINT flight to probe the Chain Home installations. (ELINT = Electronic Intelligence). (Photograph courtesy of Lew Paterson, RAF Cranwell)

near London, [3] "The rocket worked perfectly, except it landed on the wrong planet!" Von Braun had his eyes set on inter-continental and outer space rockets, something he would later achieve working with the Americans after the war.

Pre-war work on HF ionospheric sounding had often shown false returns similar to the V-2 false alarms that were presumed to be due to meteor trail echoes.

GERMAN WARTIME RADAR

As it turned out, German radar was often not far behind allied radar in design or development; in some cases they had solutions before the allies. In general, the German radar systems were considerably more sophisticated than the allied attempts and operated on higher frequencies. As Germany had more time leading up to the outbreak of war, it had managed to combine military and expert engineering design to achieve an end, a lead the British and Americans had to overcome at the outbreak of war. This is why the allied radar systems were poor relations until much later in the war. With the combined energies of the American scientists, at that time not actively engaged in the fighting, the allies had the opportunity to assess the German hardware and were quick to find its shortcomings and design effective countermeasures and more effective equipment.

Added to this, the continuous stream of German ciphered

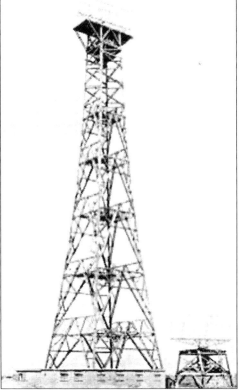

Fig 1.12: Chain Home Type 2. The smaller antenna is the Chain-Home-Low backup system for covering the elevations that the normal system was unable to adequately cover. (Chain-Home-Low was developed from the Navy Coastal Defence radar and operated on 180 to 210MHz and used a 32-dipole array). The receiving masts were constructed entirely from wood and were 240ft tall (75m). The transmitter masts were constructed of steel and were 360ft tall (110m). The picture shows the receiver tower. (Photograph courtesy of Lew Paterson, RAF Cranwell)

Fig 1.13: Typical Chain Home performance diagram

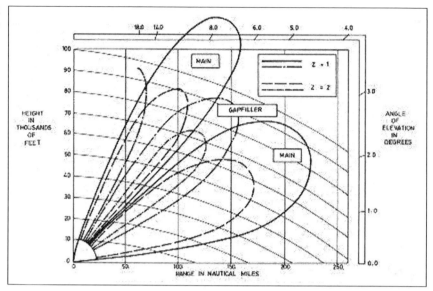

messages being decoded by the British intelligence services pinpointed the main German radar installations and the navigational beam systems used by the German air force to direct the bombers to their targets. With the expertise of the boffins, these beams were quickly rendered ineffective and the Luftwaffe lost a valuable tool to direct its stream of bombers. This was a marked turning point in the war, and explains why German bombing became almost futile and so costly in terms of machinery and manpower. Towards the end of the war, less than 20% of German aircraft were able to get to within 50 miles of the targets, such was the effectiveness of the allied radar and radar controlled guns.

Fig 1.14: Würzburg type 1. A 2m diameter parabolic antenna radar system

In fact, details are given [3] that not a single German reconnaissance aircraft was able to penetrate the London air defences between 1941 and 1944 to take photographs of bombing damage. Hence, the allies were able to give false information through captured enemy spies, making the Germans believe the bombs were falling short and they were unaware as to the true landing points of the V-1 and V-2 missiles.

Early radar systems used by the Germans were similar to the British and the 'Freya' operated on about 200MHz with a dipole array. The Freyas were situated close to the coast to detect incoming hostile aircraft and they passed the rough bearing and altitude information to the Würzburg systems. The Freya had a greater range than the Würzburg, but limited height-finding capabilities. They were also easy to detect from England and hence they were jammed successfully.

Originally, the Würzburg radar was a small parabolic dish antenna; early reconnaissance photographs showed it looked like an electric 'bowl' fire, and it was fairly low power. The later Würzburg was more sophisticated and larger antennas were employed. This second system was known as the Würzburg-Riese radar. (Würzburg is a town in Germany and 'riese' in the German language means 'giant'.) Developed by Telefunken, and operating on a frequency of about 560MHz, it could be used either as an anti-aircraft radar or coastal radar to detect shipping. The para-bolic antenna was large and the radar equipment was also more advanced com-pared with the allied ones. In total, 4,000 systems were deployed by the end of the war. The Würzburg radar used an az-el mount to point the dish at the target. Later versions used a spinning-cone antenna feed to gain more accurate elevation information.

Fig 1.15: Sketch of a Freya antenna compiled from reconnaissance photographs

Although a very advanced design, it suf-fered from several failings. The antenna beam was so narrow that two radar sys-tems needed to be employed at each site, one to track the intruder and the second to track the defend-ing fighter. The infor-mation from the Würzburg was also fed to a battery of searchlights and anti-aircraft guns. The Würzburg dishes were set up in a long line, every 50km extending from the coastline towards the heartland of Germany so the attacking bombers had to run the gauntlet of successive chains of radar.

Fig 1.16: Würzburg type 1 antenna photographed by Captain Tony Hills on an RAF recon-naissance flight at Bruneval, France in January 1942. Hills was killed soon afterwards on a similar reconnais-sance mission

Fig 1.17: German Würzburg-Riese radar. The antenna is 7.5m diameter and the f/D ratio is 0.228. The radar operated on 53cm (560MHz) and developed a peak power of approximately 8kW. The dish could be tilted down to the horizon, so making the radar dual purpose - anti-aircraft and coastal surveillance

Although the equipment was advanced the employment was far from clever. The German Air Force, which controlled the lines of defence, expected that, with the advanced equipment, the staff to operate them could be semi-skilled. This was a serious mistake. In a raid on Bruneval in February 1942, British paratroops captured the vital parts of one system and the German radar technician. This showed that, although the equipment was far in advance of the British types, it was very easy to jam as no thought had been given to this aspect by the designers. It also showed that the limited knowledge of the radar technician was insufficient to diagnose and repair faults quickly. Consequently, although there were 4,000 systems deployed towards the end of hostilities, about 50% were permanently out of service due to various faults and a lack of spare parts.

Ironically the German radar dishes, used for the Würzburg centimetric system, were quickly collected by radio astronomers after the war and put to good use both in Europe, America and Britain. At least one is still in use today at the Mullard Observatory in Cambridge, UK and one in Germany, which had originally been captured by allied forces and given to a group of Dutch astronomers in Leiden after the war, where the discovery of the Hydrogen Line emissions at 21cm were made. It is now refurbished and working as an astronomy receiver on 1680MHz, and is on exhibition at the Deutsches Museum in Munich.

Dr Bernard Lovell - Manchester University & Jodrell Bank Observatory

Bernard Lovell, a scientist from Manchester University, was extensively involved in the development of allied wartime radar at TRE Malvern [4] along with many other prominent allied scientists. Lovell was initially involved with the early airborne aircraft radar systems for detecting German night fighters (Aircraft Intercept - AI) and later in charge of the team at TRE who developed the H2S airborne radar for accurate high-altitude bombing. After the return to peacetime work at Manchester University in the autumn of 1945, Lovell, through his wartime contact with J S Hey, was able to borrow a considerable amount of wartime radar equipment in an attempt to study the effect of cosmic radiation on the ionosphere.

This work was at the instigation of Dr P M S Blackett, the head of the Physics Department at Manchester University, who had been a member of Tizard's team involved with the defence of England during the war. Blackett served on the Tizard Committee from the period prior to the war breaking out until its conclusion. It was Blackett who recruited Lovell from his own Department and sent him, just before the outbreak of war, to the first Chain Home station at Bawdsey Manor to familiarise himself with the workings of the radar. From there, Lovell was quickly recruited to the team at TRE to work on radar.

Attempts to make observations from the Manchester University campus in the city centre were fruitless, due to interference from the electric tram DC catenary overhead-wire system. Fortunately, the University of Manchester had a 10-acre botanical research farm in rural Cheshire used as part of the war effort to produce food in greater quantities. This was situated some 25 miles south of Manchester, presided over by the professor of botany, Dr Frederick Sansome, who happened to be a radio amateur. This site was free from electrical power lines and neighbouring industrial properties and ideally situated in a natural depression that screened it from the electrical noise of Manchester.

This site was known as Jodrell Bank, after William Jauderall, an archer for the Black Prince at Poitiers, and the original landowner in the 1300s, Jauderell later becoming spelt as Jodrell. (In nearby Stoke-on-Trent, the centre of the pottery industry, the steep road leading into Stoke-on-Trent that passed Josiah Wedgewood's original factory is similarly known as the 'Pot-Bank'.)

Jodrell Bank is a small farming community situated about 3km from the site of the radio telescope, but it was the nearest place of any significance, and so the research farm used the same name.

Permission was given to Lovell by the university authorities to use the site temporarily for a period of two weeks for his experiment. The army anti-aircraft radar trailers were towed to the site at Jodrell Bank, with Hey providing the necessary army vehicles and army technicians, where they became bogged down in the thick mud. Nevertheless, the equipment was soon producing amazing results. This was the start of what is probably the most famous radio telescope site in the world. The first recorded operation took place on 14 December 1945. Lovell soon outstayed his two weeks and over 60 years later a radio observatory still functions at the site.

Lovell's initial work, under Blackett's supervision, was to try to establish the effect of cosmic rays on the ionosphere by radar observations, something which he never managed to achieve although discoveries of much greater significance were soon to follow. Hey had earlier deduced that this was unlikely, because the echo from a cosmic particle was likely to be much shorter than the transmitted pulse of the radar. Although cosmic particles have subsequently been observed by radar methods, the frequency required is much higher than that of the VHF system

Fig 1.18: Army anti-aircraft radar system set up at Jodrell Bank in December 1945. The picture shows the receiver Yagi antenna mounted on the receiver trailer. This version is a 'Hey-modified' V-2 detection system (because the antenna points up at an angle). The huts adjacent were the only buildings at Jodrell at the time (they still exist) and housed the agricultural workers' tools and simple living quarters. This picture shows the radar upon arrival at Jodrell Bank on 12 Dec 1945 with one of the army technicians. (Photograph by courtesy of University of Manchester Archives)

Lovell was using. This was an error in calculation that Lovell made and Blackett failed to spot. Hey correctly guessed that Lovell would soon lose interest in the cosmic particle research and instead turn to the simpler meteor trail effects.

This early work used a wavelength of 4.2m (72.4MHz) and the low-gain four-element Yagi antennas fitted on the anti-aircraft radar system. Hey had modified the radar to use a longer time between transmitted pulses and an improved receiver front end that had been designed too late for the V-2 system. This was to achieve greater range and sensitivity than the original radar. Hey also fitted a new type of display allowing the range display to be spread out for finer measurement of the longer range. As soon as the equipment was fully operational in the spring of 1946, many echoes from the sky were observed which were of short duration, but not the results that Blackett and Lovell expected. Puzzled by this, Lovell finally concluded from the range measurements of ~100km that these were due to sporadic meteor showers and so an extensive period was spent observing these.

At the same time, Hey and his team at AORG were also studying the same meteor effects in parallel using another army radar system identical to the one Lovell was using, but operating at 64MHz. Later in 1947, when Hey and his team were called to undertake more urgent work of national importance, Hey gave his radar to Lovell.

Lovell, by his own admission, knew nothing about meteors or astronomy for that matter and, after searching through various scientific journals, found that virtually nothing had been published by the astronomical fraternity, it seemingly being a subject which was considered to be beneath them and of little importance.

Blackett suggested that Lovell approach a new member of the university staff who was involved in meteorology, Nicolai Herlofson. Blackett was apparently unaware that the study of weather was the not same as that of meteors!

Herlofson had an interesting time during the war when the Germans occupied his native Norway. Herlofson was a member of the Norwegian resistance movement passing information to the allies and was almost captured by the invading military. As the German soldiers knocked down the door of the mountain hut in which he was hiding, he escaped via the back door and found his way via neutral Sweden to England, where he worked with the intelligence services controlling the Norwegian resistance movement. After the war ended, he turned his attention to the study of the weather, joining the University of Manchester to continue his research.

Herlofson was unable to offer much assistance, but suggested that Lovell would be better off contacting the amateur astronomers who studied meteors. Lovell enlisted the help of an amateur astronomer who led a group that studied meteors. Herlofson later became deeply involved in the theory of how the meteor trails were formed and performed some vital calculations showing how the velocity of the meteor particle and the composition of the rarefied upper atmosphere influenced the reflection coefficient.

J P M (Manning) Prentice, a lawyer from Stowmarket, Suffolk, was the leader of a dedicated small group of British amateur astronomers who painstakingly kept records from visual observation of the known meteor showers. During an extensive shower in August 1946 (the Perseids) Prentice and Lovell at Jodrell Bank observed, both visually and using the radar, many hundreds of meteors. The correlation between the two methods of observation was outstanding. Later in November 1946 (the Giacobini shower) thousands of strong echoes per hour were observed using the radar, at the peak 168 per minute were observed. The sensitivity of the radar was such that on weak meteor trails, scarcely visible to the naked eye, strong echoes were obtained. A technician, recently demobilised from TRE, who had spent the latter part of the war as a lecturer at the radar training school on antenna theory, was recruited and built a new antenna system of long Yagis. This was J A Clegg, and he mounted the array on a searchlight mount

Fig 1.19: Clegg's Multi-Yagi Array. (Photograph supplied by Jodrell Bank Archives)

(again 'borrowed' from the Army due to Lovell's wartime contacts) to form a steerable array in both azimuth and elevation for the October 1946 Giacobini shower.

This consisted of five long Yagis of six elements each. Using this antenna, it was found that the maximum response to the meteor showers was when the antenna was pointed perpendicular to the observed meteor trail. A startling outcome was that many new meteor showers were discovered during the daytime, whereas all the meteor showers up until then had only been known as they occurred during periods of darkness. In total, seven new meteor showers were detected by Lovell and his colleagues in 1946 [5].

This sporadic meteor shower echo effect had been observed during the war on various radar systems, but it had not been conclusively connected with extra-terrestrial sources. At the time, the assumption was that it was deliberate jamming by the Germans or some other form of electrical interference. It was particularly troublesome for the original 26MHz Chain Home coastal protection radar system used at the beginning of the war during the Battle of Britain, causing numerous false alarms.

Radar detection of the Aurora Borealis (Northern Lights) was another early discovery by Lovell and his colleagues at Jodrell Bank in 1946. This had also been a source of interference for the Chain Home system, but not positively proved at the time. Searching back through archived war records pointed to a good correlation between interference reports and Northern Lights activity with the northern stations.

Later work adapted the radar to be able to measure the incident velocity of the meteors. This research, occupying three years, finally put to an end a long and bitter argument within the astronomical fraternity as to whether the meteors were inter-stellar or from an external galaxy. It proved that the meteors were inter-stellar.

To increase the sensitivity, Lovell, in 1947, was instrumental in constructing in an adjacent vacant field, which was rented from a local farmer at Jodrell Bank, a very large fixed parabolic antenna with the reflecting surface made of thousands of feet of wire (Lovell in his books states this was eight miles of wire), this antenna had a diameter of 218ft (66m). The available land between the newly erected laboratory buildings and the edge of the field decided the diameter of the new antenna.

This instrument was finished in the autumn and proved to be a great success. This became known as the 'transit telescope'. It was demolished some years later to allow the construction of the new Mk2 telescope. The farmer was paid

---

The velocity at which meteors enter the Earth's atmosphere varies between 12.5km/s and 72km/s. The reason there is such a wide variation in velocity is due to the orbital speed of the Earth. The Earth orbits the Sun at a velocity of 29.8km/s. Some meteors will enter the atmosphere in a direction the same as the Earth is travelling; hence the apparent velocity is low. For meteors that enter in a counter-rotating path the velocity is considerably higher.

The escape velocity of meteors orbiting the Sun is 42.2km/s; if a meteor had been observed that exceeded this velocity then it meant that the meteor was not inter-stellar but from an external galaxy.

Fig 1.20 and Fig 1.21: The transit telescope at Jodrell Bank under construction. The rim of the dish is at the height of the short masts. The feed supporting mast is the tall object, the two shorter structures visible are two of the 24 supports for the dish rim. The reflecting surface consisted of eight miles of 16-gauge galvanised wire. (Photographs by courtesy of University of Manchester Archives)

a nominal fee for lease of the field with the proviso that he may still use it for grazing his cattle! In later years the university purchased the field, and many more, so that the facility had room to expand.

The antenna pointed vertically upwards; hence the main beam of the antenna was concentrated at one point in the sky, the zenith. As the earth rotates, the sky appears to sweep across (transit) this beam every sidereal day. Thus, on each successive day, the same piece of sky is covered in a narrow strip coincident with the beam width of the antenna. The transit telescope initially operated on 64MHz, but later was changed to a frequency of 152MHz, and then had a beamwidth of approximately 2.5° and, as such, had a very large gain and sensitivity. The half-wave dipole feed was supported on top of a 126ft steel tube and stayed with guy ropes.

By tilting the supporting mast slightly (by slackening some guy ropes and tightening others), it was possible to steer the beam up to 18 degrees and allow

The collection of war surplus apparatus was something Lovell and the other scientists involved in radio astronomy were good at. After the war, there were many tons of radio and radar equipment that no longer served any useful purpose, and so a large amount was destroyed by tossing it down disused mine shafts or by burying it in bomb craters left from the war. Lovell, through his wartime contacts in the Air Ministry, was quick to see the potential of this equipment and in a few years collected a large amount that might be useful in later research. Blackett similarly, through his wartime contacts with the Royal Navy, was able to obtain more equipment from the Admiralty.

The Air Ministry was not allowed to give the equipment away but, with the help of the Air Ministry clerks, Lovell was soon to realise that if he offered a small token sum such as £10 to purchase the equipment, it would be authorised. As long as an entry was made in the disposal account book showing it had been purchased as scrap this was legal.

This equipment was stored under tarpaulins in the vacant fields. Much of this equipment was passed on to others for work in overseas countries. The radar originally set up at Adelaide, Australia, in 1952, was one of these surplus radars. In Lovell's books he states "In a short time I had amassed over £1 million worth of radio equipment for the sum of but a few hundred pounds."

Much of this war surplus equipment could not be sold on the open market because of its sensitive nature. Lovell had little difficulty persuading the powers that be that Jodrell Bank and others could use it for scientific research and so got a vast amount for literally scrap metal value. As many of the new radio astronomers then setting up research establishments had been involved in the wartime design of much of this equipment, it was nice gesture by the authorities.

Of particular importance were the two gun-elevation racks used by the Jodrell Bank Mk1 telescope for elevation. To have these made would have been too costly, but Lovell was alerted to the fact that two First World War naval destroyers were being broken up at the Clyde in 1951 and he was able to purchase the racks for a token sum.

a different portion of the sky to be probed. Adjustments to the dipole feed or change of frequency band involved hoisting a member of staff to the top in a bosun's chair; this job was often the task of young research students.

J S Hey and The AORG Research Team

Although many books written on the topic give the bulk of the praise to Lovell and his team at Jodrell Bank, this is not entirely correct. Hey and his team at AORG, during the latter part of the war and after the war ended, spent a considerable amount of time studying meteor activity using the modified radar systems.

Hey provided the radar system for Lovell and this was but one of many systems that had been modified during the latter part of the war. The V-2 detection radar that Lovell and Hey used numbered at least fifty, Hey gives details of how fifty sets were modified in a six-week period and set up for the V-2 threat before the first missile was fired. Hey in his book *The Evolution of Radio Astronomy* gives details of the work done at AORG during the spring and early summer months of 1945. In this, the discovery of daytime meteor showers, the measurement of both the optimum antenna pointing direction and head echo returns

Fig 1.22: The AORG antenna used to detect Cygnus-A

all occurred some twelve months before Lovell and the team at Jodrell Bank made similar discoveries.

At that time, the threat of the V-1 and V-2 had both disappeared following the successful D Day landings in France and the allied troops quickly overran the V-1 and V-2 launching sites, so terminating the bombardment. As the team at AORG had little work to do, Hey proposed that they spend some time before the cessation of hostilities, and before the major team members were demobilised, to try to understand some of the peculiar effects they had noticed during the war with the VHF radar systems. Hey had gathered a small but highly competent team of electrical, mechanical and theoretical engineers and scientists during the war to work on the problems with operational radar systems.

One of the experiments Hey devised involved three V-2 radar systems widely spaced to see if the meteor trails could be observed simultaneously by all three sites by pointing the antennas to a common point in the sky. This experiment used two in-service V 2 detection radar systems separated by about 60 miles and manned by army technicians and the third was the system at AORG HQ at Richmond Park. It was found that the trails were highly dependent on the pointing angle of the antennas. Only when the antenna was directed to be broadside on to the trail was a significant echo seen. It also showed that the three sites did not obtain an echo simultaneously but a time delay occurred between the sites because of the Earth's rotation. One site would acquire echoes for a time then another and then the third. From this, Hey deduced the trail was very long and thin and hence sensitive to aspect.

Later work by the team at AORG, using the same system as a receiver detected strong radio signals from a part of the sky, like Jansky and Reber, and this subsequently led to the detection of the strong source Cygnus-A. For this experiment, Hey and his team built a special antenna array of four six-element Yagis mounted on the anti-aircraft receiver cabin and this was situated at the AORG HQ at Richmond Park.

THE BIRTH OF THE BIG TELESCOPE

Jodrell Bank Mk1

Although the transit telescope performed well, it was limited in pointing direction. A small ex-US Army radar parabolic steerable antenna was obtained that was 25ft (7m) in diameter, but this was only suitable for much higher frequencies. Hence, it had less gain than the 218ft version, and soon it became apparent that, if the science was going to progress, something much bigger was required.

It was decided to build an even larger parabolic antenna that could be steered both in azimuth and elevation. A scientific instrument of such a size and complexity had never been constructed before and, after a number of false starts with various companies, Lovell enlisted the assistance of a civil engineer, Charles Husband, who normally designed bridges. Husband initially considered this to be a relatively simple task, as he originally remarked "About the same problem as throwing a swing bridge across the Thames at Westminster". However, as time progressed, it turned out to be a project fraught with many pitfalls both engineering and financial, weighing in at over 1600 tons in its final form. Not the least problem was obtaining the necessary funds to construct such an elaborate instrument. Fortunately for Blackett and Lovell, many of the grant allocation committee members had worked with them during the war either at TRE or in other establishments, and hence the initial appeal for a sum of £150,000 was quickly agreed. Within a short space of time, this estimate was revised to £260,000. In the final analysis, the original estimated cost was out by a factor of almost 5, the eventual cost being £660,000 of which approximately half was provided by the Nuffield Foundation set up by Lord Nuffield (the millionaire car mogul William Morris).

Construction was started in the spring of 1952 and was expected to take three years, but was only eventually completed in late 1957 after many dramas over the escalating cost, design problems, and supply of steel and changing require-

Fig 1.23: Jodrell Bank Radio Telescope with Bridge Farm farmhouse. (Photograph: J Fielding, 2004)

Fig 1.24: Jodrell Bank Mk1 telescope under construction. (Photograph by courtesy of University of Manchester Archives)

ments as the new science evolved. It was named The Nuffield Telescope or Jodrell Bank Mk1, a 250ft parabola, the largest of its type in the world at that time. The full account of this and subsequent developments are covered in Lovell's books, *The Story of Jodrell Bank*, *Out of the Zenith* and *Astronomer by Chance*.

The original site chosen for the erection was not optimal, and Lovell wished to move the foundations to another field nearby that did not belong to the University. During negotiations to purchase this piece of land, the landowner died and this caused a long delay. While this legal battle was in progress, the contractors continued piling on the original site, which ultimately became the car park for the Visitor Centre, erected some years later. Eventually, after a high court battle with the landowner relatives, where a compulsory purchase order was obtained, it was possible to move the contractors on to the new site. The delay ran over many vital rain-free summer months and, when the contractors were able to move into the newly-acquired field, the winter had set in and the new site soon became a quagmire, slowing the work of piling for the new foundations. The sub-strata of the new site were very different from those of the original site, and this entailed much deeper piles (160 in total) and consequent extra cost to complete the foundations.

The new site was part of Bridge Farm, and this still exists today, being a cattle farm run by the youngest son of the landowner. Today it is also a bed and breakfast establishment and the radio telescope is literally in its back garden!

Much important pioneering work was undertaken with this very sensitive instrument, including the detection using radar of the Russian carrier rocket that had launched Sputnik. This had never been possible previously, due to the lack of a sensitive enough instrument. It caused shock waves in the British and American public when the details were released to the world press and letters of congratulations from the Russian scientific community!

It also was used as the only means of detecting Russian inter-continental ballistic missiles until Fylingdales BMEWS (Ballistic Missile Early Warning

Fig 1.25: Jodrell Bank Mk1 antenna as originally constructed. Note the spindly rear 'bicycle wheel' back supporting steelwork. This, in later years, was replaced and many modifications were made to the structure to strengthen it. This picture was taken in 1957 upon completion. (Photograph by courtesy of University of Manchester Archives)

System) on the North York Moors came on stream. It says much for the foresight and the skill of the original design by Husband and Lovell that it is still in full use today as the modified Mk1A nearly 50 years later.

Another early discovery was the detection of radio emissions from new regions of the sky, as in Jansky's and Reber's earlier work, but no known star or other body could be located at the observed point. After very long-time exposure photographs were taken with the largest optical telescope, the Mount Wilson 200in, a faint smudge was detected which turned out to be a very distant nebula or gas cloud - the remnants of a long-extinct star located at a distance of 2,500 million light years. This is located in the Crab Nebula, a supernova, the explosion of which was observed by Chinese astronomers in AD 1054. From this, it became evident that radio sources at distances in excess of the penetration of the best optical telescopes could be detected. The current limit of terrestrial radio telescopes (2005) is in excess of 6,000 million light years.

Fig 1.26: Crab Nebula - Hubble telescope photograph. (Photograph courtesy of Jodrell Bank Observatory)

Fig 1.27: Jodrell Bank Mk2. The site was originally used for the transit tele-scope. The Mk1 can be seen in the b a c k g r o u n d. (Photograph by cour-tesy of University of Manchester Archives)

As the demand for more operating time grew dramatically, with many researchers clamouring for telescope time, it was necessary to build a second telescope that could share some of the workload. This telescope, built in 1964, was designated Jodrell Bank MkII, and has a smaller but more accurate surface making it usable to 10GHz. It is an elliptical design with an aluminium skin and measures 25m.

Recently (January 1996), the Hubble Space (optical) telescope has been able to see to greater distances. The great advantage of the radio telescope over the conventional optical types is the ability to operate in all kinds of weathers. Optical telescopes rely heavily on dark, clear skies, far away from earth-bound sources of light for optimum viewing and, for this reason, the best optical tele-scopes are often situated on top of mountains to reduce the amount of atmos-phere they have to penetrate. The gases in the atmosphere form a type of refract-ing lens and hence the object under observation can appear to shift in position due to the variable refraction. It also causes 'scintillation' or the apparent twin-kling of a star as the refraction varies. Radio telescopes can operate when the sky is covered in dense cloud (occluded), rain or fog and equally well during the daylight hours, from low altitudes.

More recently the development of MERLIN (Multi-Element Radio-Linked Interferometer Network) has been established with seven radio telescopes linked to the Nuffield Radio Observatory, as it was originally known. (Lord Nuffield, William Morris, the founder of the Morris motor car company, was a major con-tributor to the cost of the Mk1 telescope through the Nuffield Foundation, and in his personal capacity in finally paying off the remaining debt.)

Fig 1.28: Portable 25ft (7m) diameter ex-US Army parabolic antenna used for an interferometer network. The microwave link vehicle is parked to the left of the antenna. This picture taken in 1964 was part of a Jodrell Bank long-baseline experiment. (Photograph by courtesy of University of Manchester Archives)

Early pioneering work on radio interferometry was undertaken by Jodrell Bank and an important development was the Rotating Lobe Interferometer, designed by Hanbury-Brown and colleagues in 1955 [6].

Dr Bernard Lovell was awarded a knighthood in February 1961 for his work and retired in 1981. In 1987, on the 30th anniversary of the telescope, it was renamed the 'Lovell Radio Telescope' in his honour.

Dr Martin Ryle - Cambridge University

Ryle was a colleague of Lovell at TRE during the war and returned to Cambridge University to continue his research after peace was declared. He was instrumental in further developing the system of radio interferometry and the aperture-synthesis telescope network. Many of the early exciting discoveries of such objects as Quasars and Pulsars have been made with the Cambridge instruments.

Interferometry is based on using two small antennas to synthesise a much larger antenna; due to this the beamwidth is greatly reduced and hence the resolving accuracy is considerably enhanced over that of one antenna. By using a long baseline (distance) between the antennas the resolving power is greatly increased, and precise positional details, estimates of the size and hence distance of the radio source can be established. (The technique is similar to that used by surveyors to determine the distance or height of an object accurately.)

An interferometer of two small antennas separated by, say, 500m, gives the directivity (gain) of a single antenna of 500m diameter. Using this technique, antennas with effective diameters of up to 6,400 miles (~10,000km) have been synthesised with one antenna in Russia and one in America.

Aperture synthesis is similar to the radio interferometer but, in this system, several radio telescopes are connected in a network and the signals recorded digitally on computer disc or tape for later signal processing. The portion of sky under observation can then be 're-built' in a three-dimensional form, giving a much better picture. By moving one of the antennas to a new position and recording a new set of signals the different 'viewpoint' can give extra information [7]. Dr Martin Ryle was also awarded a knighthood for his work.

LUNAR RADAR - MOONBOUNCE OR EME

Project Diana - US Army Signals Corps

On 10 January 1946, following the cessation of war with Japan, a team of engineers and technicians of the Evans Signal Laboratory of the US Army Signals Corps in Belmar, New Jersey, led by Lt Col. John De Witt Jr, W4FU, obtained radar echoes from the moon. The official reason for the experiment was to see if the Moon could be used as a passive 'communications satellite for military purposes.

De Witt was the station engineer for one of the large US broadcast stations before the war and he had thought up the scheme some years before the war drafted him into the army. The team, largely comprising of radio amateurs, had been busy since August 1945 (when the atomic bombs had been used against Japan) modifying and experimenting with different equipment to achieve this goal. The urgency to complete the experiment was because most of the members would be demobilised in a short time, and they would be unlikely to get another chance after they left the army.

The equipment utilised a modified high-power radar system (SCR-270, the type deployed at Pearl Harbour prior to the fateful Japanese attack) with two sets of antennas combined, which then comprised 64 dipoles configured as a broadside array, using ground reflection to enhance the antenna gain. Eventually, after several unsuccessful attempts, it was proven that reliable echoes could be obtained, although the signals often showed very deep and rapid fading [8, 9].

The SCR 270 system operated on a frequency of 111.5MHz and had a peak power of 15kW with a pulse of 0.25 second. The receiver was modified to have a bandwidth of 4Hz, but due to receiver local oscillator drift a bandwidth of 50 Hz was finally used.

The Doppler shift of the signal was approximately 300Hz. The reception was initially done audibly using a quadruple conversion receiver; the person to hear the first echo was Herbert Kauffman, W2OQU, who was one of the members of the team. Later a normal A-scope radar display was used to visually display the echoes.

In order to appreciate the difficulty involved, the equivalent target has been calculated to be a metal sheet 1m square at a range of 460km.

The amount of signal returned from the moon is only about 5% of the incident power, the remainder being scattered into space. By comparison, the solar reflection (albedo) of the moon is about 7%.

Fig 1.29: SCR-270 radar with 32-element dipole array

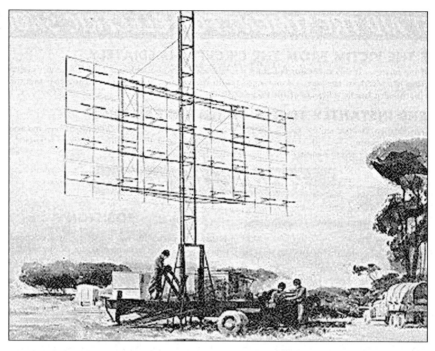

Zoltán Bay - Hungary

Bay reported that he had obtained moon echoes on 6 February 1946, just after the US Army results. Bay used a frequency of 120MHz and an antenna of 36 dipoles with a peak power of 3kW.

During the war, Bay was a radar designer and built radar systems for the Hungarian Army. Following the occupation of Hungary by German troops, his works and equipment were used by the occupying forces. When the war ended, Hungary was annexed to the Russians and all the equipment was confiscated and sent to Russia. Bay therefore had to start from scratch and this is why he used a very unusual method of displaying the echo signals. His receiver detector used a series of hydro-voltaic integrators. Ten identical voltaic detectors were used, each one corresponding to a certain range, the one that corresponded to the approximate range of the moon showed a greater amount of gas than the others [10].

Radio Australia

The 100kW short-wave transmitter of Radio Australia operating on 20MHz with the fixed wire rhombic antenna used for the North American transmissions, obtained moon echoes in April 1946. As the antenna was fixed, the time to attempt the radar experiment was limited to about 45 minutes on those days when the moon was visible close to the horizon. (The moon travels at an apparent azimuthal rate of 15° per hour but, at moonrise and moonset, the rate of change of elevation is much more rapid.)

One of the outcomes of this experiment was the observation of two distinct types of fading; one was rapid, as observed in the Project Diana tests, and the second was of much longer duration, lasting up to several minutes. The short-term fading was proved to be due to 'libration fading', the libration or rocking effect of the moon's orbit causing a slightly different portion of the moon's surface to be exposed to an observer on Earth, so causing variations in the reflectivity. The long-term fading was subsequently proved, by later research at Jodrell Bank by Murray and Hargreaves, to be due to the effect of polarisation rotation of the wave by passing through the earth's ionosphere, which is known as Faraday Rotation [11].

Jodrell Bank

Jodrell Bank was amongst the next groups to obtain lunar radar echoes using a 64MHz radar system and performed extensive studies of the moon radar problem. Initially, a large broadside array of dipoles was used but, with the completion of the transit telescope, this then became the main instrument used. The later work was done at 152MHz and 408MHz. The great strength of the echoes received using the 218ft transit telescope was such that many different types of fading could be investigated as well as precise distance measurements using standard radar ranging and measurement of the Doppler shift. Reliable echoes were achieved using as little as 100W although, normally, a 1.5kW transmitter was used. An important result of this research was the identification of the Faraday Rotation mechanism [11].

The 250ft Jodrell Bank Mk1 radio telescope was finally completed in October 1957 after many dramas, and immediately used 36MHz radar to detect the orbiting 3rd stage carrier rocket of Sputnik 1, the first time in the history of the world that such an event had occurred. Jodrell Bank also conclusively proved, in September 1959, that the Russian moon-probe Lunik had impacted on the lunar surface, much to the dismay of the American Air Force technicians present at Jodrell at the time, who had previously tried and missed a few weeks earlier. By virtue of a brilliant spur of the moment idea by one of the research students, J G Davies, measuring the Doppler shift from the onboard 19MHz beacon transmitter as it was drawn inwards by the moon's gravitational pull, it was found to be increasing up until the moment when it stopped transmitting on impact. (The first American and Russian lunar probes missed the moon by several hundred kilometres.) This new technique was to be used extensively in later research of deep-space probe tracking, to assess the gravitational pull of the planets to which the probe came close.

Later work in October 1959 was to capture the pictures from another Russian lunar probe, Lunik-3, that orbited the Moon and showed the reverse side of the Moon. These signals were transmitted as facsimile data and a fax machine was hurriedly rushed from a newspaper office in Manchester to produce the pictures. The Russians did not have a suitable receiving station and asked Jodrell Bank if they would capture the pictures and distribute them to the rest of the world!

Although all this occurred during the Cold-War between the western and the eastern-bloc countries, there was a great deal of interchange of scientific matter between all parties. In the case of the Russian lunar probe, Lovell was personally asked for assistance by his counterpart in the Russian scientific community, and was supplied with precise details of launch time and orbital data. Although the carrier rockets for both the American and Russian attempts relied heavily on military hardware, there was no restriction on the passing of scientific information and all parties had telex links to each other's stations!

Doppler shift occurs when there is relative movement between the signal source and the observer. The moon occupies a slightly elliptical orbit around the earth and so there are times when it is approaching or receding. The mean distance is 384,000km, but a variation of about 60,000km occurs due to the non-circular orbit. (For the lowest round trip attenuation, the best time for moon radar or moonbounce experiments is when the moon is closest to the earth at perigee). By observing the Doppler shift of the lunar echoes, the velocity of the moon's orbit has been accurately determined.

Initially the 218ft transit telescope was used on a frequency of 152MHz, but later work from 1957 onwards at 408 and 1240MHz using the 250ft Mk1 steerable dish, produced detailed radar maps of the moon's surface.

Jodrell Bank, along with other radio telescopes, subsequently managed to obtain radar echoes from Venus, Mars, Jupiter, Mercury and the Sun which conclusively determined the range, directions of rotation and the value of the Astronomical Unit (AU), the distance of the Sun from the Earth, which is now accepted as 149,600,000km. In the final Sun tests, a massive radar transmitter on loan from the UK Ministry of Defence developing nearly 1MW of peak pulse power was used. (This equipment was for the ICBM detection program arranged with Jodrell Bank until the Fylingdales BMEWS system was operational. In order to provide some subterfuge so as to disguise the real use of the radar it was used for the Sun experiment). It was necessary to use a very high-power transmitter because the background sun noise was high. Also it was not known at the time what the reflectivity of the solar umbra was likely to be.

Finally, as the problems of operating very high-power radar systems with other sensitive radio telescopes at the same site became more and more severe, this technique fell out of favour. Interim methods used were to feed a blanking pulse to all the receivers on site that muted the receivers when the transmitter pulse occurred; although workable, it left many problems. Today most radio telescopes are only receivers listening to the many strange noises from deep space, for which they are particularly well-suited.

Today, radio telescopes operate on frequencies from 20MHz up to 300GHz, probing the sky to determine the secrets of the universe. An important discovery was the presence of the hydrogen-line at 1420MHz. By observing at this frequency, much has been learned about the origins of the universe, as it now known that the fundamental ingredient of all galactic bodies is hydrogen. This effect had been postulated by a Dutch scientist, H C van de Hulst, in 1944, but was not released to the scientific community until much later. American and Dutch scientists in 1951 established that radio signals were present at 1420MHz due to the hydrogen. Because of this discovery, the Jodrell Mk1 dish design was modified during its construction to improve the surface accuracy to enable it to be used at these higher frequencies. Later improvements performed during the conversion to the Mk1A allowed it to be used up to 3GHz. Subsequent modifications between 1999 to 2002 extended the usable frequency to 10GHz.

PARKES RADIO TELESCOPE

The construction of the Australian radio telescope at Parkes, near Sydney was mainly due to the efforts of one person, Edward George (Taffy) Bowen. Bowen was one of the original team working on the Chain Home radar system so vital during World War 2 for the defence of England against the German Luftwaffe.

Taffy Bowen was a staunch Welshman and an excellent engineer with complex projects; he gained his doctorate under the British scientist Professor E V Appleton at King's College, London. On being interviewed by Robert (Watson) Watt for the position in 1935, Watt asked Bowen to sing the Welsh national anthem, he countered this by saying that he would be glad to do this if Watt could first sing the Scottish national anthem.

Bowen was a key person in the transmitter design in the early part of the project but he left the team to develop the Airborne-Intercept (AI) radar fitted to the RAF fighters. Bowen devised a small, lightweight; high power radar for fitting into aircraft that played an important role in the allied night fighters pitched against the Luftwaffe. During this development he needed a flexible RF transmission line and he invented what today we know as 'coaxial cable'.

Bowen was also the driving force to develop a navigational system which consisted of radio beacons that allowed RAF night fighters to safely return to base. This was the forerunner of what today we know as VOR (VHF Omni-Directional Ranging) used for navigating between way points.

Later in the conflict he was seconded to the Tizard Mission that took important British radar secrets to the USA, including the new microwave cavity magnetron (designed by Randall and Boot at Birmingham University), that got the American radar team started at MIT into the war. This mission resulted in the setting up of the Radiation Laboratory (Rad-Lab) and many important developments helped to shorten the conflict.

Towards the end of the war Tizard again visited the Rad-Lab and found Bowen at a loose end as his work was almost complete. Tizard commented that Australia was short of qualified engineers and suggested that Taffy would be better spending his efforts at the Australian lab where radar was in its infancy. Bowen made the trip and when the war came to an end he was inducted into the peacetime research team at CSIRO where radio astronomy was one of the projects to work on. (Council for Scientific and Industrial Research Organisation)

Bowen later suggested that a large radio telescope would be a useful tool and as Jodrell Bank was then building its large telescope it was felt that something similar was needed in the Southern Hemisphere to accelerate the research. Bowen with Dr John Pawsey (famous for the 'Pawsey-stub' antenna matching) and Barnes Wallace (later Sir) as a consultant drew up a design for a 210ft diameter parabolic antenna. Wallace is probably best known for his idea for the 'bouncing bomb' that destroyed the German dams ('The Dam Busters').

Wallace was also a famous airship and aircraft designer; his Wellington bomber geodetic construction was the basis for the antenna design. This was a lightweight but immensely strong form of construction. Bowen enlisted financial

Fig 1.31: Parkes radio telescope

support from two American foundations, the Rockefeller Foundation and the Ford Foundation who offered a sizeable cash donation to the project, the Australian Prime Minister agreeing to match this from public funds. The project was put out to international tender and the German MAN enterprise won the bid to construct the telescope. The construction was on budget and time, a rare event in those days. Upon completion the telescope was an instant success with performance exceeding the design parameters. Today it is still considered one of the first class radio telescopes and has recently been upgraded to improve its performance. The original design was the basis for the NASA deep space tracking network that grew into many telescopes dotted around the world.

This has been a very condensed account of the early work, and many books and thousands of papers have been written since the 1930s work of Jansky on this fascinating topic. The points covered above will be analysed in greater detail in subsequent chapters.

REFERENCES

[1]   Jansky, Karl G, 1933 'Electrical Disturbances apparently of Extra-terrestrial Origin', *Proc IRE*, 21, 1387.

[2]   *Astrophysical Journal.*

[3]   Jones, R V, *Most Secret War.*

[4]   TRE - originally known as AMRE - Air Ministry Research Establishment, changed to MAPRE [Ministry of Aircraft Production Research Establishment] and in 1942 to TRE - Telecommunications Research Establishment, it is today known as RSRE - Royal Signals Research Establishment, based in Malvern, Worcester.

[5]   Lovell, A C B, *Meteor Astronomy*, Clarendon Press.

[6]   Brown, R Hanbury, Palmer, H P and Thompson, A R 1955, 'A Rotating Lobe Interferometer and its Application to Radio Astronomy', *Phil Mag*, 46, 857.

[7]   Ryle, M, 1952 'A New Radio Interferometer and its Application to the Observation of Weak Radio Stars', *Proc Roy Soc Astr*, 211, 351.

[8]   Mofenson, J, 1946 'Radar Echoes from the Moon', Electronics, 19, 92 - 98.

[9]   Dewitt, J H jr, & E K Stodola, 1949 'Detection of Radar Signals Reflected from the Moon', *Proc IRE*, 37, 229 - 242.

[10]   Bay, Z, "Reflections of Microwaves from the Moon", Hung. *Acta Phys.*, vol. 1, pp. 1-22, April,1946.

[11]   Murray, W A S, & Hargreaves, J K, 1954 'Lunar Radar Echoes and the Faraday Effect in the Ionosphere', *Nature* (London), 173, 944 - 45.

2

Radar Astronomy

In this chapter:

- Radar display
- Simple radar receiver
- Maximum range limitation of radar systems
- Minimum detectable signal and maximum range
- Post-detection processing signal enhancement
- Relevance to amateur meteor scatter communications

- Receiver IF parameters
- Target reflectivity
- Antenna beamwidth
- Doppler effect
- Requirements for radar transmitters
- Spectral spreading
- Transmit pulse shaping methods
- Modern meteor radar systems

The early radio astronomy work after the Second World War by Hey, Lovell and others on meteor showers and other planetary objects relied extensively on the use of radar. Whereas today, radar is a well-refined and commonly-used technique for all manner of things, in the period during the Second World War, the equipment was relatively insensitive and hence limited in range and positional accuracy.

The equipment used by Lovell from late 1945 for his experiments at Jodrell Bank was anti aircraft (AA) gun-laying (GL) equipment operating on a frequency of 72.4MHz (4.2m) with a pulse length of ~3µs and a pulse repetition frequency (PRF) of 150Hz. Why Lovell used this in preference to the higher frequency systems requires some explanation.

> *Note: RADAR is the acronym for Radio Detection and Ranging*

Generally, in order to establish the maximum surface detail and position of the target, a very high frequency (short wavelength) is normally used. Dr Bernard Lovell was extensively involved in the development of the H2S airborne radar used for high-altitude bombing of German industrial targets during the Second World War. This accurate bombing had a significant effect in reducing the length of the war. In this system, a frequency of 3GHz and later 10GHz was used and highly-detailed ground returns (echoes) enabled the radar operator to pinpoint the target during night time raids, as if he was looking at a map, so containing the bombing to the selected targets.

The writer has managed to establish the radar type used by Lovell. This was the AA No1 MkII referred to as the GL MkII or GL2 (code name 'George') and, in its standard form, developed a peak pulse power of 100kW using two NT57 or VT98 valves operated in push-pull. Lovell's radar system was provided by J S Hey of the Ministry of Supply, Army Operational Research Group (AORG), and was a version of the V-2 detection type modified by Hey for the experiment. Hey also modified several other GL2 radars, identical to the one given to Lovell, and carried out meteor observations in parallel from the AORG HQ in Richmond, UK. Fuller details are given in Hey's book [1].

In the radar scenario there are two main types of system, the tracking radar and the search radar. In the tracking radar, the antenna accurately follows a moving target to establish range and trajectory. For this system to work, the operator needs some prior knowledge of a likely trajectory or track.

The search radar, on the other hand, as the name implies, is used to find a target, often at a great distance, the direction and speed of travel of which is unknown. Consequently, the antenna needs to have a fairly wide beamwidth. If the beamwidth is made very narrow, the target object may pass by without the antenna beam impinging on it and so no echo will result. Also, the frequency needs to be fairly low as the dilution or attenuation of the signal is directly related to the frequency. A high-frequency signal suffers more attenuation for a given distance than a low-frequency one; hence, for long detection ranges, where the limitation of generating high power is a problem, a low frequency will often give better results.

In Lovell's early experiments, a low frequency radar was chosen, as this was a search radar using four-element Yagi antennas; consequently, the antenna positioning was not so critical and the antenna could be tens of degrees off the target without a severe loss of sensitivity.

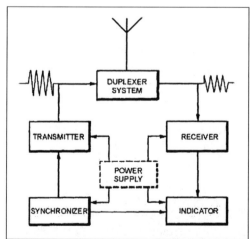

Fig 2.1: Simple radar block diagram

Lovell at first had no idea where to start looking in the sky so this type of radar was a very good choice. Another fortuitous reason for choosing a low frequency, although Lovell was not aware of this at the time, was that echoes from meteor trails are strongest when a low frequency is used. Frequencies above about 300MHz give little or no meteor echoes from the ionised trail. (See the later section on 'Head Echo Effect' for a more detailed description.)

The German radar systems were evolved differently from the British systems. They used a dual-radar system. The wide-beamwidth, low-frequency Freya system was used for the initial detection of a hostile target and the information was then passed on to the Würzburg stations for tracking and more accurate positional information.

It is also probable, but not confirmed by Sir Bernard Lovell in his books, that as the war had recently ceased, there were many of these low-frequency anti-aircraft radars available, and so it was easier to obtain one of these than the scarcer microwave air-borne radars such as H2S, of which only a limited number were actually made. The H2S radar was commonly only fitted to a few 'PathFinder' bombers or Mosquito fighters which laid marker flares for following bombers to home-in on. The size and weight of the H2S radar precluded any significant bomb-load in the lead aircraft. The H2S radar allowed the bombers to fly at very high altitudes, so largely avoiding enemy anti-aircraft fire and German night fighters. A smaller version was also later fitted to allied fighters to allow them to home-in on enemy aircraft at night from a range of 20km. Later versions were also fitted to the allied bombers as a tail-warning radar.

Today's search radar is considerably more sophisticated than the Second World War systems then in common use. A technique of rapidly scanning the feed-point of the antenna to sweep a narrow pencil beam in azimuth and/or elevation coupled with a gigahertz-frequency, today gives good accuracy, long range and considerable details of the target type.

The type of radar 'borrowed' by Lovell consisted of three trailers. Two of the trailers were the size of a small caravan. One contained the transmitter and the second contained the receiver and display unit. One antenna was mounted on top of the transmit cabin and the second was mounted on top of the receiver trailer cabin which was parked about 50m from the transmitter. The two trailers were linked by a variety of cables. The portable diesel generator in the third trailer was placed some distance away to reduce the noise generated. The trailers were each towed by an army lorry. As this system used two separate antennas it was known as a bi-static system and each antenna had to be pointed to the same point in the sky [2]. According to the scientific paper published by Lovell and others in 1947, the antennas were directed vertically upwards for the initial experiments.

RADAR DISPLAY

During the early part of WWII, the displays used by radars utilised conventional cathode-ray oscilloscope (CRO) tubes. The vertical displacement of the trace gave an indication of the strength of the received signal echoes. A strong return echo made the trace move towards the bottom of the screen. (The early radar display had the trace inverted; the zero signal trace was at the top of the screen). The operator, using a manual RF gain control, could control the sensitivity of the receiver to keep the trace above the bottom of the screen. When the echoes were weak, the gain could be advanced to bring the trace further up from the noise floor (or 'grass', as it was known).

The use of the name 'grass' arose because the random noise looked like grass viewed from the side; the CRO tube used a green phosphor with a long persistence. The trace was swept horizontally at the pulse repetition frequency (PRF), in the case of the anti-aircraft radar sets, at 1000Hz. Using a long-persistence phosphor meant the trace remained visible for a short time due to the 'afterglow', and this formed a type of integration to make the signal easier to distinguish.

This type of display was known as a range amplitude indicator or 'A-Scope'. The modern types we now associate with radar are known as a Plan-Position-Indicators (PPIs) and use a circular tube with a rotating line that shows the current position of the antenna as it rotates through 360°. As each pulse returns the received signal is displayed on a radial timebase, synchronised to the antenna position. The return echo is shown in distance from the centre of the cathode ray tube and the angular location is marked around the outer of the circle in degrees azimuth.

The horizontal axis was an indication of range. The extreme left hand side corresponded with zero range (a zero marker blip was formed by the transmitter pulse), and the extreme right hand side was maximum range. The horizontal axis bore a ruler marked in increments of distance, the range. The range indicator was normally calibrated in either nautical miles for naval systems or in thousands of yards for land-based systems. Adjustments to the receiver to add or remove delay could be used to shift the trace along the horizontal axis to centre it and allow a more accurate determination of range. This is known as range-gating.

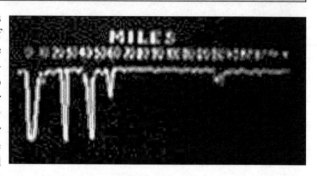

Fig 2.2: Type 1 Chain Home A-scope display. The extreme left-hand blip (known as the 'main-bang') is the transmitter pulse; the large right hand blips are range markers, the small blip at the extreme left is the target echo. In the early radar systems, the display was an inverted form, hence the strongest signal is close to the bottom

The early search radar did not use a continuously-rotating antenna as is common today; instead, it was moved to a particular direction where the threat was expected. The antenna could be moved by hand to a new azimuth or elevation. Many of these early radars were situated on cliff-tops overlooking the channel separating England and Europe. The V-1 detection version had the antennas pointed close to the horizon, as the altitude of the V-1 flying bomb was low, usually less than about 5,000ft.

SIMPLE RADAR RECEIVER

A simple radar receiver is a single-conversion superhet, with a manual gain control for the RF and IF stages. The GL2 used a 9MHz IF with a bandwidth of about 300kHz.

In the GL2 radar system, the complete trailer cabin was rotated on a turntable by a gearbox fitted with crank handles. The receiver and transmitter trailers were adjacent and the operators followed one another to keep the two sets of antennas aligned on the target. An indicator in each cabin showed the operator where the other antenna was pointed.

Another reason that AGC cannot be used is that it is impossible to switch off the receiver completely when the transmitter generates a pulse - the recovery time would be too slow. Receiver muting or 'blanking' is used to reduce the sensitivity to prevent overload. If AGC were fitted, the receiver would be very slow to return to full sensitivity. Without blanking, the receiver AGC would be driven hard on and reduce the sensitivity, this would take a long time to recover. With a fixed gain receiver, the time to return to full sensitivity after the transmitter pulse is very short. Today, logarithmic amplifiers are used, which have recovery times of the order of a few nanoseconds.

Automatic Gain Control (AGC)

The early receivers did not have any form of AGC; in fact, AGC is exactly the opposite of that required by a radar receiver. The return echoes are of very short duration, being the same length as the transmitted pulses, and conventional AGC with its attack and decay time would limit the response of the receiver to weak signals in the presence of strong signals. If a strong echo preceded a weaker echo at a greater range the AGC would reduce the receiver sensitivity and the weaker echo might go undetected.

The IF signal after bandwidth filtering and amplifying is applied to a fast-response amplitude-detector that gives a DC output voltage proportional to RF level. This DC voltage is amplified and applied to the vertical plates of the CRO tube.

The display timebase is swept with a sawtooth waveform to cause the trace to start at the left and continue to the right. The sawtooth wave is synchronised to the transmitter pulse generator. The time from the transmitter pulse to the echo being received gives a delay in time proportional to the signal's round trip from transmitter to receiver. This time delay is read off the horizontal axis when the trace shows a received blip. From experience, the height of the trace and the displacement from left to right provide an indication of target size and range. A large target will cause a bigger echo than a small target. Multiple targets, closely grouped, such as aircraft, will give bigger or multiple blips on the trace. From this, an estimate of the number and size of targets could be made by a skilled operator.

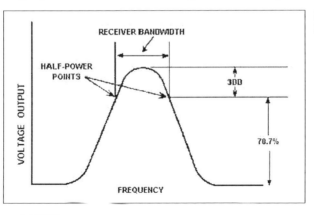

Fig 2.3: IF passband response.

Sensitivity Time Control (STC)

A problem with the early radar systems, where the target could be very close to the observer, was receiver overloading. As the receiver gain was set to allow maximum range this meant that for close-in targets the received signal might be large enough to paralyse the receiver. The way this was countered was a system known as STC. This uses a variable gain amplifier preceding the main IF

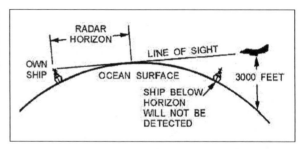

Fig 2.4: Line of sight radar range and how the height of the antenna and the curvature of the earth affect the radar's range

amplifier, the gain of which can be varied according to the position of the time-base trace. For an echo which occurred immediately after the transmitter pulse, the gain was low and, as the timebase swept the trace across the display tube, the gain was ramped up to maximum. The sawtooth voltage driving the display X-axis controlled the gain of the amplifier.

MAXIMUM RANGE LIMITATION OF RADAR

Range, or, more correctly, the ability to detect a target at a great distance, is determined by several factors in the radar system.

The first is the directivity or gain of the antenna. For maximum directivity, the antenna collecting area needs to be large in terms of wavelength. This measurement is generally reduced to the aperture or collecting area in square metres (m^2).

Gunther Hoch, DL6WU, an engineer at the German Post Office antenna test facility, has pointed out in his articles on antenna design that it is incorrect to say that an antenna has gain, it cannot have gain, as it is a passive device. The power radiated cannot be more than the power fed into the antenna. What we have come to call 'gain' is the increase in power flux density radiated in a particular direction, at the expense of power flux density radiated in other directions. However, it has become common to say an antenna has gain and little will be served here to contradict this otherwise commonly-accepted statement.

The antenna gain has a two-fold effect; it 'amplifies' the output power of the transmitter to produce a greater effective radiated signal in a particular direction; this is often expressed as effective radiated power, or ERP, and it also produces similar effects during receive. (This assumes that the same antenna is used for transmit as well as receive, the mono-static system. Some radar systems are bi-static using separate transmit and receive antennas separated by some distance - see earlier).

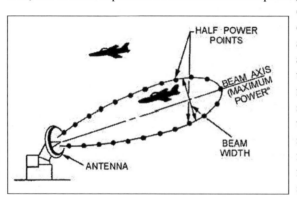

Fig 2.5: Antenna beamwidth and how it affects the target acquisition

Effective radiated power is expressed in watts. An antenna with a power gain ratio of 10, when fed from a 10W transmitter, develops an ERP of 100W. This will generate a field strength the same as a unity gain antenna fed with 100W. In amateur terminology, the half-wave dipole is often used as the unitary gain antenna. The correct engineering definition does not use a dipole antenna as the reference antenna but an isotropic antenna, because a dipole is itself a directional antenna, having two major lobes with a gain of 2.14dB over an isotropic source. The isotropic antenna is an abstract point source with no directional ability. Hence, for an unambiguous effective radiated power the isotropic source is preferred. Then the nomenclature is 'effective isotropic radiated power', or EIRP.

The second factor is the output power of the transmitter. The higher the output power, the greater distance the signal will travel before being diluted to an unusable level. The generation of high power during the Second World War was limited compared with that of today.

The dilution of the radio wave as it travels through space obeys a square law, and the attenuation, or 'free space path loss' as it is known, is conventionally measured in decibels (dB).

The attenuation over a distance of, say, 10km will be one-quarter or 6dB less than for a distance of 20km.

The attenuation in free space can be calculated from the following formula:

$$\text{Path loss (as a power ratio)} = \frac{4\pi d}{\lambda},$$

where: d is the distance in metres, and
         λ is the wavelength in metres.

$$\text{Path loss (dB)} = 20\log_{10}\frac{4\pi d}{\lambda}.$$

This formula is often reduced to:

$$A = 32.45 + 20\log_{10}(f) + 20\log_{10}(d),$$

where: A is the attenuation in dB,
         f is the frequency in MHz, and
         d is the distance in km.

The decibel (dB) is a sub-unit of the Bel, and is one-tenth of a Bel. The Bel was defined by the Bell Telephone Company to denote the attenuation occurring in telephone circuits. The attenuation or gain expressed in Bels is the logarithm of the attenuation or gain ratio. Hence, a gain or attenuation of 1Bel is the same as ±10dB. Conventionally, the Bel is no longer used in engineering circles today, although it is the correct unit to use. A gain or attenuation of, say, 45dB would be written as ±4.5B, the plus sign indicating gain, the minus sign indicating attenuation.

For example: A 144MHz signal transmitted over a distance of 10km will suffer an attenuation of approximately 96dB. For a 20km path the attenuation will be approximately $96 + 6 = 102$dB. For a 144MHz signal transmitted from the Earth to the Moon, the one way attenuation will be about 188dB.

In the radar case, the attenuation occurs on both the outwards and the return paths, so in this case it becomes a fourth-power law. Hence, a target at 20km will give a receiver signal that is one-sixteenth (-12dB) of a target at 10km, assuming the two targets are of the same cross sectional reflecting area.

The third factor is the sensitivity of the receiver; a high sensitivity is necessary to maximise the range performance. In Lovell's low-frequency radar, the equipment utilised thermionic valves. From available literature, it is known that the front-end amplifiers consisted of low-noise grounded-grid triodes; these would not have had a particularly good sensitivity by today's standards. At the time, a noise figure of 6dB at 75MHz was the best that could be achieved with the available devices. As it happened, this was not of too much significance, because the overall limitation was the background atmospheric sky noise and man-made noise which is fairly high at these low VHF frequencies. J S Hey, in his book *The Evolution of Radio Astronomy*, recounts how experiments during the war to improve the V 2 detection radar showed no significant increase in the range when special low noise front-ends were made. This was due to the high intrinsic background noise at these low VHF frequencies.

The fourth factor is the size of the target; a large target will intercept and hence reflect a greater proportion of the signal than a small target.

The final factor is the reflectivity of the target; a metallic sheet, sphere or ionised meteor trail will act as a good reflector, whereas soil, vegetation and cloud, for example, reflect to a lesser degree. The factors mentioned above have been incorporated into what is known as the 'standard radar equation'; the equation shown below is the simplest form and can be expanded to cover other factors.

$$ R_{max} = \left(\frac{P_t G_t A_e \sigma}{(4\pi)^2 S_{min}} \right)^{1/4} , $$

where: R_{max} is the range in metres,
P_t = transmitted power in watts,
G_t = antenna gain, expressed as a power ratio,
A_e = antenna effective aperture in m²,
σ = radar cross section of target in m², and
S_{min} = minimum detectable signal in watts.

Note: The range, R_{max}, is the one-way distance.

Since

$$ \text{Gain } G = \frac{4\pi A_e}{\lambda^2} $$

if Ae is replaced by

$$ \frac{G\lambda^2}{4\pi} $$

then there is a version of the radar range equation:

$$R_{max} = \left[\frac{P_t \, G^2 \, \lambda^2 \, \sigma}{(4\pi)^3 \, S_{min}} \right]^{\frac{1}{4}}$$

where λ is the operating wavelength and the same antenna is used for transmit and receive. Where separate antennas are used for transmit and receive the term G^2 is replaced by $G_t \times G_r$ which are the antenna gains expressed as a power ratio.

> The antenna gain (G) is shown as squared, as the same antenna is assumed to be used for transmit and receive (mono-static system). In bi-static systems the antenna gain comprises two terms $G_t \times G_r$, which are the transmitter and receiver antenna gains expressed as power ratios. The receiver and transmitter antennas may have different gains in some cases.

The 'range' derived from the above equation is the distance travelled by the signal to the target. All of the factors are, to some extent, under the control of the radar designer except the size and reflectivity of the target.

Note: The maximum range is also a function of the pulse repetition frequency. For long ranges, the transmitter pulses need to be widely spaced to allow the signal to travel to the target and back again before the next transmitter pulse. (See the later section 'Range Ambiguity' for a more detailed description.)

> In order to increase the range by any significant amount, it is necessary to increase the transmitter power by a large factor. If the range needs to be doubled, the power output needs to be increased by $2^4 = 16$, which is 12dB. Similarly, if the power were only doubled (3dB), the increase in range would be small.
>
> One important fact to be aware of is the limitation of the available transmitter power due to suitable power amplifiers. Assuming no further improvements can be made to the antenna or receiver, the only recourse is to increase the transmitter power.

From the radar equation, it can be seen that, if very long ranges are required,

- The transmitter must generate very high power.
- The radiated energy must be concentrated into a very narrow beam (high antenna gain)
- The received echo must be collected with a large antenna aperture (high antenna gain).
- The receiver must be sensitive to weak signals.

> It is important not to confuse path loss attenuation and total signal loss. It can be shown that the difference between the original transmitted power and the received power is composed of two parts. The attenuation over the two paths can be accurately determined from the free-space path-loss equation; the additional losses are due to non-perfect reflection properties of the target, non-perfect antenna efficiency and variations in the propagation medium.

MIN DETECTABLE SIGNAL AND MAX RANGE

The ability of any receiver to detect a weak signal is limited by the noise energy that occupies the same portion of the frequency spectrum as the signal energy. The weakest signal the receiver can detect is called the 'minimum detectable signal', or 'minimum discernible signal', or MDS. This corresponds to a Signal to Noise Ratio (SNR) of unity (0dB). Usually, for reliable detection, the SNR needs to be greater than two (3dB).

Detection in a radar system is normally based on establishing a threshold level at the output of the receiver detector. If the receiver output exceeds the threshold, a signal is assumed to be present. If the expected signal were small, the threshold level would need to be adjusted close to the intrinsic noise level of the receiver and background noise, but not so low that the quiescent noise crosses the threshold. In such a case, the probability of detection becomes more difficult as the change in receiver output is small and could be due to a small variation in the receiver noise level or some external interference (for example ignition interference) causing a false alarm.

Matched Filter Signal Enhancement

A special technique developed for the radar receiver after the WWII is the concept of a 'matched-filter'; this is not matched in the sense of being the same as the system impedance. Here the receiver bandwidth, B, is the reciprocal of the transmitter's rectangular pulse width, τ. A matched filter is the receiver noise bandwidth which is the reciprocal of the time period for the transmitted pulse, $(B = 1/\tau)$.

In the Project Diana Moon-echo experiment, described in Chapter 1, the transmitted pulse was 0.25s and the matched receiver bandwidth required would then be 4Hz. In practice, this could not be used due to start-up drift in the receiver local oscillator and the transmitter. (In a simple radar system, the receiver local oscillator is normally turned off during the transmit pulse and re-activated during the receiving period.). The typical modern short-range radar uses a transmitted pulse width of about 1μs; hence the matched filter bandwidth would be a minimum of 1MHz. The GL2 anti-aircraft radar used a pulse duration of ~3μs and a repetition rate of 1000Hz, which gives a time between adjacent transmit pulses of 1ms. The receive period would therefore be a maximum of 1ms. The matched filter bandwidth would have been about 300kHz.

Zoltán Bay, for his moon radar experiments, used a transmitter pulse of 60μs and a receiver bandwidth of about 200kHz. If a matched bandwidth filter had

In modern radar receivers, the receiver is not turned off completely, due to problems of re-establishing it in the very short time between transmit pulses ~1μs. Desensitising (or 'desensing') the receiver is used to prevent overload and damage to the sensitive front-end and mixer stages. Here a device known as a 'spark-gap-switch' or 'T/R cell' (Transmit/Receive cell) is used to clamp the signal from the transmitter to a safe level, to prevent damage to the early stages of the receiver. A T/R cell is a device filled with ionising gas, such as neon or xenon which, when the transmitter provides a pulse of energy, perhaps as much as 1MW, the gas ionises and causes a short circuit to appear across the receiver input. When the transmitter is off, the receiver is connected via the T/R cell to the antenna with a low loss. In effect, the T/R cell is a very fast antenna changeover relay.

been available, it would need to have had a bandwidth of about 17kHz. (The receiver bandwidths quoted are not the normal -3dB bandwidth but the 'effective noise bandwidth', which is approximately 1.2 times the -3dB bandwidth, taking into account the IF filter shape factor.)

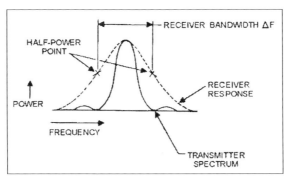

Fig 2.6: Receiver half-power bandwidth - dotted line, and radar transmitter spectrum - solid line

The maximum and minimum ranges achievable are directly related to the transmitter pulse length and the pulse repetition frequency (PRF). For high resolution of

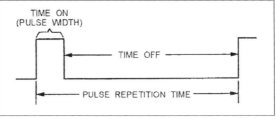

Fig 2.7: Transmitter pulse repetition rate (PRF)

close targets, a very short pulse is required with a short duration between adjacent pulses (high PRF). For maximum range sensitivity, a long pulse is needed with a long duration between adjacent pulses (low PRF).

In practice, early radars of this type had maximum ranges of about 30 to 150km. For radar using 1µs pulse repetition, period the minimum range would be 150m.

The MDS is determined by several factors. Some of these are not under the control of the designer, for example the atmospheric background noise. The ultimate sensitivity is largely determined by the noise performance of the early receiver stages and the transmission line loss between the antenna and the receiver RF amplifier stages.

The available thermal noise power is defined by the formula:

$$Av = kTB_n$$

where: k = Boltzmann's constant = 1.38×10^{-23}jK^{-1},

   T = temperature, K,

   B_n = bandwidth of the receiver, Hz.

If T is taken to be 17°C = 290K, then the factor kT = 4×10^{-21} WHz^{-1}.

A second factor is the bandwidth of the receiver. As the receiver noise power per unit of bandwidth is constant, by reducing the receiver bandwidth the SNR of the echo is increased. As has been already mentioned, the ideal radar receiver IF bandwidth is approximately the reciprocal of the period, τ, of the transmitted pulse. This is a typical engineering case of conflicting parameters. By reducing the receiver bandwidth the sensitivity increases until the matched filter bandwidth is reached. Further reducing the bandwidth causes the sensitivity to decrease as the bandwidth of the echo signal is greater than that of the filter; this causes a loss of detectable energy.

For very long-range targets, the transmitted pulse can be made very long, up to a maximum of 2.5s in the case of the Moon, and hence the receiver bandwidth can be extremely narrow to maximise the sensitivity. Receiver bandwidths of 1Hz and below (if they can be achieved) become beneficial in such cases. With modern digital signal processing this is readily achieved. The only limitation to this is the frequency stability of the transmitter and receiver oscillators and any Doppler shift.

POST-DETECTION SIGNAL ENHANCEMENT

Post-detection processing can be used to give an enhanced SNR. In a typical radar receiver, by utilising video processing with a bandwidth of half of the IF bandwidth, a theoretical 3dB increase in sensitivity can be achieved.

It is as well to explain how this 'half-bandwidth' filtering works. The received signal, when it is processed by the detector, is effectively a double-sideband signal, similar to AM but without a coherent central carrier. In the AM detector the signal is 'folded' about the centre into a single signal containing the sidebands. As each sideband is a mirror image of the other, the information in each is the same, but 180° out of phase. By folding the signal at the centre, the two sidebands are added together in phase and a 3dB increase in amplitude occurs. Since the signal now only occupies half of the original bandwidth the video-filter-bandwidth required to pass the signal is halved.

Range Measurement

The determination of the range to the target is relatively simple for the perfect radar case, in practice it is more difficult due to various factors. In the perfect case, the assumption is made that the target is clearly identified, free of background clutter and causes specular reflection, such as a perfect mirror would exhibit. The time taken for the transmitted pulse to travel from the transmitter antenna to the instant of the reception of the echo gives the range. The velocity of radio waves, c, is the same as that of light, $c = 3 \times 10^8$ ms^{-1}. (The velocity of light is known to within about one part in 10 million, but it is of little practical importance).

By accurately determining the epoch time of the pulse and the instant of the echo reception, the distance travelled can be determined as this gives the 'flight-time' from the transmitter to the target and back to the receiver. The range is half the 'flight distance'. Accurate atomic clocks allow the range to be determined with great precision. (the distance to the Moon has been measured to within 3mm).

However, the typical radar target is not specular and the echo signal does not therefore appear to emanate from one point. This causes the returned pulses to be smeared in time and is equivalent to slight defocusing of the target. This gives an uncertainty to the absolute value of the range. If the case of the Moon is taken, which has a radius of 1780km, the extra time taken for the signal to penetrate to the outer limbs is approximately 1ms.

A secondary factor is that not all the energy impinging on the target is reflected directly back towards the receiver, some is reflected outwards at an angle away from the radar. (In the case of the Moon the reflection ratio is only about 5%). In some cases, this wave could then strike another object which acts like a secondary reflector. This causes multiple echoes that appear as an aberration in the range. In the case where the target, the secondary reflector or the observer is moving, variable aberrations in range are produced.

A replica of this effect is 'ghosting' on television reception from multipath signals. If the transmitted wave strikes a moving object, such as an aircraft, the ghosting will appear to vary rapidly. The rapid variation in signal level, or 'flutter' as it is commonly called, is due to wave interference between the wanted and unwanted return signals. At one instant the waves are in phase and so reinforce the received signal, at another instant the waves are out of phase and cause destructive cancellation.

The Moon has a very rough surface, and the many craters cause the radar signal to be reflected into deep space and hence away from the receiver. It also has a secondary factor, the 'libration effect'. The Moon does not prescribe a pure circular orbit around the Earth.

At one time it is moving faster and at other times slower; this causes the two limbs of the Moon to be seen at different times in its orbit. An observer on Earth hence sees more than 50% of the surface pointed towards Earth. This rocking, or libration, causes the Moon's surface to give variable reflection over a period of time. This causes a fading mechanism that varies the received signal echo, known as 'libration fading'

A further complication is that the strength of the receiver output is directly proportional to the duration of the echo signal. If the transmitter pulse width, τ, were very short, it would be difficult to detect the resulting echo in the intrinsic background noise, as a wide bandwidth would need to be used at the receiver. Therefore, it is common to use a relatively long pulse for the transmitter to obtain sufficient illumination of the target, and hence optimum performance.

(Optimum does not mean 'best'; more correctly it means the best that can be attained *given the conflicting circumstances*).

A final problem is any delay caused by the IF filtering. Any narrow-band filter has an inherent delay for the signal to pass through it. The narrower the filter the longer the delay. In conventional receivers this is of no importance, except in the case of television and radar receivers.

In television receivers the IF filters are known as linear-phase, as the television picture signal is several megahertz wide. The filter is designed to have the same amount of phase shift across its passband. Without this, the picture quality would be severely compromised. In radar receivers, a similar technique is employed and these filters are known as 'time-delay-equalised'. By employing time-delay-equalised filters of a known delay, the display can be calibrated to correct the error.

In some very long-range radar systems, for example the US Navy space debris tracking system operating on 216.98MHz uses an 800kW transmitter which radiates a continuous carrier. Reception of echoes is performed by a remote-receiving site that has a high attenuation to the transmitter (bi-static system). This is the way that Doppler speed detectors work, except in this case the transmitter and receiver are housed in the same unit and a small portion of the transmitter output is used as the receiver local oscillator. This is a zero-IF type of receiver. When the target is not moving, the DC output from the detector is a constant value. When the target is moving the receiver output varies in voltage at the Doppler rate, which is an audible frequency. By feeding the audio into a frequency-sensitive circuit, the relative speed is calculated.

An interesting fact is that for the original detection of Venus by the Millstone Hill radar of MIT's Lincoln Laboratory, a relatively short transmitter pulse of 2ms was chosen with a pulse repetition frequency of 30Hz. The one-way flight time was predicted to be about 4.5 min. After 4.5min, the transmitter was turned off and the receiver activated for a period of 5min. The assumed distance to Venus was approximately 45.5 x 10^6km at the closest point (perigee). At apogee, Venus requires a flight time of over 28min.

Using the equipment (265kW transmitter, a dish of 25m diameter and a low-noise receiver with an effective noise temperature of 170K), the predicted SNR was -10dB, at the expected range of 45.5 x 10^6km. This was far too low a value to give a reliable result. The expected path loss was 314dB.

A process of integrating (adding) each successive received pulse to the previous ones enhanced the signal over the 4.5min receive period and gave the expected result. This was done by receiving the echo pulses, buried in the noise, converted by an analogue-to-digital converter; it was then recorded in a digital format onto magnetic tape. By comparing this to another tape containing a replica of the transmitted signal, correlation was done using an IBM-704 computer, and so the detection was conclusively proved.

However, it was later shown that the range obtained was incorrect by approximately 10,000km. A second measurement by the Jet Propulsion Laboratory (JPL) of the California Institute of Technology, using a more sensitive system, fixed the distance to Venus and hence the Astronomical Unit, the standard for measuring all other objects.

The Astronomical Unit, (AU), is the distance from the Earth to the Sun. The Venus radar experiment fixed the value at 145,599,000km to within 1 part in 100,000. Today, the accepted figure is 149,600,000km after further measurements by Jodrell Bank refined the measurement by repeating the Venus radar experiment in 1961. The reason an incorrect range resulted was because the MIT radar counted one pulse too many in the 8100 transmitted during the 4.5min transmit period.

Venus is a better reflector of radio and light waves than the Moon. The ratio of reflected radio waves (albedo) is about 14% and for sunlight 76%, whereas the Moon is only 5% for radio waves and 7% for sunlight. (For comparison purposes, the Earth reflects 36% of the light falling on it and Mars 16%).

Venus, the morning and evening star, appears as a very bright object to the naked eye (due to its high albedo) in the sky to the west and is usually observable just before or immediately after the Sun has set and remains visible for a period of about 4h before itself setting. It was also later discovered to be an intense radio source.

The reason for the superior reflection was found to be due to the dense hydrocarbon clouds surrounding the planet; these act as a better reflector than the Moon, which has no discernible atmosphere. It has been postulated that the clouds are the source of the intense radio noise under the action of the strong magnetic field of the planet.

Subsequent radar investigation revealed some details of the planet surface by using a much higher frequency to penetrate the atmosphere and obtain ground echoes.

Range Ambiguity

As has been described, the maximum range possible is a function of the time between adjacent transmit pulses. However, there is one pitfall awaiting the unwary. The possibility exists of a target being detected at an incorrect range.

Consider a short pulse radar with a pulse length of 1µs and a repetition frequency of 1000Hz. The time between adjacent transmit pulses is therefore 1ms. As the radio wave travels at the speed of light (3×10^8 ms^{-1}), in a time of 1ms it can travel 300km. The range is half the total distance, as the signal has to travel to the target and back again in this time. A PRF of 1000Hz hence gives a 'maximum unambiguous range' (Ru) of 150km. Now consider a target slightly more than the maximum unambiguous range of 150km. This will give a range indication much closer than it actually is.

For the echo to be seen at an unambiguous range, it must arrive at the receiver before the next transmit pulse, hence 150km is the maximum range possible with a 1ms receiver time. If an echo arrives during the next transmit pulse, the receiver being blanked will not see it. Now if the echo is due to a target at a slightly greater range than 150km and if it takes, say, 1.1ms to travel to the target and back again, the receiver will see this echo at a range corresponding to ~100µs or 15km, which gives a false range. (The correct range is 150 + 15 = 165km.) This effect is known as 'second-time-around'. In order to get long unambiguous ranges the PRF needs to be low, hence a long time between transmit pulses.

The second-time-around effect can also occur for 'third time around' and longer range targets. Hence, a target at 325km would give rise to an echo that occurs at a range time of 2.166ms. Because the range gate is set to 1ms in our example, the target would appear to occur at 0.166ms or a range of 25km. The only clue to whether this is a valid target is the receiver detector amplitude. For a target at such a great distance the echo would be very small and could possibly be undetected. However, if the target were very large the signal level could be as large as a close-in target. To get around this problem modern radar systems use multiple pulse coding. In this technique the transmitter might generate one pulse for the first transmission, the second transmission will use two pulses very closely spaced. Hence, a second time around echo can be distinguished by counting the number of received echoes for each sweep of the time base.

In the original Jodrell Bank meteor observation paper published in 1947 by Prentice, Lovell and Banwell [4], a curious anomaly is apparent. The paper states the radar used a PRF of 150Hz with a pulse width of 8µs, and a transmitter peak power of 150kW. This is in conflict with the official specification of the GL2, which used a PRF of either 1000Hz or 2200Hz and a transmitter pulse width of 2 to 3µs and 100kW peak power. The maximum range for a PRF of 150Hz is approx. 1000km. The antennas were also different from the original GL2 types, being replaced by four-element Yagis. This radar was sourced from J S Hey and was modified for improved long-range from a V-2 missile detection radar; hence the lower PRF used. In total, 1679 GL2s were manufactured during the war, (204 were supplied to Russia) and a small number were later modified by J S Hey for improved V 2 detection by fitting a Yagi antenna tilted upwards to 60° elevation. It appears from the photograph of the Jodrell Bank radar that this was one of the later V-2 sets.

However, the ranges shown as being measured by Lovell do not correlate with the expected ranges for meteor trails, which occur in the range of about 70km to 120km altitude. In a table published in the paper, the ranges of the majority of meteor reflections are shown as being a grouping around about 80 to 120km, within the accepted ranges of meteor trails, with two lesser groupings at about 270km and 400km.

The amplitude of the A scope readings are given in an arbitrary manner related to SNR and the size of 'blip' seen on the A-scope display; the majority of the reflections at about 120km range are shown as being of value three. The odd thing is the amplitude values for the 270km and 400km reflections. These are also shown as being three.

The values to be expected from such long ranges, (using the standard radar equations and assuming the targets were of similar size and reflectivity), would be very much smaller and probably below the noise floor of the receiver. Equivalent relative amplitudes would be approximately 0.4 and 0.01. After consultations with several radar specialists, the only logical explanation as to how these distant targets could possibly give such reflection amplitudes is they must have been due to reflections from the ionosphere E-layer, which we call Sporadic-E or Es. Es has a very high reflection coefficient and can cover areas of tens or hundreds of square kilometres, hence giving large echo returns. Eli Brookner in his book *Radar Technology* [5], gives details of erratic echoes observed at long ranges on L-band radar systems due to E-layer anomalies. The long range echoes observed by Lovell must have been due to signals that struck this highly ionised patch and were then deflected to strike the Earth's surface at some distant point. The signal would then be reflected off the Earth's surface to the Es cloud and then back to the radar. This assumption seems correct as the echo periods where much longer than for normal meteor trails, being up to 90s in some cases. All of the very long-range echoes were of long duration.

Quite why Hey and Lovell chose such a long time between pulses is a mystery as they should have been aware of the signal amplitude limitations from targets at a range of 1000km. The official specification of the GL2 was a maximum range of 40,000 yards or about 38km.

This is with the original GL2 dipole antennas; with the four-element Yagi antennas, the range would only extend to about 150km. The paper states the antenna gain was "7.5 as a power ratio" which is approximately 9dB over an isotropic source or 6.9dBd (dBd = dB relative to a single dipole), which agrees with the four-element Yagis used on the radar.

The sensitivity calculations given in the paper stated that the receiver had a MDS of 2×10^{-14}W in an IF bandwidth of 250kHz. In the paper, the value of received signal corresponding to an amplitude of 3 is given as 18×10^{-14}W, hence it was a healthy size signal, being about 7.5dB above the receiver MDS. The original GL2 radar had an IF bandwidth of about 300kHz, which agrees with the matched filter bandwidth figure of the 2 - 3μs transmitter pulse of the GL2. The paper states the IF bandwidth was 250kHz, hence the 8μs pulse stated is not in agreement; it would need to be about 125kHz to give optimum performance. This factor was, however, not known at the time the equipment was manufactured.

Taking into account all the stated system improvements, the increased transmitter power (50%) and the antenna gain increase (~15dB), the maximum range still does not add up to much more than 300km, unless a significant receiver improvement also occurred, which is not mentioned in any of the literature.

Hey in his book *The Evolution of Radio Astronomy*, states that experiments with improved receivers did not give any significant increase in range due to the high atmospheric noise at the low VHF frequencies being used.

To support this theory further is the way the meteor reflection is generated. The meteor will only generate a reflection upon grazing the Earth's upper atmosphere; this generates the ionised electron trail. At altitudes of 270km and 400km there is no significant atmosphere and so it would not be impossible to generate an electron trail.

Dr Graham Elford of Adelaide University, Australia, has considered this possibility and confirmed that no meteor reflection could occur at these altitudes. In his experiments with the Buckland Park MF radar operating on 1.98MHz, the greatest altitude observed is approximately 150km.

It is the writer's belief that the original Jodrell Bank paper contained an error regarding the transmitter pulse period. At the same time as the first Jodrell Bank paper was published, a second paper was printed in the same issue of the MNRAS Journal [6]. Lovell's paper occupied pages 155 to 163, Hey's paper occupied pages 176 to 183.

In between these two papers was the second Jodrell Bank paper also covering the Giacobinid Meteor Shower. *Radio Observations of the Giacobinid Meteors*, 1946 submitted by A C B Lovell, C J Banwell and J A Clegg. This occupied pages 164 to 175. Hence, the three papers spanned from page 155 to 183 and would no doubt all be read in sequence.

As we now know from Hey's book *The Evolution of Radio Astronomy*, published in the early 1970s, the two radar systems were 'twins', and both had identical parameters apart from the operating frequency, Hey used 64MHz whereas Lovell's radar was on 72MHz. In Hey's paper, the details gave the transmitter as "3µs pulses, 150kW peak power and a PRF of 150Hz". It seems fairly certain that the 8µs stated in Lovell's paper was a typographical error and it should have read 3µs, not an uncommon mistake for someone such as a secretary typing a manuscript from handwritten notes, a badly written '3' being read as an '8'.

One wonders however as to why neither person spotted the mistake, Hey undoubtedly was intimately aware of the system he had 'loaned' to Lovell, as he was responsible for modifying it and delivering it in person to the University of Manchester and then spent over a week setting it up and training Lovell and his people on how to operate it. That it should have taken almost 60 years for the error to be spotted is remarkable, as the error should have been spotted either during proof-reading the typed manuscript or later when it was published in the *MNRAS Journal*.

In actual fact, Hey's book gives details of another experiment involving the same radar systems where he and his colleagues used three radars to observe from different sites simultaneously so, in fact, there must have been several of these special radars available after the war [7].

NOMENCLATURE COMMENTS

To eliminate confusion as to the various names quoted about meteors in general, it is useful to note the International Astronomical Union's (IAU) recommendations for the names and their definitions.

- **Meteoroid**: Dust particle moving in space or entering the Earth's atmosphere, where it is ablated.
- **Meteorite**: Residual body that reaches the Earth's surface from space.
- **Meteor**: The phenomenon of a meteoroid's interaction with the atmosphere, usually appearing as a transient trail of light ('shooting star'), and/or forming an ionised trail.
- **Meteor Trail**: The linear nature of a meteor, implying luminosity or ionisation extending from the head. The term 'meteor' is frequently used in place of 'meteor trail'.
- **Meteor Reflection Equation**: The method in which the ionised trail is generated depends on several factors. The velocity of the meteoroid entering the Earth's atmosphere and the density of the atmosphere are the two main factors. A meteor travelling at high velocity will generate more free electrons to form the trail than a slower one. The amount of ionisation per unit length of trail depends roughly on the cube of the speed of the meteoroid. Also, as the density of the atmosphere is greater at low altitudes, the expectation is that, upon first entering the rarefied upper atmosphere, the generation of the trail will initially be weak and it will increase as the meteoroid plunges lower into the denser atmosphere. When the friction generated becomes high enough to start vaporising or 'ablating' the meteoroid, the 'shooting-star' or meteor trail will become visible to the human eye.

A similar effect occurs when a spacecraft re-enters the Earth's atmosphere. Here the massive cloud of ionised electrons generated form a radio reflector preventing any radio communications until the spacecraft slows to below the critical velocity. The electron cloud generated causes the 'radio-blackout' during the re-entry phase.

It is also important to note the importance of the approach angle of a meteoroid. If the meteoroid strikes the Earth's upper atmosphere at an angle shallower than 7° it will 'bounce' off and not enter the lower atmosphere. For larger bodies' the meteoroid on first entering the upper rarefied atmosphere will be slowed by the friction generated and the approach angle will steepen as the object is slowed down and the Earth's gravitational attraction acts on the large mass. In certain cases, the angle can reach 45° to the Earth's surface.

In correspondence with Dr Graham Elford, a research scientist at Adelaide University, Australia, the following description is given as to how the meteoroid generates both the ionised electron trail and the visible shooting-star which we associate with meteoroids. Graham Elford has been researching meteoroids since the 1950s when, at the suggestion of Dr Bernard Lovell, the University of

Adelaide was encouraged to take up this challenge. Currently Adelaide University has several new VHF radar systems (~30 - 54MHz) as well as a system operating on 1.98MHz at Buckland Park near Adelaide.

Below is reproduced the relevant portion of Graham Elford's letter to the author in 2004.

The formation of a meteor trail is generally described along the following lines -

Assuming that the meteoroid has a stony composition, (inferred from the spectra of bright meteor trails), collisions of the particle with atmospheric molecules cause the particle to heat and eventually reach ablation temperature. Just prior to ablation a small particle will have melted right through, while larger one may have substantial radial thermal gradients. The transition size is about 200µm. Thermal gradients can cause fragmentation of the larger meteoroids, producing a bunch of particles all moving in essentially the same direction but becoming slightly spread along their path by differential deceleration depending on the size of the daughter particles. At the present time, there is no consensus as regards the prevalence of fragmentation, but my recent work in this area is partly directed to this question.

Having reached ablation temperature (~2000K) atoms of the meteoroid commence evaporating into space while maintaining the speed of the parent body. Subsequent collisions of the individual meteoroid atoms with the (essentially stationary) atmospheric molecules cause excitation of the meteoroid atoms (typically Na, Mg, Ca, Si, Fe) which emit light as they decay to less excited states. Molecules of atmospheric gases have higher excitation energies and thus there is only weak visible radiation associated with oxygen and nitrogen. Occasionally, a collision process is favourable to ionisation of the meteor atom and a free electron is formed. The associated ions are rapidly 'thermalised' by further collisions with the atmospheric molecules (~10 collisions in about 1ms) and they and the free electrons form an ionised column (meteor trial) behind the ablating meteoroid.

Ablation commences at a height of about 120km for meteoroids with speeds of 60 - 70kms^{-1} and at about 85km for those with speeds of 10 - 15kms^{-1}. The ionised trail diffuses radially at a rate controlled by the positive ions; a process called ambipolar diffusion. The physics of this process is well known from laboratory studies, and the ionisation distribution across the trail rapidly becomes gaussian. As is shown in McKinley's book [8], diffusion causes the reflection coefficient of the trail for radar waves directed orthogonal to the trail (sometimes called transverse scattering) to fall off exponentially with time if the trail is under-dense (line density $<$~2 x 10^{14} electrons/m). The significance here is that this effect sets a height ceiling for scatter of VHF radar signals that is about 105km for under-dense trails. For most meteor radars, the bulk of the echoes comes from under-dense trails. Thus, most VHF meteor radars detect almost all trails produced by meteoroids with speeds $<$40kms-1 (assuming the trail line density is sufficient to give a *detectable echo), but trails from meteoroids with speeds in excess of about 50kms⁻¹ form at heights above the 'diffusion ceiling' and are thus undetectable (unless they are members of the small population of over-dense trails).*

There is evidence, from the Giotto spacecraft observations of the dust around Halley's comet, that there is a significant fraction of 'tar-like' dust, rich in hydrocarbons. Such material entering the Earth's atmosphere will ablate much more readily than stony material, and thus will form trails at greater heights, possibly as high as 150 - 160km. Such trails will not produce visible light, as the particles are deficient in metals. However, the trails will be ionised and should be detectable by a suitable radar.

"Such a radar exists at Adelaide. Using an array of dipoles on 2MHz covering an area of about 1km², we produce a relatively narrow beam that can be directed down to 45° elevation. With this system, we have detected echoes up to a height of 140km (roughly the 'ceiling' of the 2MHz system), thus confirming the existence of meteor trails at this height and by implication the presence of low ablation temperature material. The experiment is difficult as one has to wait until the E-region has decayed sufficiently, which means observations are only possible for a few hours just before sunrise.

At the present time, we have no idea of the fraction of 'tar-like' dust entering the atmosphere. I have conjectured that it might be the dominant form of meteoroid dust. Maybe the Stardust space probe will tell us. For the radio amateur, it is worthwhile keeping in mind that MF radio signals may be forward scattered by trails at 150km when the underlying ionisation is weak.

The most important thing to note from this correspondence is that not all meteoroids produce a visible trail.

In fact, the scientific community is now tending towards the idea that as little as 50% of meteoroids entering the Earth's atmosphere will be stony and produce visible trails. Hence, although no visible trails are seen, the chance of a meteor trail occurring is quite high at any time of the day or time of year.

The equation for the radio frequency power scattered back to the radar receiver is -

$$\varepsilon = 3.3 \times 10^{-28} \frac{\alpha^2 \lambda^3}{R^3} P_0 G^2,$$

where: α = number of electrons produced per cm path by the meteor,
λ = wavelength (cm),
P_0 = peak transmitter power (W),
G = antenna gain (power ratio),
R = range of echo (cm).

The dependence of α on size and velocity is given in the theory of meteor ionisation developed by Nicolai Herlofson, whose calculations indicate that, for a meteor velocity of 40km/s, a meteor near the limit of visibility will produce $\alpha = 10^{10}$ electrons cm^{-1}.

Also of significance is the effect λ has on the echo signal amplitude. For low frequencies, the echo amplitude will be much greater than that for a shorter wavelength. As the factor is a cube law, doubling the frequency will produce an echo signal that is one-eighth (-9dB) that of the lower frequency, for the same conditions. Hence, 50MHz will give correspondingly larger echoes than a 144MHz signal, the difference being about 24 times stronger (14dB) on 6m than on 2m.

Using the published parameters of the Jodrell Bank system gives a received signal power of 3 x 10^{-14}W for meteors at a range of 95km near the limit of visibility. As the detectable sensitivity is 2 x 10^{-14}W, this is a signal slightly above the receiver noise floor and can be expected to be detected. For meteoroids travelling at higher velocities, the echo signal will be considerably stronger.

Head-Echo Effect

The Head-Echo effect is very similar to the spacecraft re-entry problem.

A recent study undertaken in Scandinavia in 1997 & 1998 has identified a second mechanism for echo reflection. This is called the 'Head-Echo effect'. The size of a typical meteoroid is extremely small, being about the size of a grain of sand. This was not expected to cause a reflection, as it is so tiny. However, scientists have now concluded that an echo is possible because the particle rushing into the Earth's atmosphere generates an electron cloud in front of it. This electron cloud is capable of reflecting a radar signal.

The target size is small in comparison to the electron trail generated by the particle burning up, and hence a very high frequency needs to be used to detect the object. Hey and Lovell both reported observing Head-Echo reflections using the VHF radar systems, but the number was very small in comparison to normal echoes and of much shorter duration.

The Scandinavian experiment used 930MHz radar with extremely high power and three very large parabolic antennas (32m) connected as a tri-static antenna to form a 3D-search radar. Out of approximately 200 meteors observed, using conventional VHF radar running in parallel, 10 meteors showed the Head-Echo effect. As a high frequency gives little or no reflection from the ionised trail, the distinguishing of this from the Head-Echo effect was the clue to why echoes were observed in some cases.

In another recent study undertaken by Australian and American scientists several very high power radars were used to observe the Head-Echo effect. These used military radars situated at Roi-Namur in the Kwajalein Atoll, Republic of Marshall Islands and are defence radars operated by the Australian and American Air Forces. In addition to the main radar, known as ALTAIR, which transmits 6MW peak power on 160MHz and 422MHz simultaneously, several other radars took part in the observation. These other radars were TRADEX, (L- and S-band radar), ALCOR, (C-band radar) and MMW, (operating on Ka-band and W-band). Hence, the spectrum was covered from VHF to the upper microwave bands.

Fig 2.8: Arecibo dual frequency radar display of a terminal meteor event. The initial head-echo obtained by the 430MHz UHF radar is shown on the top trace, and is caused by the ionised cloud surrounding the head, which quickly decays to zero. At the time the head-echo disappears, the longer-wavelength 40MHz VHF radar shows the longer normal reflection from the ionised trail. The VHF echo is smaller in amplitude than normal because the antenna is pointed 'up the trail' (to acquire the head-echo signal), and not orthogonally, as would normally be the case

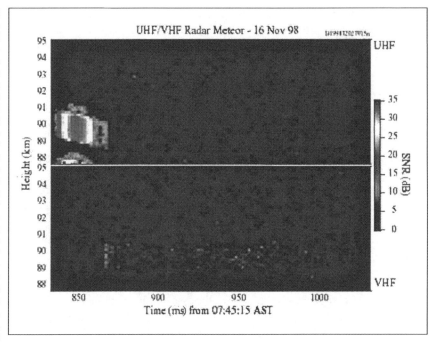

ALTAIR used a 46m parabolic antenna and either right-hand or left-hand circular polarisation to determine the echo polarity and range. It was found that approximately 1.6 Head-Echo returns per second occurred during the peak of the Leonid shower.

RELEVANCE TO AMATEUR METEOR SCATTER

In a very recent study performed at Arecibo Observatory (operated by Cornell University) in Puerto Rico during 1998 and 2003, a definite factor emerged which is of great importance to amateurs involved in meteor scatter communication. It has been known for some time that the use of the UHF bands is not very productive, but the exact reason was not known. In this study, Mathews [9] used a dual-radar system operating at 40MHz and 430MHz to observe meteoroid reflections simultaneously.

From this it became apparent that the Head-Echo effect is the predominant mode at UHF and, as the echo decayed away after a very short 'ping', the VHF radar showed a longer and more pronounced reflection from the ionised trail. (In the Head-Echo, the ionised cloud is pushed forward in front of the rapid body and the target area is extremely small, being only a few tens of metres in diameter, and hence requires an extremely powerful radar to illuminate the target sufficiently.) The ionised trail which follows is a much larger target and extends for several kilometres behind the meteoroid, and hence will act as a better reflector to VHF signals. The Head-Echo effect occurs at altitudes higher than traditional trail reflections, and these exist in the region of 120km down to about 90km.

The picture is one taken from an earlier study using the Arecibo radar during 1998. In this is clearly seen the UHF echo which abruptly disappears and reappears at the lower VHF radar frequency.

RECEIVER IF PARAMETERS

If the radar receiver uses an IF amplifier that compresses the signal amplitude, such as a FM limiting amplifier, before passing the IF signal to a linear detector, the echo trace from a target at 15km or 50km is apparently the same amplitude. So range estimation from the target amplitude is not possible. In early radar receivers, the IF amplifier was a linear gain-controlled stage and the gain was manually adjusted by the operator to suit the requirements ruling at the time: a close-in target would give a large deflection on the A scope display; a target at great range would give a very small deflection, hence a skilled operator could, to some extent, distinguish between second-time-around signals, assuming both targets have a similar cross sectional area. With modern radar receivers the logarithmic amplifier gives accurate echo size indication and so this problem is alleviated.

TARGET REFLECTIVITY

A further problem is the reflectivity of the target. A large metallic object, such as an aircraft, will give a strong echo because the amount of radio wave energy striking it will be high. A bird, being of much smaller cross-section, will give a much smaller echo. But if the bird is several kilometres from the radar it could be falsely confused with a larger target at a greater range if only amplitude was used as the range criterion.

A technique used during WWII to jam the enemy radar was the use of aluminium foil cut into strips of length $\lambda/2$ at the radar frequency. These acted like dipoles and caused a radar receiver to be saturated by many strong echoes. This was known as 'chaff' or 'window', and was initially dumped by hand from aircraft to flutter slowly down to Earth. The effect was very good and caused the enemy radar to be put out of action for several minutes. Later versions used strip-filled canisters, fired from cannons on the aircraft, to cover many square kilometres of the sky. This technique is still widely used today. With modern microwave radar, a similar effect is observed during rainstorms. Consequently, it is often found that a strategic radar site has two different operating frequencies so that it can switch to a lower frequency to reduce the chaff- or rainstorm-generated reflections.

ANTENNA BEAMWIDTH

In the ideal radar case, the antenna beam width would be chosen to be the same as or smaller than the apparent diameter of the target. In most low-frequency radio astronomy cases, it is impractical to do this without resorting to a type of interferometer technique.

If the case of the Moon is considered, the angle the Moon subtends to an observer on Earth is about 0.5°. At VHF and UHF it is not practical to achieve such a narrow antenna beamwidth using a single antenna. Jodrell Bank Mk1 - a 250ft dish at 152MHz - has a -3dB beam width of 1.5°, and at 408MHz it has a -3dB beam width of 0.7°, and so it illuminates a considerably greater portion of the sky than the Moon occupies. Because of this, the Moon only receives a portion of the transmitted signal and the remainder is lost.

The penalty of not concentrating all the power on to the target is twofold: one is the obvious partial illumination of the target and hence a weaker return echo; the second is that the antenna 'sees' a much greater portion of the sky. This causes degradation of the received echo signal as the portion of the sky may contain other radio sources which radiate interfering signals and reduce the SNR of the radar return from the target.

> The case of the Moon is not too serious, as the target is large and relatively close and hence the echoes are likely to be strong. Tests performed at Jodrell Bank, soon after the Mk1 telescope was commissioned, showed that as little as 1W was required to obtain audible echoes at 152MHz.
>
> A former colleague of mine had been employed at Jodrell Bank during this period and, as he was a radio amateur, he was asked to help in setting up the first Moon radar tests.
>
> Using a 10W AM mobile radio, connected to the feed-point with about 100m of coax cable, he succeeded in hearing his own voice echo using the Mk1 dish. Unfortunately, it was transmitting on 152MHz and not 144MHz, otherwise he could have claimed to be the first UK amateur to achieve a moonbounce echo on 2m.

If the case of Venus is considered, where the target subtends an angle of much less than 0.01°, the effect is very much more severe due to the far greater range. The system sensitivity for detecting Venus by radar needs to be nearly 10 million times better than that for the Moon (68dB).

One simple way to decrease the antenna beamwidth for a given size parabolic antenna is to increase the frequency. Provided the profile of the parabolic antenna is accurate enough, this seems an attractive alternative; however, there are negative effects to this.

The gain of the antenna will be greater at the higher frequency but, against this must be weighed the higher path loss, the extra difficulty of designing low-noise receivers, the additional transmission line losses and the difficulty of generating high power at these frequencies.

The final outcome must be reviewed on a case-by-case basis. If this is being considered as an alternative to building a larger-aperture antenna, there is a finite practical and economic upper limit for the size of a single parabolic antenna. The largest fully-steerable parabolic dish, at present, is the 100m diameter dish at the Max Planck observatory near Bonn, Germany and the largest fixed dish is that in Arecibo, Puerto Rico which is 1000 ft (300m) in diameter.

Although larger antennas have been proposed several times, - the 600ft American dish which was started and abandoned due to the escalating cost, and the proposed Jodrell Bank Mk5, a 500ft dish which was never successfully funded are just two examples - it is unlikely that any larger single dish will be now constructed in the foreseeable future.

The estimate of the cost of a 200m (600ft) diameter steerable dish is approximately $300 million at present prices. It is believed that a comparable-size dish may exist in Russia, but details are sketchy at present. A far cheaper solution is to use two or more smaller antennas as an interferometer system, which gives far greater resolving accuracy.

The GL2 radar originally used dipole arrays, which therefore had a very broad polar pattern, which was preferred for a search radar. To obtain accurate azimuth and elevation information,n a simple 'split-beam' system was used. The two azimuth bearing receiver dipoles were orientated so that a known offset was obtained; this was done by mounting one antenna some distance from the other with a separation of $3\lambda/2$. The receiver had dual phase-sensitive detectors.

The two detectors each fed the A-scope display with an offset so that two blips appeared side by side. As the receiver antenna was turned towards the target, one blip would rise to a maximum and then begin to fall. As one fell, the other blip rose on the display.

When the received signals from both antennas were the same height on the display the antenna was pointed exactly at the target. Hence, the operator rotated the receive antenna to obtain equal heights on both blips. Azimuth accuracy was about 1°. The elevation system used a similar method. The dipole antenna used open-wire feeders to connect to the equipment.

In search mode, the receiver used the single 'range' dipole. When a target was acquired, the receiver operator changed to the two bearing dipoles. The transmitter similarly used a single dipole for search with a beamwidth of about 80° in azimuth and approximately the same in elevation. In the 'follow' mode, the transmitter used four dipoles combined to give a pattern of 21° in azimuth and a large elevation angle spread of about 80°.

Fig 2.9: GL2 radar system. The receiver cabin is in the foreground and the transmitter cabin is behind. The generator is the smaller cabin adjacent to the receiver. (Photograph courtesy of Lew Patterson)

Fig 2.10: GL2 antenna arrangements. (Photograph courtesy of Lew Patterson)

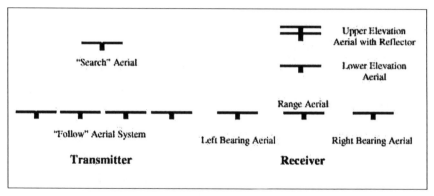

Before we leave the subject of antenna beamwidth, it is useful to see how this effects the determination of a target's position. For the case where the antenna has a wide beamwidth, the determination of the precise direction is very difficult. Consider the antenna has a beamwidth of 40°, and it is rotated to point exactly at the target. The 40° parameter is the 3dB beamwidth. Turning the antenna so that the received signal falls to 3dB below the highest signal level is an angle of 20° either side of the target, assuming the antenna has a perfectly symmetrical pattern. If the antenna were connected to a sensitive receiver used as a transit telescope, the target would appear to be an angular size of 40°. By using a much narrower antenna beamwidth, the apparent angular size falls closer to the correct value. In the case of the Moon, we know that the optical angular size is about 0.5°, but even a very large amateur antenna array at, say, 144MHz cannot be expected to have a 3dB beamwidth of much less than about 3°. In the case of EME, this is not of much concern unless there is also a large interfering source within the antenna beamwidth, possibly the Sun. In the case of a radio telescope, this situation is chronic as we might be trying to separate two radio stars which are only 0.1° apart. In a case such as this, we would need to use an interferometer to achieve the necessary angular resolution.

DOPPLER EFFECT

As has already been mentioned, one of the factors that needs to be considered is the effect of Doppler shift. If the two objects are not moving relative to one another, the Doppler frequency shift will be zero. In many cases the target is moving relative to the observer - in the case of the Moon, the Doppler shift is quite low (210Hz typically at 144MHz), but is still present.

The formula for calculating Doppler when radar is used is -

$$f_d = \frac{2v_r}{\lambda},$$

where: f_d is the frequency shift in Hz,
v_r is the relative velocity in metres per second,
λ is the wavelength in metres.

In normal systems where one-way communications is used the formula is -

$$f_d = \frac{v_r}{\lambda}.$$

For example, in a meteor radar system, one would expect a large Doppler shift because of the high velocity of the meteors. Typical meteor relative velocities vary between approximately 15km/s to 70km/s. This is because the meteors can enter the Earth's atmosphere in the same direction as the Earth's rotation, hence the relative velocity will be low, or the meteors can enter in a counter-rotating manner, in which case the relative velocity will be high. The Earth rotates in orbit around the Sun at a velocity of approx. 29.8km/s.

In the case of 144MHz (2m), the Doppler shift to be expected would vary between 14.4kHz to 67.2kHz. This would require a receiver that can be 'side-stepped' in frequency from the transmitter to ensure the echo is within the IF bandwidth of the receiver if the bandwidth is narrow. Simply listening on the transmit frequency would yield no echoes as the Doppler shift makes the signal appear several channels away in frequency. Using a wider bandwidth IF to encompass all possible Doppler shift eventualities would require an IF band-width of approximately 140 kHz and would result in a severe loss of sensitivi-ty with the possible consequence that the echo could be undetected. (See later sections for receiver sensitivity calculations.)

In practice, the major reflection when using VHF is not from the meteor, it being a very small target, but from the ionised trail that the meteor generates and leaves as a relatively stationary cloud of electrons as it burns up in the Earth's upper atmosphere. Hence, the Doppler shift to be expected is much lower than the theoretical value.

This has been proved by amateurs using meteor scatter propagation where the frequency offset required is very small. Later observations by Jodrell Bank con-firmed that some meteors generated what are termed 'travelling-echoes', where the apparent position of the target varied at up to 15kms-1. This effect was stud-ied by using the Doppler information from the receiver to determine the veloc-ity of the electron trail. In about 20% of meteors observed, it varied between 2 and 15km/s

REQUIREMENTS FOR RADAR TRANSMITTERS

In order to achieve a long detection range, it is necessary to develop a very high peak power in the transmitted pulse. Although the peak power needs to be very high the average power does not need to be, unless a very long pulse transmis-sion is required. A typical medium-range radar might use a pulse length of 1µs and operate at a pulse repetition frequency of 1kHz. The PRF determines the average power.

For example, taking the original GL2 radar, we know that the peak power was 100kW and the PRF was 1kHz. As the transmitter is only transmitting for 3µs and the time between pulses was 1ms, then the transmitter 'off-time' is 1000µs.

$$\text{Average power} = \frac{\text{Pulse time}}{\text{Off time}} \times \text{Peak power} = \frac{3}{1000} \times 100\text{kW}.$$

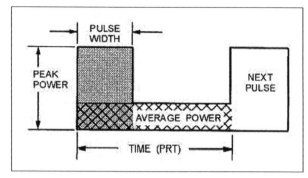

Fig 2.11: Radar transmitter peak and average power

Hence, the average power is only about 300W. If you were to insert a through-line wattmeter in the feed-line it would measure 300W.

The safe operating conditions for pulsed amplifier devices is normally given in terms of duty cycle. This is the percentage of time the device is generating power. For a 1µs transmit pulse at a PRF of 1000Hz, the duty cycle is 0.1%. Hence, the amplifier is in the off state for 99.9% of the time and this allows time for the heat developed to be dissipated, giving a low rise in anode temperature.

This factor may explain one or two discrepancies about the radar system used by Lovell. The official specification for the GL2 lists the peak output power at values of 30kW to 100kW, depending on the modification record. The early versions used the lower power and the later ones had uprated output valves. The same valves were also used in the earlier versions of the Chain Home radars. The peak power stated by Lovell in the 1947 paper is 150kW, but with an 8µs pulse instead of the more normal 2µs or 3µs used in the GL2. The other factor is the PRF. The GL2 had a PRF that could be varied between two settings, 1000Hz and 2200Hz, the lower PRF being used for the search mode. Lovell and Hey state that the PRF used was 150Hz. This is consistent with the higher power stated.

If the official figures were correct, the duty cycle of the GL2 was 0.3% with the lower PRF and, at a 100kW peak power, the average power would be 300W. Lovell's 8µs radar transmitted at a duty cycle of 0.12% with a 150kW peak power, and hence the average power was 180W. These figures are completely plausible, but it does not explain the Ru problem discussed earlier.

Many transmitting valves designed for radar applications are capable of very high peak powers but only limited average powers. An example is the original 2C39 used in early L-band radars and radio altimeters. The official continuous CW rating of the 2C39 is 40W output and the anode dissipation is 100W, but it is capable of 3kW of pulse power with a pulse length of 10µs and 10kW with a 1µs pulse. The limitation is due to the dissipation of the anode and the ease (or otherwise) with which the heat can be extracted. If the heat is not extracted as fast as it is being generated, the valve will overheat and fail. The 2C39A was the original glass-sealed version, which had a limited peak anode voltage rating and, if this was exceeded, the envelope would puncture due to the intense RF field existing in the cavity resonator. Later versions such as the 2C39B,

2C39BA or the 7289 have approximately the same anode dissipation and average power but, because they utilise a ceramic envelope, are capable of much higher peak power outputs. A typical peak power specification is up to 30kW for the 7289 at 1µs pulse length.

The QQVO6-40 double tetrode is capable of 60W continuous CW output at up to 450MHz in Class-C with an anode dissipation of 40W but, under radar medium pulse length operation, it is safe to 1kW peak. It was, in fact, originally designed for UHF radar duty. Many of the modern radar high-power valves are water-cooled and this greatly raises the average power rating and hence the peak power they are safely able to generate. Often the limiting factor is the peak anode voltage the valve can safely sustain without flashover occurring. The 4X150A series of valves were used in US Air Force 200 - 400MHz airborne jammer after WWII and used four valves connected in parallel. These jammers generated up to 100kW peak pulse power.

SPECTRAL SPREADING

One of the major problems associated with high-power radars is the spectral pollution they generate. If the transmitted waveform were the ideal rectangular pulse, with zero rise and fall times, the signal would occupy an infinite bandwidth. This is due to the very fast rise and fall times of the waveform. In a rectangular- or square-wave-modulated signal, the spectrum includes all the harmonics of the modulating frequency up to a very high order. Fourier analysis confirms that adding all the harmonics together algebraically can generate a square-wave pulse.

The main problem is the close-in products caused by the harmonics of the modulating pulse (rise and fall times) related to the PRF. This is unacceptable, and hence great efforts are made to shape the rising and falling edges to limit the bandwidth occupied. This is normally done by passing the rectangular pulse through a 'root-raised-cosine-filter', or Hanning filter. This limits the bandwidth

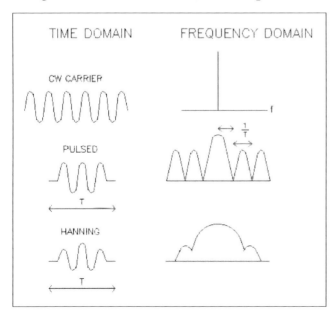

Fig 2.12: Comparison between a CW signal, a pulsed signal without shaping, and a shaped pulse. The left shows the time-domain signal and the right shows the frequency-domain signal

Fig 2.13: Spectral plot of a shaped pulse signal

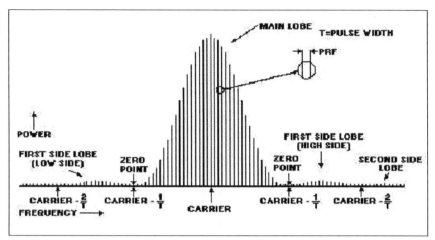

to acceptable proportions. Without frequency shaping, the spectrum envelope would be of (sin x) / x form and spread to infinity with each successive sideband being a little lower in amplitude than the one preceding it.

If the filter were designed for a 10kHz cut-off frequency, the bandwidth would be constrained to about 20kHz.

If the rise and fall times were 1ns, the minimum bandwidth occupied would be 2GHz. This is clearly unacceptable, as it would cause severe interference to other spectrum users.

Often with an L-band radar (23cm) the spectrum is confined to approximately 100MHz by pulse shaping. The degree of shaping possible is obviously a function of the duration of the pulse. If the pulse was 1μs and the shaping used was to achieve a rise and fall time of 0.5μs, the pulse would rise only to about half the peak power, with a consequent loss of range.

Hence, shaping is limited to about 10% of the pulse duration to ensure adequate peak power is achieved. With 10% shaping, the maximum peak power is ~95% of the rectangular pulse case.

Pollution caused by out-of-band signals is normally constrained by high-power band-pass filters in the transmitter output stage. These filters need to handle very high peak powers and they present some severe challenges to limit the amount of power lost as heat, often requiring water cooling, and they need to have an exceptionally high breakdown voltage because of the high power being transmitted.

When the author lived in the UK, he was active on all VHF/UHF bands up to 13cm. When operating on 23cm, the Heathrow Airport approach radar (L-band 1215 - 1260MHz) would be such a large signal that the S-meter would rocket over to full scale every 4s. This coincided with the times when the radar antenna was pointing at his amateur station. The author was resident in Liverpool a distance of about 200 miles (320km) away. A similar situation occurs with the Durban Airport approach radar, also an L-band system. The Fylingdales BMEWS (Ballistic Missile Early Warning System) operating on 425MHz caused widespread interference to the 70cm band for the same reason.

TRANSMIT PULSE SHAPING METHODS

As the pulse shape of the transmitter is a critical factor to prevent spectral spreading, it is necessary to look at the various ways this can be applied. The simplest way to generate the required pulse shape is to perform this at a low power level. A simple method is to utilise a linear variable attenuator with a large attenuation range driven by voltage or current with the necessary-shaped waveform. The shaping filter can be an op-amp with a feedback network to establish the cut-off frequency. This is a classic active-filter design, and simply changing component values can make many different filter types. For example, Butterworth, Chebyshev, raised cosine etc. The rectangular pulse is applied to the filter and the output is a pulse with rounded rise and fall edges.

Pulse Modulator

If a true rectangular pulse is desired, there are many methods to achieve this at low power. One of the simplest is to use a PIN diode operated as a switch in series with the RF. The RF signal is applied to one side and an amplifier follows it. The amplifier can be a Class-C type as used in frequency multipliers. Hence, the non-linear amplifier helps to steepen the rise and fall edges. The PIN diode is switched on and off with a square-wave current of the required pulse length. The fact that the PIN diode only has a limited amount of attenuation in the 'off' state is not too serious, as the multiplier stage will cease conducting when the drive level drops below a critical level. Hence, the multiplier gives extra isolation and attenuation levels of 100dB are not too difficult to achieve.

In a conventional radar transmitter today, the output stage is a type of magnetron. The energy to be transmitted is stored in a large storage device, often an inductor, that is pulsed to provide the high voltage pulse of many kilovolts. This very high voltage 'spike' is generated when the transmitter is required to generate the radio frequency signal and applied to the anode terminal.

Shaped Pulse Modulator

In the case where accurately-shaped pulses are required, another method is often used.

A popular method is to use a 'double-balanced ring mixer' as a variable attenuator. The signal from the transmitter oscillator is applied to the LO port and the modulated carrier is taken from the RF port. The IF port is fed with a current shaped after the square wave is passed through a root-raised-cosine low-pass filter. This method generates a very accurately-shaped pulse, but the power level is low. A typical +7dBm mixer (5mW) will have an insertion loss of approximately 3dB when used as a linear modulator. However, the drive power applied to the LO port needs to be approximately 10dB lower than when the device is used as a mixer. When used as a mixer, the LO power causes the diodes to switch hard on and off. We require the diodes to behave as linear attenuators, and so the drive needs to be well below that which causes the diodes to switch. Hence, the output power from the RF port will be only about -6dBm. This requires a lot of amplification in subsequent stages to reach the required power. There are special versions of ring-mixers designed for linear modulators that have better linearity than a standard mixer.

The technique is the same as that used for keying-shaping in a CW transmitter. Here, with Morse code dots and dashes, the transmitter drive is turned on and off by the keyer. If the rise and fall times were not carefully controlled, the generation of key-clicks would be excessive. A radar pulse transmitter is no different. The key-clicks are caused by $(\sin x)/x$ components.

The problem with this technique is that all the stages following the modulator need to be perfectly linear, much more so than an amplifier for SSB. If any of the amplifier stages start to saturate, the fidelity of the pulse suffers. If the amplifiers are very non-linear, such as a Class-C amplifier, the carefully-shaped rise and fall edges of the pulse will approach a square wave again. The sort of linearity required is severe and requires almost full Class-A amplifiers to achieve the necessary pulse fidelity. As all linear amplifiers are inherently inefficient, a better solution is often required.

Final Stage Pulse Shaping

It would be preferable for all the amplifier stages to operate in an efficient manner to minimise the power lost as heat. This means Class-C would be the best choice, where efficiencies of 70% or higher are possible. A Class-C final stage would allow a far greater power output to be achieved for the same anode dissipation.

Unfortunately a Class-C stage is not a linear amplifier in the common sense. If an AM or SSB signal is applied to the input of an amplifier operated in Class-C, the resultant signal would be very distorted. However, AM transmitters using Class-C output stages are capable of good efficiency and very low distortion if the anode and screen electrodes are correctly modulated. In the old AM valve transmitters, the modulation is applied via a modulation transformer and the anode and screen grid voltages are varied as the modulation is applied. By having the screen grid and anode voltage rise and fall in the correct ratio, very low distortion is possible. The grid of the amplifier is driven with a constant level of signal and the varying anode and screen voltages provide the modulation. This technique is now commonly used for solid-state amplifiers in cellular telephones which use time-division-multiplexed transmitters, where the collector or drain voltage is raised in sympathy with the crest of the modulation pulse. This brings about a substantial improvement in efficiency and linearity.

Anode modulation in a pulsed transmitter is not a very attractive method as the audio power required is quite high; the power required is 50% of the total DC input power. Not only that, but because of the very rapid rise and fall times, the back-EMF generated in the transformer causes very high voltages to be developed which can breakdown the transformer or the valve. A simpler method using just screen grid modulation of a tetrode gives almost the same results with very little modulating power. This is known as 'efficiency modulation' and the older amateurs who used AM will be familiar with this technique. It does not require a modulation transformer and can be achieved with low-power valves or transistors.

Pre-Distortion Techniques

Although the application of modulation to only the screen grid of a tetrode does not give the same low distortion as full anode and screen modulation, but with

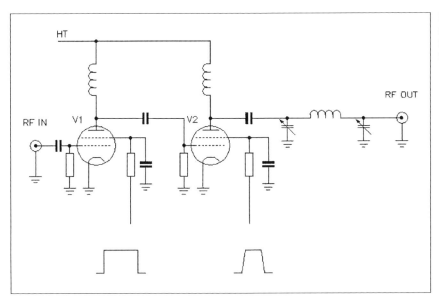

Fig 2.14: Simplified diagram of Class-C final stage modulation

a little bit of extra circuitry we can achieve equal results. The modulation of just the screen grid results in distortion at low modulation levels and at high modulation levels, due to the non-linear transfer curves at these points. The portion in between is substantially quite linear. By pre-distorting the modulation signal for the low and high modulation levels, the inherent distortion due to the transfer characteristics of the valve can be eliminated. This is a case of 'two wrongs making a right', and it is a technique widely used in television broadcast transmitters to deliver linear amplification with non-linear amplifiers.

In the case of a pulsed transmitter, when the transmitter is supposed to be off the RF drive signal is gated off and the output stage screen voltage is clamped to zero. Hence, no power is radiated. When the pulse should occur, the drive is first applied (square-wave signal) and then the screen voltage ramped up to a maximum with the required slope to give the spectral confinement. When the transmitter turns off, the screen voltage is first ramped down and then the RF drive is turned off. This needs to be carefully timed so that adequate RF drive exists before the screen voltage is applied or spectral spreading will be introduced. By using solid-state drivers for the high voltages, the fast turn-on and turn-off time of the driver stages can be controlled to suit our requirements. High voltage MOSFETs, as used in off-line switch-mode power supplies, are ideal for our needs, having switching times measured in nanoseconds and are readily available at low cost.

In the diagram, the low-power drive is applied to V1 and the screen grid of V1 is supplied with a square-wave high-voltage supply to switch the valve on and off. The output stage V2 screen grid is supplied with a ramped voltage to perform the pulse shaping. An alternative scheme is to apply the shaped voltage to both the driver and output valve screen grids. This is somewhat better, as at the point when extra drive is required by the output stage, the driver valve is able to supply it.

This technique will be described in more detail in a following chapter describing a meteor radar system.

71

MODERN METEOR RADAR SYSTEMS

The study of meteors using VHF radar continues today with many countries having high-power systems. The American scientific community has several systems in use; Japan operates high-power radar from near Kyoto, and the Australian Antarctic Research base at Davis has recently installed a 55MHz system. This last system uses a 120kW transmitter with 144 x 3-element Yagis pointed vertically, occupying a 1.2km²area.

Many amateurs in America use the American Navy space tracking radar for observing meteor scatter signals. This transmitter radiates an 800kW CW signal on 216.98MHz. Many amateurs have received EME signals using simple low-gain Yagis.

Daily Meteor Counts

It has been estimated from collected data that as many as 100,000 meteoroids enter the Earth's atmosphere every day. Of these about 50% are large enough and travelling fast enough to give rise to ionised trails.

Sporadic meteoroids occur at any time of the year, whether day or night. The highest incidence is normally after midnight and before sunrise. Quite how many occur in an average day is an often-debated topic. Recent studies performed by the Buckland Park station at Adelaide, Australia have, to some extent, answered this question. This station uses 31MHz and 54.1MHz high-power radars with a broad antenna beamwidth to collect as many echoes as possible. This study took place between April 2001 and July 2003.

Discounting erroneous echoes, which were due to other signals such as interference, aircraft reflections etc - by rejecting echoes which apparently are due to ranges outside those to be expected from normal meteoroid activity - the daily count rate varies between 9,000 and 14,000 per day. This is far higher

Fig 2.15: 55MHz meteor radar antenna installation at Davis Base, Antarctica

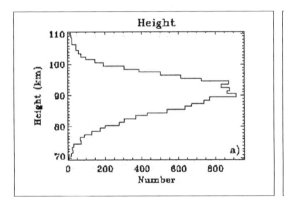

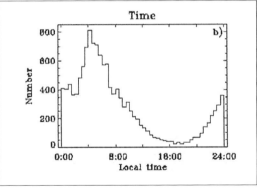

than was originally estimated. The measurements occupied five different operating periods between 2001 and 2003, and the highest number of echoes or other signals received peaked at almost 38,000 in a day. Many of these were spurious and, after the computer algorithms rejected the erroneous ones, this left the daily average of valid echoes that fitted the criteria for an echo from an under-dense trail. The incidence of meteor echoes does increase during traditional meteor showers (Leonids, etc) but, even so, the figure is still more than was expected.

This study was made in five different operating periods between April 2001 and July 2003 and used two separate radar systems, one operating with a PRF of 2kHz and the second with a lower PRF of between 400 and 500Hz to resolve the range ambiguities. (The higher-PRF radar had a range of 6 to 66km and the lower-PRF a range of 70 to 310km.) The antenna system consisted of crossed dipoles, one being the transmit antenna and five further antennas being used for the receivers. The transmitter had a peak power of 7.5kW. The receiving antennas were arranged to give an omnidirectional azimuth pattern with elevation angles of 20°, 40°, 60° and 80°.

The plots here show a typical distribution of meteoroid altitude and the occurrences versus local time. As expected, the peak is between midnight and sunrise, being at approximately 0500, where almost 800 appear in an hour and the minimum occurs 12 hours later, at 1700.

The information shown is for the operating period of 24 July 2003. From this it can be seen that meteor scatter communication is very unlikely during the mid-afternoon but, for night owls, the dividends are enormous!

Plots of Meteor Activity

One of the things apparent when one studies the results from the scientific stations working on meteoroid echoes is the extent of how little we still know about the subject. A classic example concerns the area of sky to examine. The picture below is one obtained from the Buckland Park radar in Adelaide, Australia. This shows a period of 24 hours and the apparent position of the meteor trails. As the radar is essentially operated in the same way as a transit telescope, where the antenna is fixed and the sky rotates with respect to the observer, the position of the echoes cover 360° of the observed sky. The Buckland Park radar has four different receive antennas that cover elevations of 20°, 40°, 60° and 80°.

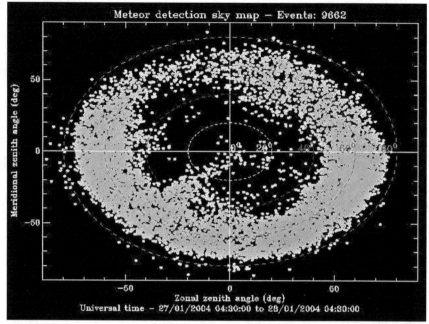

As one can see, the majority of the echoes occur between an elevation angle of 60° to 80° and very few occur below 40° elevation. In this plot, the total number of echoes is nearly 10,000 during a 24-hour period.

Special Antenna Systems

Many of the large VHF meteor radar system in use today use antenna systems that to amateurs seem strange. Often, only simple dipoles are used and others use multiple low-element-count Yagis. The scientists operating these systems are more concerned with collecting as many echoes as possible than a few from a discrete point in the sky.

It should not be overlooked that if you point an antenna straight up at the zenith, the Earth, as it rotates, will cause the beam produced to act like a transit telescope and the beam will be swept over a narrow strip of the sky. Hence, meteors entering the atmosphere close to the observer's horizon will not be detected unless they also transit across the antenna beam.

Another version commonly used is two Yagi arrays pointed in different directions - for example due south and due west. These antennas are coupled to two separate receivers and the sky illuminated by a transmitter using a wide beamwidth dipole array. As a meteor approaches, it will transit first one antenna and a little later the second antenna. By using trigonometry, it is possible to ascertain the altitude, velocity and the track of the meteor trail.

Because the Earth's surface is curved, pointing an antenna at the observers horizon will only detect meteor trails at a very long range, and the sky noise will be at its highest level under this condition, but the altitude could be only 80km above the Earth's surface. This limits the number of echoes that can be detected because, for maximum reflection using VHF, the trail needs to pass through the antenna beam at right angles. It is far more productive to elevate the antenna to a high angle, perhaps as high as 80° above the horizon.

Fresnel Zone Signal Level Variation

One of the earliest discoveries by the scientists occupied with meteor trail detection was the rapid variation in the received level. This is due to the refraction of the ionised trail and caused by Fresnel Zone effects. By using a high-PRF transmitter, the trail could be illuminated by many pulses during its brief life. This showed up as large changes in the received signal level and, by measuring the peaks and troughs of the signal over a longer period, one can ascertain the velocity of the meteor trail as it decays to zero.

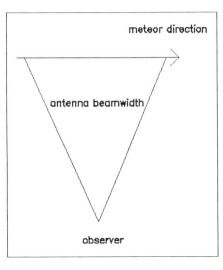

Fig 2.19: A meteor echo will occur only while the trail is within the antenna beamwidth. Hence, a wide beamwidth will yield better results than a narrow beamwidth

Typical meteor trails show a signal level variation of about 15Hz.

The use of a high PRF does not allow a measurement to be made of the range, but this is of little importance, as the expected altitude of meteor trails is known to be in the 70 to 110km region. Often secondary radar with a longer PRF is operated in parallel to obtain altitude data.

REFERENCES

[1]   *The Evolution of Radio Astronomy*, Science History Publications, New York. ISBN 0 88202 027 7.

[2]   Today, *bi-static* refers to a type of radar where the transmitter and receiver are situated a considerable distance apart, similar to the expected range.

[3]   Prior to this discovery by D O North in 1946, the radar systems used a receiver bandwidth that was selectable between 1/ and 2/ . North showed that the ideal bandwidth is 1.17/ .

[4]   J P M Prentice et al, 1947, 'Radio Echo Observations of Meteors', *Monthly Notices of The Royal Astronomical Society* (MNRAS), 107, No 2.

[5]   Artech House, Inc, ISBN 0 89006 021 5.

[6]   J S Hey et al, 1946, 'Radar Observations of the Giacobinid Meteor Shower', *Monthly Notices of the Royal Astronomical Society*, 176 - 183.

[7]   The writer subsequently discovered that at least 50 of these specially-modified GL2 V-2 detection radar systems were in use towards the end of WWII.

[8]   McKinley, D W R, 1961, *Meteor Science and Engineering*, McGraw Hill, New York.

[9]   Mathews, J D, 2004, *Journal of Atmospheric and Solar-Terrestrial Physics*, 66, 285 - 299.

[10]   Holdsworth et al, in publication.

3

Receiver Parameters

In this chapter:

- Limitations to sensitivity
- Typical signal levels
- Noise contribution
- Receiver bandwidth
- Main receiver details
- Modern approach to receivers
- Dicke switching receiver
- IF bandwidth considerations
- Radio flux units
- Radio Horizon

- In-band interference signals
- Radio astronomy frequencies
- Noise performance calculations
- Cryogenic cooling
- Antenna noise temperature
- Effects of sky noise
- Special receiver techniques
- A low-cost amplifier
- Special filtering techniques
- System calculations

B y definition, a radio receiver is 'a device which accepts the electrical signal from an antenna and, by a process of amplification, filtering and detection, outputs an intelligible signal'.

In the early radio astronomy systems, the receiver output was not normally used to drive a loudspeaker, as in a normal radio, but was used to drive a meter, chart recorder or oscilloscope. The chart gives the amplitude of the received signal in the same way as the signal strength meter (S-meter) on a communications receiver. Today, the receiver output is digitised via analogue-to-digital converters and either processed in real time by a computer or stored on magnetic media for later study.

In a communications receiver, the signal strength meter is intended for 'casual observation' by the operator to give some indication of the strength of the received signal. In the radio astronomy system, the chart recorder gives an accurate and permanent record of how the received signal varied with time. Time can be translated into various other meanings, for example - in the case of the transit telescope, it can be used to give an exact position in the sky.

The superheterodyne (superhet) receiver is the most commonly used type today, the reason being that the bulk of the amplification and filtering can be performed at a low frequency, the 'intermediate frequency', or IF. The superhet uses a process of frequency mixing to bring the input signal to a lower frequency.

At this lower frequency the amplification and signal filtering to reject out-of-band noise and other interfering signals are more easily performed. Hence, it is possible to achieve the very high signal amplification required and good selectivity without the difficulty of instability that could occur at the higher input frequency.

LIMITATIONS TO SENSITIVITY

In receiving systems, the concept of signal-to-noise ratio (SNR) is used. The signal is the wanted output and the noise, by definition, is either internally-generated in the receiver or externally-generated by an interfering source. Noise, therefore, by definition, is any signal other than the desired one. In a radio telescope receiver, the wanted signal is extremely weak for most cases and is often broad-band; it is not a coherent single carrier - it resembles noise, but it may have a frequency dependence about a particular frequency, for example the Hydrogen Line at 1420MHz.

The limitation to the ultimate sensitivity of the receiving system is the noise performance of the receiver's first amplifier stages, the front-end or low-noise amplifier, LNA. For maximum sensitivity, the front-end amplifier stages need to have the lowest possible noise figure with adequate gain.

As the first stages in a receiver effectively determine the overall receiver sensitivity, it is important to strive for the lowest noise figure in the early RF amplifier stage(s).

Contributing factors to the overall receiver noise figure include the transmission line and connectors that connect the antenna terminals to the first amplifier stage. This can be a large contributor to the overall noise figure if lossy coaxial cable or connectors are used.

In a normal radio telescope system, the LNA would be connected directly to the antenna feed-point, reducing the insertion loss of any cable to essentially that of the connector losses.

The VSWR mismatch between the antenna and the LNA can add another fraction of a dB to the noise figure. In many cases the LNA will present a severe mismatch to the antenna feed point in order to obtain the optimum noise figure. A VSWR mismatch of 10:1 or more is not uncommon for certain types of LNA.

TYPICAL SIGNAL LEVELS FOR ASTRONOMY

It is as well to appreciate that the sort of sensitivity required is greatly in excess of even a very good communications receiver. In order to understand the very small signal levels involved it is necessary to get a benchmark against a typical radio telescope receiver and a commercial two-way radio receiver operating at VHF. A typical sensitivity figure often quoted for a commercial two-way radio VHF receiver is 0.25μV for 12dB SNR. In a 50Ω system this is -115dBm, or a minimum discernible signal of 115 + 12 = -127dBm. By comparison, the signal to be expected with an average radio telescope is approximately -190dBm; in many cases, the lower limit will be of the order of -260dBm when additional signal processing and long-term integration techniques are employed. This level of signal is very much weaker than a system for Moonbounce (EME).

To put the signal levels into perspective, it is useful to calculate the path loss for some strong noise sources. Taking our Sun and Cygnus-A as two examples. The Sun is situated at 149.6 x 10^6km from the Earth and Cygnus-A is approx. 550 x 10^6 light years away. A light year is 9.6 x 10^{12}km, so Cygnus-A is 5.3 x 10^{15}km distant.

Using the path loss calculation formula in Chapter 2, we can calculate the attenuation the signals suffer. If we observe on 144MHz, the value for the Sun is 239dB and for Cygnus-A it is 390dB. Assuming our 144MHz antenna has a gain of 30dB and the Sun radiates a signal of 1MW, the expected signal level at the LNA input will be -119dBm. In practice, the observed Sun noise can as much as 10dB above the receiver noise floor for a quiet Sun and as much as 20dB above the receiver noise floor for a disturbed Sun when solar flares or sun spots occur.

For Cygnus-A using our 144MHz antenna of 30dB gain, assuming the power radiated is 1GW, the expected signal level will be -240dBm. However, we know from the received signal of Cygnus-A that the power radiated is about 10 billion TW (1x 10^{22}W). [1 terawatt (TW) = 10^{12}W]

NOISE CONTRIBUTION

Image Noise

An important factor in superhet receiver design is the noise power contained at the image frequency. Due to the mixing of the input signal and the LO to produce a lower IF, two possible input signal frequencies can produce the same IF for a given local oscillator frequency. One is the wanted frequency and the other is the image frequency. In a receiver down-converter using low-side LO injection, the upper of these two is treated as the wanted frequency and the lower one as the image frequency.

If the image frequency is not sufficiently suppressed by either filtering in the RF amplifier stages or by some other technique, the image noise, if it is of equal signal level to the wanted signal (this is the case for pure noise caused by resistive means), will cause a 3dB (50%) degradation of the SNR. In many cases, due to interfering sources, the image noise power can be much greater than the wanted signal. There is, however, a trade-off to be made between the sensitivity gained by image noise filtering and the noise figure degradation caused by the loss in the first filter section before the amplifier stage.

It is possible to select too narrow a filter in an effort to suppress image noise; hence it will have appreciable loss. It is as well to remember that any loss before the first amplifier device will add directly to the noise figure of the amplifier. Whereas the receiver SNR may be improved by reducing the image noise component, it may well be that this is more than negated by the noise figure degradation caused by the image filtering loss. Low-noise amplifiers have little or no filtering before the active amplifier device in order to minimise the noise figure.

It also is prudent to select the local oscillator frequency to avoid potential interfering signals at the image frequency. For each input signal and IF combination there are two possible local oscillator frequencies that may be used. Often, for ease of construction, we would wish to choose the low-side injection in preference to high-side injection. Choosing low-side injection means that the multiplication for the local oscillator chain is less than for high-side injection and the LO frequency is consequently lower. But it may be that the image frequency potentially contains strong interfering carriers. For example, if 144MHz was the input frequency and the IF is 21.4 MHz then the choices of LO are (144 -21.4) = 122.6MHz or (144 + 21.4) = 165.4MHz. The image frequencies would be 101.2 MHz for low-side injection and 186.8 MHz for high-side injection. The choice of low-side injection places the image in the middle of the FM broadcast band where strong interfering signals will be present. The choice of high-side injection places the image within the television broadcast Band III, where strong interfering signals at the image frequency may also be present. For these two cases the image rejection would need to be in excess of 100dB to prevent interference. By selecting a different IF, and hence LO, the image can be moved into a quieter portion of the spectrum.

Image Rejection Mixers

An alternative to image signal rejection by filtering is the use of an image-rejection mixer which is a common technique used at microwave frequencies where filtering is often difficult. An image-rejection mixer (IRM) consists of two double-balanced mixers, two 90° phase shifters and a 0° power combiner. By using this technique, the unwanted image band of frequencies is cancelled out. A block diagram of a typical IRM is shown. Today for microwave applications the mixers and phase shifters are often constructed in chip-form directly on an IC.

The conversion loss of an image-reject mixer is usually only a fraction of a dB higher than a normal type; in some cases it is a little less than a conventional mixer. However, one important fact to be aware of about image-reject mixers is that, although they reject coherent carriers at the image frequency, they do not reduce the image noise, which is our primary concern. So, although we can utilise an image-reject mixer, we will also still need some image filtering to improve the system noise figure.

In practice, if the image signal noise power is reduced by approximately 10dB, the image noise contribution becomes insignificant. It is possible to achieve 25dB of image suppression to coherent carriers in an image-reject mixer without introducing significant losses and, in addition. by using wide-band-low-loss filtering in the RF input, a suppression of 40dB or more is achievable. Only in the case of the image frequency containing a strong coherent interfering signal would any greater suppression be required. Here it is preferable to utilise a notch or trap filter tuned to the image frequency that introduces minimal loss at the signal frequency. High-performance HF communication receivers typically have image rejection figures of 70dB to 100dB due to input filtering alone.

Another way around the lossy image filter problem is to use a double-superhet with a very high first IF, as the image frequency is situated at a frequency of twice the IF away from the wanted frequency. This, for a low-frequency input signal (in the HF or VHF range), will entail firstly mixing the signal

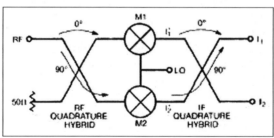

Fig 3.1: Image rejection mixer diagram

up to a higher frequency of typically 1GHz, then a second narrow-band down-converter is used to bring the signal to a normal IF of typically 70MHz or less. The input amplifier band-pass filter can then be replaced with a low-pass filter, rolling off in response a little above the receiver frequency. Low-pass filters generally have lower insertion loss than a narrow-band symmetrical band-pass filter. The filter losses after the mixers at 1GHz and 70MHz are relatively small and can be tolerated in such a system.

Equipment for measuring noise figure will, if the receive mixer is not preceded by an image filter, give an optimistic noise figure due to the image noise adding to the wanted signal.

If the receiver consists of a wideband LNA (no image filtering) and a single double-balanced mixer, the noise figure measured will be 3dB less than the actual figure. Noise figure measurements need to be done using a single-sideband technique and not a double-sideband type, which an unfiltered mixer with image noise contribution inherently gives.

LOCAL OSCILLATOR NOISE CONTRIBUTION

The assumption for optimum noise performance is that the local oscillator signal is a perfect sinusoidal carrier of zero bandwidth, in the real world, this is not the case. If the local oscillator is noisy, either in amplitude or phase and contains significant noise power or other spurious response at the image, the noise will be mixed on to the wanted IF signal. This is known as reciprocal mixing, and will cause degradation of the signal. Receiver local oscillators need to have extremely low noise performance for radio telescope duty in order to maximise the sensitivity. A crystal-controlled oscillator is usually far superior to a synthesised oscillator. If the radio telescope is required to operate on several different frequencies, a local oscillator, mixer and LNA are required for each new band. This imposes a problem with switching the LNAs with minimal losses. Often the LNAs are mounted at the antenna feed-point and, because any form of switching relay introduces a slight but unwanted loss, changing frequency band often requires a technician to climb the antenna and physically disconnect the old antennas and LNA and reconnect the new antenna and LNA by hand. This can be a time consuming process, not to mention the potential hazards involved.

Jodrell Bank Mk1 originally got around this problem by stationing a technician at the dish in a weatherproof cabin slung under the dish centre. The cabin pivoted on a hinge so that it was always vertical. A lift from the ground allowed quick entry into the cabin.

This then involved a short climb through a trap door to the dish floor and to the feed-point box, via a ladder fixed to the tower, to make the changes. Even so, the climb was some 20m and at night, this can be quite daunting, especially as the bottom of the dish is already about 80m in the air.

To make this work, the dish needed to be driven to the zenith (the dish pointing directly upwards) each time the LNA needed changing. The local oscillators were originally contained in the technician's cabin and these then fed the resulting 1st IF to the main receiver by a long coaxial cable to the central control room some 200m away.

Fig 3.2: 20GHz liquid-helium-cooled receiver front-end under development at Jodrell Bank Radio Observatory. (Photograph: J Fielding 2004)

Fig 3.3: A receiver carousel fitted to a cassegrain-focused antenna. (Photograph courtesy of Jodrell Bank Observatory)

With the advent of liquid helium cooling of the LNAs this became an impractical method and the availability of better coaxial relays with much lower insertion losses meant that all the changes could be done remotely from the control room. Today the preferred technique uses the LNA and mixers incorporated into the 'front-end' module, all of which is cryogenically cooled. The various front-ends are arranged in a carousel that can be rotated to bring the required one to the focal point of the dish.

Currently (2005) the Jodrell Bank Mk1A radio telescope does not have a carousel fitted due to the limited space in the focus box. On the author's last visit in September 2005, the four-channel Hydrogen Line receiver was doing double duty as a pulsar and Hydrogen Line receiver.

BROAD-BAND NOISE AND NOISE POWER

As the noise power contained in a 1Hz bandwidth for a particular condition is constant then the same follows for other bandwidths. Suppose we measure the absolute level of power in the 1Hz bandwidth - let us say it is $1\mu W$ in a 50Ω impedance for convenience. If we now use a measuring bandwidth of 1kHz, the level of power we expect to measure is 1000 times as high, being 1mW. (You can imagine this is 1000 windows stacked side by side, each one is 1Hz wide, each of which lets $1\mu W$ pass. The total amount of power is therefore the sum of all the windows.) This is an increase of 30dB. If we use a 1MHz measuring bandwidth, the power level will be 1000 times higher still, it will be 1W. Therefore it is much easier to measure the power in a wide bandwidth than it is in a very narrow bandwidth. As the level of noise power in a 1Hz bandwidth is likely to be very small, it is easier to use a wider measuring bandwidth and then calculate the effective 1Hz bandwidth figure. In fact, we can choose any suitable bandwidth and then work back to find the 1Hz-bandwidth value. Everything can be scaled to a new bandwidth.

The noise power in a resistor at an ambient temperature of +17°C (+290K) is a noise power of 4 x 10^{-21} WHz^{-1} = -174dBmHz^{-1}. Lowering the ambient temperature to close to absolute zero reduces the noise power considerably.

Now imagine a bandwidth 1MHz wide in the centre of which we place a carrier that occupies a bandwidth of 1Hz. If the noise is measured in a broadband power detector the carrier will need to be more than 1 million times greater in amplitude (60dB) to appear above the noise floor. If we now reduce the measuring bandwidth to 100kHz the signal only needs to be 100,000 times greater (50dB) to appear above the noise floor. Taking this concept further, if we further reduce the measuring bandwidth to, say, 1kHz the signal only needs to be 1000 times greater (30dB) than the noise to appear above the noise floor. When the measuring bandwidth is reduced to 1Hz only the signal will be left and all the other 1Hz segments containing noise will be excluded. Hence, by reducing the measuring bandwidth the signal appears to rise out of the noise floor. This causes the SNR to improve as the system bandwidth is reduced. The situation for radio astronomy receivers is a little different and this is covered later.

Sky Noise

The noise we measure when an antenna is pointed to different parts of the sky is determined by various factors. One of these is the operating frequency. At low frequencies, the sky noise is high, reducing as we increase the frequency. The second factor is the elevation angle of the antenna and where the main antenna beam is pointed. At low elevation angles, the antenna sees a far greater portion of the warm lower atmosphere than when pointed vertically. Excluding any radio stars that might be in the antenna beamwidth will give a uniform noise temperature for a particular operating frequency and antenna elevation angle. There are, however, exceptions to this general rule. These are due to additional noise sources such as the oxygen frequency and others. These occur in the higher frequencies (microwave bands).

Fig 3.4: Sky noise temperature against frequency and antenna elevation angle

The graph below shows the general level of noise to be expected for different frequencies and antenna elevation angles. The lowest frequencies have the highest noise temperatures and the higher frequency generally the lowest noise temperatures. There is, however, an ambient background microwave radiation (BMR) noise level of approx. 2.7K at the higher frequencies.

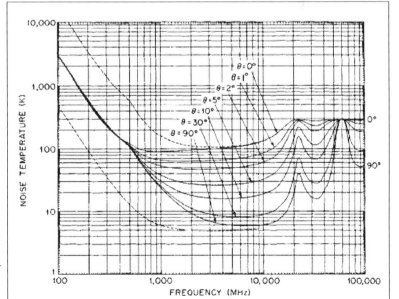

From this graph can be determined the minimum and maximum sky temperatures for the various frequencies. The lower dashed curve is the lowest temperature to be expected when all other sources of noise are excluded. If you examine the lower dashed curve you will see that at 144MHz the lowest sky temperature is about 200K. This sets the lower limit to the noise figure required. Reducing the receiver noise figure below this point does not bring any significant improvement in sensitivity and is likely to cause intermodulation products to be generated by strong in-band signals if excessive gain is used.

Of interest are the two bumps in the noise curve at 22GHz and 60GHz; these are due to water absorption and the oxygen resonance effects respectively. Therefore it is not useful to observe at these frequencies from the Earth because they will cause severe attenuation. However, if the receiver were mounted on a space probe listening on these frequencies it would identify water and oxygen by the increase in noise level.

As mentioned above, radio-astronomy systems usually operate close to the theoretical noise limits. With a few exceptions, signals are usually extremely weak. One such exception is the Sun. Depending on frequency, solar cycle, antenna size, and system noise temperature, pointing an antenna at the Sun normally increases the received power several fold. Toward other sources, it is not unusual to detect and measure signals that are less than 0.1% of the system noise. The increase in power, measured in K, due to the presence of a radio source in the beam is given by

$$T_a = \frac{AF}{2k},$$

where: A is the effective aperture (m2), or aperture efficiency times physical aperture,
F is the radio flux density in $Wm^{-2}Hz^{-1}$, and
k is Boltzmann's constant, 1.38×10^{-23} $WHz^{-1}K^{-1}$ (more commonly JK^{-1}).

The factor of 2 in the denominator is because radio astronomers usually define the flux density as that present in both wave polarisations, but a receiver is sensitive to only one polarisation. Radio telescopes use linear or circular polarisation depending on the type of observations being made, and with two LNAs and two receivers, two orthogonal polarisations can be detected simultaneously. In order to detect and measure signals that are a very small fraction of the power passing into the receiver, signal averaging, or integration, is used. If the receiver gain were perfectly stable, our ability to measure small changes in signal is given by the noise equation, where ΔT is the 1σ measurement noise.

If the receiver bandwidth is 1MHz and T_{sys} = 100K, for example, we can measure down to 0.013K in one minute. For a sure detection, we need to see a change of 10 sigma or about 0.1K change. The receiver gain in practice is seldom exactly constant, and the additional spill-over noise and atmospheric noise may also be changing, so it will be difficult at this level to distinguish a real signal from a change in gain or atmospheric noise. There are several solutions to this problem, depending on the type of observation, all of which rely on some way of forming a reference. If we are making spectral-line measurements, the reference is often just adjacent frequencies. If we scan the frequency or simultaneously divide the spectrum into many frequency channels, then the gain or atmospheric noise changes will be largely common to all frequencies and will cancel with baseline subtraction in the final spectrum. In making measurements of broadband, or continuum, radio emission, we usually use a synchronous detection technique known as 'Dicke switching' after its inventor Robert Dicke. An example of Dicke switching is the use of a switch to toggle the input of the LNA between two antenna outputs that provide adjacent beams in the sky. If we switch fast enough in this case and take the difference between the power of the two outputs synchronously with the antenna switch, receiver gain changes will largely cancel. Furthermore, if the two antenna beams are close together on the sky, then changes in the atmospheric noise will tend to be common to both beams and will also cancel. Since we are taking a difference and spending half the time looking at the reference, the T given above will have to be doubled.

Another powerful technique for extracting weak signals from noise is correlation. The radio telescope in this case has two or more receivers either connected to the same antenna, or, more often, two or more separate antennas. The signal voltages are multiplied together before averaging instead of multiplying the signal voltage by itself to obtain the power. With separated antennas, the correlation output combines the antenna patterns as an interferometer, which generates lobes on the sky that are separated in angle by the wavelength divided by the projected baseline between the antennas. Correlation techniques are common in radio astronomy, and they are becoming popular also in communications. Correlation is used, for example, to detect and demodulate spread-spectrum signals as in code-division multiple-access (CDMA) digital cellular telephones.

RECEIVER BANDWIDTH

The signal from a distant radio star or other object is inherently a very wideband type, perhaps occupying several GHz of spectrum. A radio star is the same as our Sun and it generates a large amount of broadband noise, hence we need to use a receiver bandwidth of similar value. In practice, this is normally not possible because of other users of the spectrum. However, the noise power per unit bandwidth is relatively constant, so it makes little difference if we observed at 144MHz, 432MHz or 1296MHz. Typical radio telescopes use bandwidths of anything up to 100MHz or more at the microwave end of the spectrum to try and encompass as much of the noise as possible and avoiding other occupied frequencies. By international agreement, there are special portions of the spectrum exclusively allocated to radio astronomy, in which no other services are allowed to operate.

If you consider the amateur bands, this approach will not work, because there are so many signals present. In a case such as this, we would need to utilise a receiver bandwidth that can exclude all but the wanted signal. In the radio telescope, there is normally only one signal under observation and the choice of the observing frequency is not normally very critical, except in a few specialised cases. One of these is the Hydrogen Line at 1420MHz. Here, the receiver needs to be centred on the nominal frequency, but also needs to have sufficient bandwidth to accept as much of the noise power as possible. Another problem is

Doppler shift. If the object under investigation is moving away from the observer, the signal will be shifted in frequency; this is a function of the operating frequency and the velocity of the object. The average velocity of a receding star or other object is of the order of 50kms[-1] or higher; hence the Doppler shift can be quite high. Typically, this requires a receiver with about 50MHz bandwidth. (50MHz bandwidth at 1420MHz is approximately 3.5%.)

One radio telescope might use an observing frequency of 160MHz, whereas another might use 250MHz. When both are pointed at the same radio star, the magnitude of the signals received will be different. Although the absolute noise power received is different for the two cases, this can be attributed to the different antenna gains and beamwidths, the receiver noise figure and the receiver bandwidth in use. If each radio telescope were to be normalised, the signal power would be the same for the same radio star.

Some powerful radio stars can be used as 'calibration sources'. The two strongest radio stars, Cassiopeia-A and Cygnus-A, have similar signal levels, but the radio star with the greatest output power is the weaker of the two. This is because it exists a far greater distance away. Note: The signal powers quoted are in 'janskys' (Jy), the accepted way of measuring radio stars.

Cassiopeia-A	57×10^{-24} Jy
Cygnus-A	38×10^{-24} Jy

These signal levels were established by Dr John D Kraus, W8JK, using the Ohio State University radio telescope at 250MHz using a 4MHz receiver bandwidth. Irrespective of the actual receiver bandwidth used, the two radio stars will still have the same ratio of signal levels, being 57/38 = 1.5:1.

If the receiver uses a very narrow bandwidth, the received signal power falls to a lower value. This is exactly the opposite of the case where a very narrow band signal is being searched for in a wideband background noise floor.

As the wanted signal is, in most cases, a broadband noise, the way this can be detected is quite difficult. Connecting a voltmeter to the receiver output is one way. If the antenna is positioned to point at a vacant spot in the sky, we will measure the ambient background noise plus any receiver noise. When the radio star transits the antenna beam we will see a gradual increase of the voltmeter reading and then a gradual decreases as the source passes through the antenna main beam. If the telescope is a transit type, this occurs at the rate of 15° per hour due to the Earth's rotation. By measuring the half-power points on the voltmeter, and knowing the antenna beamwidth, we can estimate the apparent size of the object.

MAIN RECEIVER DETAILS

In many radio telescopes, the main receiver is used for all the different frequency bands. The receiver often utilises a frequency of around 70MHz to 100MHz and contains the necessary different bandwidth filters for IF filtering and the logarithmic detection. Often the main receiver can be tuned in 1MHz or smaller steps around its nominal frequency, which then gives variable frequency coverage at the input frequency. The receiver is permanently connected to a chart recorder or digitising computer for signal processing.

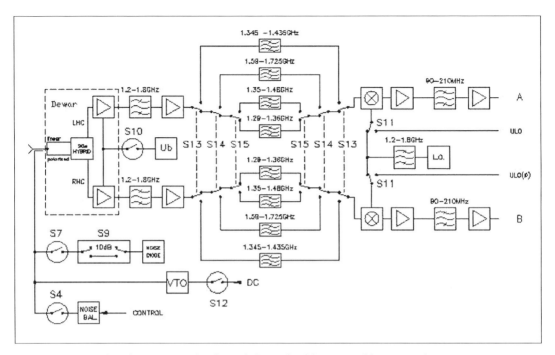

As the main receiver is an expensive item, it is preferable to use this approach. The different frequency bands are provided for by up- or down-converters, each with its own LNA, mixer and local oscillator. These are often mounted at the antenna and the coax cable from them to the main receiver carries the 70MHz to 100MHz signals to the operating room. This means it is simple and quick to change frequency bands by remote control to the antenna-mounted components in the receiver. The feeder cable can be quite long. In the case of Jodrell Bank Mk1, it is approximately 200m long. By utilising a relatively low IF, such as 70MHz, the feeder loss is not as serious as the sensitivity has already been defined by the LNA and mixer stages.

Fig 3.5: Typical hydrogen line receiver front-end block diagram. (Courtesy Max Planck Radio Observatory)

For radio telescopes using GHz front-ends, the 70MHz to 100MHz IF is often too low, and a higher first IF of about 1.5GHz is often used. This is then further down-converted to the normal IF for processing.

Today, the predominant method is to use two parallel receivers contained in one front-end unit. These cater for left-hand and right-hand circular polarisation and supply two parallel IFs to the processing equipment.

MODERN APPROACH TO RECEIVERS

Today, the use of a dedicated receiver is more the norm. For example, Jodrell Bank and many other radio telescopes have chosen a different technique, where each 'receiver' is dedicated to a particular band. In the new approach, the receiver front-end is still much as before, but the IF processing is quite different. At Jodrell Bank, the receiver first LO is carried by a low-loss coaxial cable from the observing room to the dish focal point where the LNA and first mixer are situated. For an L-band receiver, the loss in the coax may be too high, so a lower frequency is used that is then multiplied up to the final frequency in the front-end and then filtered to remove spurious products. The technique at Jodrell

Fig 3.6: The equipment racks contain the receiver first LO generator and the first IF processing equipment. (Photo: J Fielding 2005)

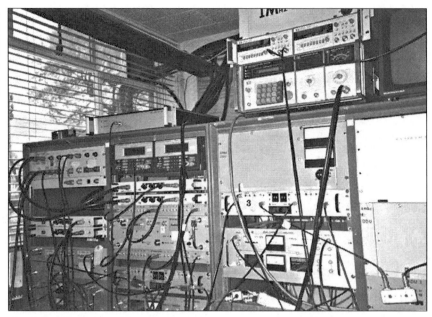

Fig 3.7: Simplified diagram of Jodrell Bank Hydrogen Line receiver for one channel

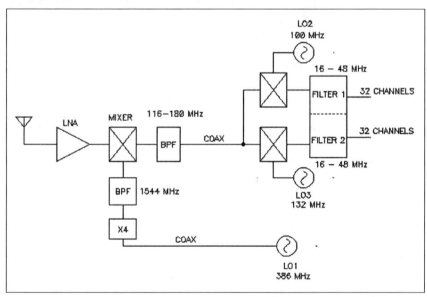

Bank uses the Hydrogen-Line receiver at about 1.42GHz (1364 to 1428MHz) where LO1 is 386MHz; this is then multiplied by 4 to 1544MHz. This produces a wideband first IF of 116 to 180MHz. The first IF is then carried back to the observing room by another low-loss coaxial cable.

In the observing room is a series of band-splitting filters. These are 32MHz wide and consist of two banks of 32 separate filters, each of 1MHz nominal bandwidth. The filters are supplied with two 'channels' each 32MHz wide by using two second LO signals. These LO signals are at 100MHz and 132MHz. The 116 to 180MHz wideband first IF has a total bandwidth of 64MHz. The second mixers, therefore, supply two new 'channels' of 32MHz bandwidth. The filter bank outputs 2 x 32MHz (64 channels each 1MHz) wide of 16MHz to 48MHz. These are then fed into 64 separate DSP detectors that process the signals in parallel. Hence, there is a contiguous coverage of the first IF over a 64MHz bandwidth. Each DSP processor is clocked at 1.2GHz and is able to sweep across each individual 1MHz wide slot to search for signals. The search for a signal within the Hydrogen Line spectrum is then possible by resolving the signals down to as little as 1Hz bandwidth in real time.

Fig 3.8: Jodrell Bank IF filter bank (Photograph: J Fielding 2005)

Fig 3.9: One of the IF filter bank cards containing 16 filters. (Photograph: J Fielding 2005)

The simplified diagram of the Hydrogen Line receiver showed only one polarisation channel. In practice, there are two separate polarisation receivers contained within the front-end unit. One receiver accepts the right-hand-circular signal from the antenna, and the other the left-hand-circular signal. There are therefore three coaxial cables running from the front-end unit to the observing room, one carries the 1st LO and the other two carry the wideband 1st IF, which the 2nd IF filter bank processes in the same way. There are 2 x 64 1MHz-wide filters in use, each one feeding a DSP processor, making a total of 128 processors running in parallel.

The main Hydrogen Line receiver contains four separate front-ends, each with a dual IF output for LHC and RHC antenna polarisation. Therefore, when all four receivers are in use, they require eight separate coaxial cables to carry the 1st IF back to the observing room and to the entire available band-splitting filters. For most applications, only one front-end is used.

To measure spectral-line emission or absorption from molecules or atoms, we need a device to measure power spectra - a spectrometer. An intuitive method to measure power spectra is to scan a narrow tunable band-pass filter across the frequencies to be measured and record its power output as a function of frequency. A variant of this scheme, actually used in spectrum analysers, has a fixed filter in the IF that is scanned, in effect, by scanning a LO in a heterodyne configuration.

A significant improvement in observing efficiency results from having a comb or bank of band-pass filters placed side-by-side in frequency and recording all their outputs simultaneously. Fig 3.8 and 3.9 show an example of such a filter bank. Choosing filter shapes and spacing for such a spectrometer is, however, not intuitive. The popular almost-square filters placed just touching, for example, give spectra that are difficult to interpret whenever spectral features are comparable to the filter widths. With today's technology, filter banks are expensive and troublesome compared to various digital alternatives.

Digital Signal Processing

With the advent of digital signal processing (DSP), the main receiver design has changed considerably over the last 10 years. Whereas, in the early days of DSP, it was difficult to manufacturer fast Analogue-to-Digital converters (A/Ds) with acceptable noise performance and dynamic range, today it is possible to make very fast converters that work in real-time, with clock rates up to 2GHz. Today, the receiver does not consist of much hardware, the IF amplifiers have been replaced in some receivers with a simple wide-band amplifier and then this is fed into the A/D converter.

In earlier days, because of the limitations in the available ICs, the A/D converter worked at a very low IF and the signal was down-converted and then applied to the A/D converter. With very fast A/D converters becoming affordable, the DSP now directly converts the noise spectrum at the input frequency into a digital bitstream for later processing. With computers becoming more powerful, it is now possible to do the processing in something approaching real-time. Modern DSP receivers are zero-IF types and the mixing, filtering and detection are performed directly in software using the raw digital bitstream. The advantage of the DSP approach is that it is possible to make continuously-variable

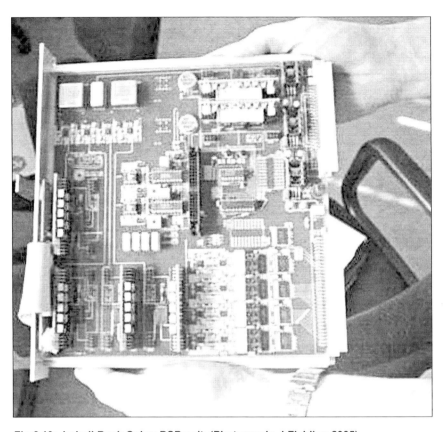

Fig 3.10: Jodrell Bank Cobra DSP unit. (Photograph: J Fielding 2005)

Fig 3.11: Cobra digital signal processing rack. (Photograph: J Fielding 2005)

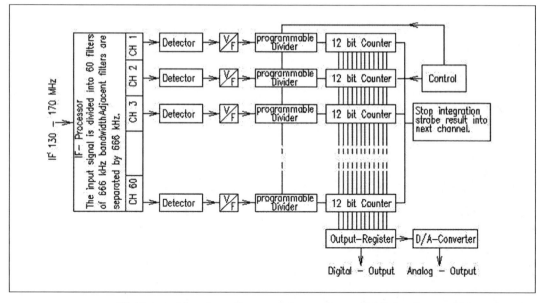

IF filters with only software and one piece of DSP hardware. This makes the DSP receiver approach much more cost-effective because, once the initial high cost has been overcome, the receiver depends entirely on the software used.

The most advanced system to date is the new Jodrell Bank Cobra DSP system which can simultaneously sweep across up to 96MHz of IF 'channel' in real time, although normally only 64MHz is used.

Many other radio telescopes use similar techniques. The diagram below is the method used by the Max Planck observatory in Germany. Here, the 1st IF at 130 to 170MHz is split into 60 x 666kHz segments and then processed by fast digital circuits to provide a composite serial bitstream.

Signal Integration

One of the ways we can extract a very weak signal from the background noise is to use a process known as integration. Integration is the process of continuously adding one signal on top of the previous ones to build up a stronger signal. A similar technique is used in the spectrum analyser and, in this case, it is known as video averaging. If integration is used on a very weak source over a long time period, the wanted signal rises up out of the background noise and then can be detected more easily. Integration of radio signals is exactly the same principle as used by the optical astronomers using long time-exposure photography. In an optical telescope, the light from a distant star is so weak the human eye or any electronic means such as Charge Coupled Devices (CCD) cannot see it. However, if the object is photographed with a long time-exposure, some detail is visible from the photographic plate.

One of the most persistent and difficult problems in spectral measurements in radio astronomy involves the difficulty of obtaining good flat baselines, the parts of spectra with no signal. The corresponding baseline problem with continuum measurements involves stable measurements off-source (ie cold sky) to subtract from on-source measurements. There are numerous instrumental effects that contribute to bumpy baselines, and many of the effects are a substantial percentage of the system temperature and are typically much larger than the signals to be measured. To reduce the severity of such instrumental effects, almost all radio-astronomy measurements are made using one of several possible switching schemes. The ideal switching scheme would have the source itself turn off and on synchronously with a prescribed periodicity and with nothing else changing. Then the difference between signal and comparison is precisely the desired measurement. Provided that Ts does not change between the on-source and off-source observations, it can be shown that noise is minimised by spending half the observing time on-source and half the time off-source.

Another method used is phase-switching of the antennas. If the phase of one antenna is rapidly switched with a $90°$ delay added and the signal is compared to another antenna with no delay, the net result is that the sky noise is nulled and only the wanted signal is left.

Among practical switching schemes, we can move the antenna pointing on and off the source either by actually moving the antenna or by offsetting the effective pointing by moving the feed or its image. But this works only if the source is confined in angle. Or we can move the source in and out of the pass-band by moving the LO frequency. But this works only if the source is confined in frequency. Or we can switch the input to the receiver alternately from the feed to an absorber or load. This last scheme is less good because many of the instrumental effects to be ameliorated are in the feed and beyond. This technique is known as the Dicke Switching method (see later).

Switching schemes are needed for either continuum or spectral measurements. A price to be paid for switching is increased noise. There are two contributions to the added noise. The receiver spends only half the time looking at the signal, and the result is the difference between two equally-noisy measurements. The result is twice the noise compared with not switching for the same integration time or four times the integration time to achieve the same noise.

DICKE SWITCHING RECEIVER

This was developed by a Canadian engineer working on radar receiver design during WWII. R H Dicke was working at the Massachusetts Institute of Technology (MIT), where a similar problem existed of trying to discern a weak return echo against a background of noise. In the Dicke receiver, an antenna relay rapidly switches the receiver between the antenna and a load resistor. When the switch is connected to the load resistor the output is simply the residual noise generated in the receiver plus the thermal noise of the resistor at ambient temperature. When the switch is connected to the antenna the noise is the product of the inherent receiver noise plus any signal within the bandwidth. A

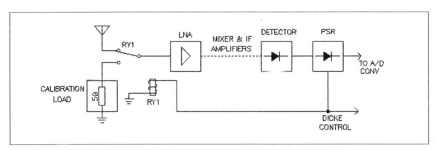

Fig 3.13: Dicke switching receiver

switch-frequency rectifier, synchronised to the switching waveform, performs detection. By using the Dicke switching method, it is easier to see if a signal is present. Dicke, in his original experiment, was able to measure a change in temperature of the Moon of 0.5K using a microwave receiver with a bandwidth of 8MHz and an integration time of 2s. This is equivalent to about 0.01dB change in signal level.

IF BANDWIDTH CONSIDERATIONS

Because the noise power per unit bandwidth from a radio star is relatively constant, we would ideally use a fairly wide band IF filter to allow the maximum amount of signal to be collected. If a very narrow band IF filter is used, the time it takes to build up a detectable signal using integration is longer. So the IF bandwidth is normally quite wide. For a radio telescope, this is not normally a problem because, by international agreement, certain portions of the spectrum are allocated only for radio astronomy. For an amateur band this cannot work; you cannot expect everyone else to stop transmitting while you are trying to receive. Consequently, if an amateur band is chosen as the receiving frequency we need to use narrower band IF filters than are optimum. A good compromise might be a filter with a 50kHz bandwidth. These can be constructed with LC filters because the widest crystal filter commonly available is only about 30kHz bandwidth.

RADIO FLUX UNIT

When one considers that the signal may have travelled a distance corresponding to more than 5 billion light years to arrive at the antenna, it can be appreciated that the signal is extremely weak and great efforts must be made in order to resolve and detect it with the least degradation.

Because the levels of signals we are dealing with are so small, it is impractical to use conventional measures of signal strength. Accordingly, a notation of 'radio-flux-units' is used to quantify the signal level that takes into account the antenna collecting area and system bandwidth. This is known as the jansky (Jy), and was defined by J S Hey in the 1950s in honour of Karl Jansky, and is defined in watts per square metre per unit bandwidth. 1Jy is defined as being 1 x 10^{-26}Wm^{-2}Hz^{-1}.

This means that if the effective aperture of the antenna is 100m^2, and the receiver being used has a bandwidth of 1MHz, and a flux unit of 1Jy is being received, the power collected is 10^{-18}W. The example given is equivalent to a signal of 10^{-15}mW or -150dBm. Present-day radio telescopes can directly detect radio sources down to 10^{-3}Jy flux units (-180dBm) without post detection processing or integration.

It is important to appreciate the significance of the flux unit, as it relates absolute received power to the antenna aperture and receiver bandwidth. By using this, it is possible for two radio telescopes to compare the received signal strengths in an unambiguous way. The two radio telescopes will most probably not have the same antenna or receiver bandwidth, but it is possible to directly calculate the signal strength for each one, from the antenna size and receiver characteristics, by knowing the flux of the distant object. Conversely, if the parameters of the receiver and antenna are accurately known, it is possible to assign a radio flux figure to a particular object.

It is different from the case of two communications receivers fitted with S-meters. Here, the sensitivities of the S-meters will most probably be different, as will the antennas, so to get any meaningful relationship is practically impossible. At best, the S-meter is purely a rough guide.

Calibration of the radio telescope system is done by injecting a precise known level of signal or noise into the antenna from a small sub-antenna or via a directional coupler directly into the LNA. Periodic checks are made to ensure the receiver sensitivity is not degraded. A crude noise source is the Sun but, as the solar radio flux varies widely, it cannot be considered an accurate means. Jodrell Bank Mk1, when operating at maximum gain, saturates and overloads the receiver when pointed at the Sun.

RADIO HORIZON OF RADIO TELESCOPES

It is difficult to visualise the vast distances that the signals from remote radio stars travel before we on Earth are able to receive them. One of the biggest problems is designing the correct antenna and receiver to observe a remote radio star. This factor sets an upper limit to the range at which radio stars might be detected with a particular radio telescope.

If one considers Cygnus-A as being typical of the brightest radio star, we can estimate the radio horizon for other stars of a similar power output. Cygnus-A is situated approx. 550×10^6 light years from Earth and is the strongest known emitter of radio-frequency energy.

To calculate the 'ultimate radio horizon', we need to calculate the ultimate sensitivity of the radio telescope system. This is done using the formula

$$S_{min} = \frac{2kTN}{A\sqrt{nt\Delta f}},$$

where: S_{min} = minimum detectable power flux density (Jy),
    k = Boltzmann's constant (1.38×10^{-23} JK^{-1}),
    T = receiver ambient temperature (K),
    N = noise factor of receiver,
    A = effective aperture of antenna (m^2),
    n = number of records averaged,
    t = time constant of output integrating circuit,
    f = receiver bandwidth in Hertz.

Note: The factor 2 is included because the telescope is only sensitive to one polarisation component of the signal.

Calculating for the Ohio State University telescope at 250MHz gives an ultimate sensitivity of 1.9×10^{-27} Jy. Using Cygnus-A as a reference, which is 550×10^6 light years distant, gives the radio horizon as 28×10^9 light years.

Because of receiver gain instability and interfering signals, the horizon will be somewhat less than the above figure. However, the value given is the ultimate that might be achieved under favourable conditions. It should be mentioned that the range calculated is unlikely to be achieved for one very important reason. The objects at or near the radio horizon are travelling at a great velocity away from us, approaching the speed of light, and hence the chance of detecting a signal from these is very unlikely. At a range of about 7 billion light years, the rate of recession equals the speed of light, so above this range no signals can be expected to be detected. The range of 7 billion light years is known as the 'celestial horizon'. The Ohio State University radio telescope exceeds the celestial horizon by about a factor of 4, and the best Earth-bound optical telescope equates only to half the celestial horizon at the present time. However, we now know from measurements recently made (2004) that the age of the universe is approximately 13 billion years, so the 28 billion light years predicted is out by a factor of more than 2:1.

Sufficient sensitivity does not necessarily imply the ability to detect an object. If the observed object is very close in angular displacement to other stronger sources, the telescope may not be able to resolve it from the other interfering signals. In such a case, the telescope is said to be resolution limited. Conversely, at short wavelengths, where sufficient antenna resolution is usually possible, the telescope may be limited due to insufficient sensitivity because of too high a noise figure; in such a case the telescope is said to be sensitivity limited.

IN-BAND INTERFERENCE SIGNALS

A serious problem affecting all radio telescopes is the radiation of weak signals that fall within the bandwidth of the receiver. A typical case occurred in the UK in the 1970s. An amateur 70cm converter utilised a 404MHz local oscillator to convert down to 28MHz. This was a home-made unit, not very well screened, and some of the local oscillator energy was able to leak into the antenna feeder and was radiated. The amateur lived approximately 20km from Jodrell Bank and caused the wiping out of the telescope whilst it was receiving on the 400MHz portion of the spectrum. The reason was that the Jodrell Bank receiver tuned in steps across the 400 to 410MHz spectrum to find deep space signals. Today the 400 - 408MHz spectrum is heavily polluted by many ISM, LPD and other devices, making the radio telescope usage difficult. Hence, this portion of spectrum has largely fallen into disfavour by astronomers.

When radio astronomers first started searching the sky for signals, there were not many interfering signals from man-made communications systems and plenty of spectrum to choose from. Today, the situation has changed radically. Frequencies that in earlier days were unused are now crowded with many different types of radio communication systems. Also, the broadband noise power radiated by some of these is far greater than the radio telescope sensitivity, so causing interference. If one imagines an aircraft flying overhead nearby radiating a signal from its radio altimeter in the 1.5GHz band of perhaps 100W, this will severely affect a receiver trying to receive on 1.4GHz. Although the receiver is operating 100MHz away, it has a wide first IF of maybe as much as 100MHz, and the broadband noise spectrum from the aircraft radio altimeter is only some 100dB below the transmitted power. This will be seen as an increase in the received noise floor and cause a false signal. Other typical problems are cellular telephone systems. When you visit a site such as Jodrell Bank, there are notices asking the visitors to switch off any cellular handset to stop interference to the telescope. Although the cellular handset is transmitting about 500MHz away from the 1.4GHz receiving frequency, the broadband noise radiated from the simple handset is quite high and this can spread over into the radio telescope band.

An Interference Case at 21cm

Man made noise can be the result of many different electrical and electronic items. An unusual case occurred during the early commissioning of the Durban University of Technology (DUT) Indlebe 21cm transit radio telescope. During this phase the team was attempting to calibrate the receiver against known celestial objects and was running the system in semi-automatic mode. For this the antenna was aligned so that Sagittarius-A would pass through the antenna beam, a drift scan method. At the time the constellation Sagittarius-A in the centre of the Milky Way only appeared late at night around midnight and the logging computer collected data from about 2pm local to 7am the next day. The faculty is closed from about 4-30pm.

On examining the plots the next day an odd trace was observed. Before 5pm the receiver noise floor was at the expected low level but at about 6pm the noise floor jumped up about 6dB and apart from the peaks of Sag-A and a few other identified objects as they drifted through the antenna beam the noise floor remained at the higher level. At about 6am the following day the noise floor abruptly dropped back to the lower level.

This had the team puzzled for a while until it occurred to them that something was being switched on and then off the next morning. Enquiring with the maintenance staff they discovered that the passageway fluorescent lights were operated by a time switch. The times in question correlated with the timer settings. To prove the point the time switch was altered by 15 minutes for the on and off time and the plots the next day showed that the noise had also altered in time when the noise floor jumped up and returned to normal. Although nothing could be done to solve the problem it highlighted how sensitive the 21cm receiver was.

Sometime later the writer came across an old book on radar which showed an X-band noise source which consisted of a short piece of waveguide with a 12-inch fluorescent tube slant across the guide, used to test the 10GHz receivers. The plot shown is the DUT drift scan showing the bumpy noise floor

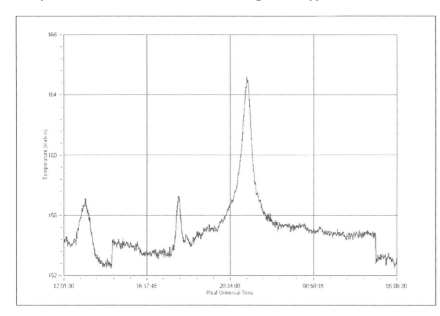

3.14: First calibrated source temperature plot showing from left to right Vela X (3K), Centaurus A (3.5K) and the Milky Way. The anomalies in the signal (step change near the beginning and end of the plot) are due to fluorescent lighting in the passageways of each floor of the buildings flanking the antenna switching on and off. Local time is UTC+2. (Note the absence of cellular phone interference). [Picture: Durban University of Technology]

3.15: Plot from sensitive radio telescope. [Picture courtesy Durban University of Technology – South Africa]

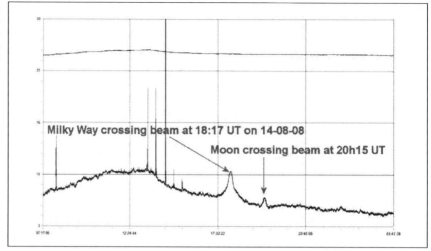

Milky Way crossing beam at 18:17 UT on 14-08-08

Moon crossing beam at 20h15 UT

As an indication of how sensitive a good radio telescope can be, look at the plot above from the DUT Indlebe transit telescope. This shows two objects in a drift scan. The first is the response from Sagittarius-A in the centre of the Milky Way; the second is the Sun radiation reflected off the Moon. The large spikes are man made interference from cellular telephones on campus, a real problem!

RADIO ASTRONOMY FREQUENCIES

The allocation of spectrum for radio astronomy is performed by the ITU, and the usage is controlled by the Committee for Radio Astronomy Frequencies (CRAF), a division of the International Astronomical Union (IAU). Some of the spectrum allocated is exclusively set aside for radio astronomy, and some is shared with other services. The spectrum covers from 13.36MHz to 141GHz.

The following radio astronomy frequency bands were recognised at the 1979 World Administrative Radio Conference. Many are shared segments, not specifically protected from interference by other authorised users, but are nevertheless generally accepted spectral regions for radio astronomical observation. The lower two segments are generally used for solar and Jupiter observations; the 73, 150 and 406MHz segments are quite popular for pulsar detection, and the 1400MHz band is used for hydrogen line and Pulsar measurements.

13.36	--	13.41 MHz
25.55	--	25.67 MHz
37.50	--	38.25 MHz
73.00	--	74.60 MHz
150.05	--	153.00 MHz
322.00	--	328.65 MHz
406.10	--	410.00 MHz
1400.00	--	1427.00 MHz

There are also many higher frequencies set aside purely for radio astronomy work, but these are in the upper microwave spectrum and unlikely to be suitable for amateur observation.

As can be seen, many of these border traditional amateur bands, and so the modification of equipment is quite simple. Note that these frequencies are designated for passive use, which is receive-only and no transmitting is permitted within these bands.

RX NOISE PERFORMANCE CALCULATIONS

The formulæ for calculating the system noise performance are listed below:

$$\text{Noise factor } F = \frac{\text{Available SNR at input}}{\text{Available SNR at output}}.$$

$$F = \frac{P_{si}}{P_{ni}} \times \frac{P_{no}}{P_{so}} = \frac{P_{no}}{G_a P_{in}},$$

where: P_{si} = input signal noise power,
          P_{so} = output signal noise power,
          P_{no} = available noise power at the receiver output,
          G_a = available power gain, and
          P_{ni} = available input noise power (W) due to kT_oB_n.

Note: Noise Factor and gains are expressed as power ratios.

Noise factor (F) is a unit-less measurement. Noise Figure (NF) is the logarithm of noise factor and is expressed in dB.

$$NF = 10\log_{10}F$$

Hence: Noise factor of 1 is equal to a noise figure of 0dB,
          Noise factor of 2 is equal to a noise figure of 3dB,
          Noise factor of 4 is equal to a noise figure of 6dB, etc.

The available input noise power, P_{ni}, is the noise power resulting from a matched source resistor at temperature T_o.

The SNR at the output of an amplifier will always be less than that at the input, as any practical amplifier will add some noise. Noise factor, F, is a measure of the amount of noise added. F will always be greater than unity (or NF > 0dB).

When several stages are cascaded to form a system, the following formula is used (Friiss's formula).

$$F_{total} = F_1 + \frac{F_2 - 1}{G} + \frac{F_3 - 1}{G_1 \times G_2} + \frac{F_4 - 1}{G_1 \times G_2 \times G_3} \dots$$

Note: Noise Factor and gains are expressed as power ratios..

From this it can be seen that the overall noise performance is largely determined by the first stage (F_1), and that the addition of later stages degrades the overall noise figure to a lesser extent, defined by the gain of the first stage (G_1), provided the first stage is not a lossy line with G < 1.

In a radio telescope, the noise contributions of the second and possibly the third stages can be significant, and so extra care must be taken with the design of the receiver. Due to the very low noise figures that are typically used in a radio telescope, it is more convenient to express these in terms of equivalent noise temperatures. The noise power at the output of an amplifier stage (P_n) is defined as:

$$P_n = \frac{F-1}{kT_0BG_a},$$

where: k is Boltzmann's constant $= 1.38 \times 10^{-23}JK^{-1}$,
          To is the equivalent noise temperature of the amplifier,
          B is the bandwidth of the amplifier (Hz),
          Ga is the gain of the amplifier as a power ratio.

The noise characteristic of this stage can alternatively be represented by assuming that it has an equivalent noise temperature such that the noise power produced at the output of the stage due to internally generated noise is given by

$$P_n = kT_eBG_a$$
Thus

$$kT_eBG_a = \frac{F-1}{kT_0BG_a} \quad \text{or} \quad T_e = \frac{F-1}{T_0}.$$

The cascaded noise factor equation can be written in noise temperature format (modified version of Friis's equation)

$$T_e = T_e1 + \frac{T_e2}{G_a1} + \frac{T_e3}{G_a1 \times G_a2}\ldots$$

As an example:
The current generation of 5GHz LNAs used by Jodrell Bank use HEMT devices and liquid helium cooling. The published noise temperature of the system is 5K.

The noise figure of a 5K device is

$$NF = 10\log(1) + \frac{5}{290} = 0.074dB.$$

CRYOGENIC COOLING

Many modern radio telescopes today use some form of cooling to lower the ambient temperature of the LNA to achieve a lower system noise temperature. Common forms are liquid nitrogen and liquid helium. Helium is usually the preferred medium. Liquid helium exhibits a temperature of about -260°C or about 13 degrees above absolute zero.

Fig 3.16: Decanting liquid helium in the Jodrell Bank Receiver Design Laboratory. (Photograph: J Fielding 2005)

In practice it is normally possible to hold the LNA and associated metalwork to about 15K. Whereas this technique works very well it is not the sort of thing that amateurs are likely to incorporate in a low noise amplifier because of the engineering problems encountered.

Using liquid helium to lower the temperature of the LNA and other parts of the front-end unit brings about some very interesting engineering problems. In the picture below, there is a white former to the left and near the bottom of the unit with several enamelled copper wires wrapped around it. It looks a bit like a RF choke; in fact it is a 'thermal choke'.

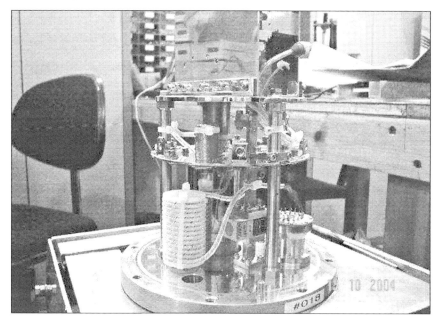

Fig 3.17: Close-up of a typical microwave receiver unit. (Photograph: J Fielding 2004)

The wires run from the DC input connector to the right, which has feed-through capacitors and other RF filtering to stop interfering signals getting into the unit. However, the biggest problem is stopping heat getting in and raising the temperature of the LNA and other components.

The wires wrapped around the plastic former carry the various DC supply lines and control signals and they exhibit a high thermal resistance and help to prevent the ambient heat getting to the LNA. It takes about 1h to lower the temperature from ambient to the required 15K (-258°C). The rate of change of temperature needs to carefully controlled to prevent rapid contraction of the metal-work or components from causing a stress-related failure, particularly in surface-mounted components. The liquid helium is pumped up the main support tubes to the top plate, which serves as a heat sink (heat-extractor) to which the LNAs and other parts are mounted. Having passed through the extractor the heated liquid helium exits via another supporting pipe and is then sent through an external heat exchanger to remove the heat energy. It is then sent back to the helium pump for another circuit. The liquid helium is pumped by a DC powered 'shuttle-pump' mounted on the bottom of the unit.

ANTENNA NOISE TEMPERATURE

The concept of equivalent noise temperature may be extended. If an arbitrary source of noise (thermal or non-thermal) is random, it can be modelled as an equivalent thermal noise source and characterised with an equivalent noise temperature. Thus, components and systems can be characterised by saying that they have an equivalent noise temperature.

For example, a non-thermal device, such as an antenna, may be associated with an effective noise temperature, T. If the noise power received by the antenna is Pn in a system bandwidth, B, then Tant may be expressed as

$$T_{ant} = \frac{P_n}{kB}$$

where: k is Boltzmann's constant = $1.38 \times 10^{-23} JK^{-1}$, and
B is the system bandwidth (Hz).

The term T_{ant} includes all noise contributions up to the 'reference plane', which is normally taken as the input to the first amplifier stage (commonly referred to as the Low Noise Amplifier, LNA).

There are basically two major contributors to antenna noise temperature, namely sky noise and noise from ohmic losses in the antenna or coaxial cable. Sky noise comprises all external noise that enters the antenna. In satellite and radio astronomy systems, the sky noise is due to extra-terrestrial noise, thermal radiation from the atmosphere and man-made noise reflected from the earth.

The atmosphere affects external noise in two ways. It attenuates signals passing through it from outer space, and also generates noise because of the energy of its constituents. Sky noise generally varies with frequency, elevation angle of the antenna, (at low elevations the antenna 'sees' a greater portion of the atmosphere and some of the warm earth), and surface water vapour concentration.

EFFECTS OF SKY NOISE

As the sky noise reduces so dramatically as the operating frequency rises, it is often more productive to choose a higher rather than a lower frequency to observe a distant object, even though the expected path loss is greater. One can safely assume that for frequencies up to about 144MHz half the system noise temperature is due to antenna and sky noise and the remainder is due to the LNA. Therefore, there is no significant benefit to be gained by reducing the LNA noise figure much below half of the total system temperature.

For example:

At 144MHz, with the antenna pointed at the horizon in an urban environment, the typical sky noise will be of the order of 1000K. With the antenna elevated to 45°, it will be reduced to approximately 200K. This is an equivalent LNA noise figure of 1.15dB. With the antenna pointed at the horizon with a 1000K sky noise, the lowest noise figure required is about 6.5dB. In a rural environment, the ambient noise with the antenna pointed at the horizon will be lower, perhaps as low as 300K, and then a lower noise figure can be used to advantage. Even so, it is limited to about 3dB.

At 432MHz, the sky is less noisy and the typical figures for these two cases will be approximately 150K and 20K. This is an equivalent minimum LNA noise figure of 0.3dB.

At 1296MHz, the sky noise has dropped to about 5K for an antenna pointed vertically upwards, assuming no radio star is in the beam. This is an equivalent LNA noise figure of 0.07dB. It is extremely difficult to get anywhere near this with conventional microwave transistors at a modest cost. To achieve this very low noise temperature requires cryogenic cooling.

Turning this fact around explains why there is no great improvement to be gained by using an extremely low noise figure on the lower bands. At 144MHz, for all modes except satellite or EME, there is no advantage in striving for less than about 2dB NF. For 144MHz EME, going down to as low as 1dB is all that is required. On 432MHz and above, the lowest noise figure that can be achieved is of benefit as the sky noise is so low at the higher frequencies.

An equation for determining the antenna noise temperature up to the reference plane is:

$$T_{ant} = \frac{(l_a - 1)290 + T_{sky}}{l_a},$$

where l_a is the numeric value of the system ohmic losses up to the reference plane.

For an antenna-receiver system, the total effective system noise temperature, T_{sys}, can be defined as

$$T_{sys} = T_{ant} + T_{rx},$$

where Trx is the equivalent noise temperature of the receiver.

SPECIAL RECEIVER TECHNIQUES

In a receiver for very weak-signal detection there are several techniques we can use to enhance the probability of detection. Apart from the obvious one of ensuring the system noise figure is as low as necessary, the detection process in the intermediate amplifier stages and post detection signal processing are particular areas that have involved a great deal of study. Much of this is due to the development work done on long-range military radar systems. Here, a similar problem exists - how to determine if a response in the IF and detector is in fact a genuine target or simply a random burst of noise. Today, with digital signal processing (DSP), the IF signal is converted in an analogue-to-digital converter and the final filtering and detection is performed at a digital level.

In a radar system, unwanted small changes in the detector output give rise to false alarms. If a radar system has a high false alarm rate, the user quickly loses confidence in its ability to identify a threat target at a long range. This is what happened with the SCR-270 radar system set up in Hawaii during the WWII. The radar correctly detected the Japanese aircraft moving towards Pearl Harbour some 50 minutes before the fateful attack began, but the operators incorrectly concluded they were American friendly aircraft returning to base.

In simple radar receivers, the amplifier stages could all be fixed-gain linear amplifiers and the detector a simple amplitude detector similar to an AM detector. The increase in IF level when an echo signal is received causes the DC component to rise above some preset level and then a target is assumed to be present. This works for the perfect case but, in practice, many factors can effect the detectability. Common problems are insects or birds flying through the antenna beamwidth at a few miles range. These will give a radar return (echo) similar to an aircraft at much greater distance. If only amplitude information is available, the operator could assume it was a threat. With range information, the operator could distinguish between close-in targets and those further away. A target closing on the radar would in each successive echo show a shortening of the range

TYPICAL RADIO TELESCOPE SYSTEM NOISE TEMPERATURES

Some typical system noise temperatures can be quoted for the various large radio telescopes in use around the world. These are taken from Skolnik's Radar Handbook, published in 1970, so are indicative of that period (see the table). Today, considerable improvements have taken place with receivers for radio astronomy.

Site	Year	Antenna Dia (ft)	Gain (dBi)	Freq (MHz)	Tsys (K)	Noise Figure (dB)
MIT (a)	1964	1800 x 220	34.5	38.26	12000	16.3
AIO (b)	1967	1000	37.0	40.12	10000	15.5
NBS (c)	1962	1000 x 500	40.0	49.92	6000	13.3
JB (d)	1961	250	47.3	408	1000	6.5
MH1 (e)	1961	84	37.5	440	240	2.6
USSR (f)	1963	8 x 50	47.4	750	100	1.28
MH2 (e)	1963	84	47.3	1295	70	0.93
JPL1 (g)	1964	85	54.2	2388	30	0.42
JPL2 (h)	1968	85 + 210	*54.2 + 62	2388	221	0.30
HS1 (i)	1966	120	66.0	7750	100	1.28
HS2 (i)	1967	120	66.1	7840	5	0.07

Notes on table

(a)   Phased dipole array at El Campo, Texas. Operated by Massachusetts Institute of Technology.

(b)   Fixed 1000ft-diameter spherical reflector; movable feed (±20°). Operated near Arecibo, Puerto Rico, by Cornell University. 40.12MHz and 430MHz.

(c)   Phased dipole array at Jicamarca, near Lima, Peru. Operated by the US National Bureau of Standards. Antenna comprises approximately 5000 dipoles.

(d)   Steerable paraboloid at Jodrell Bank. Operated by the University of Manchester.

(e)   Steerable paraboloid at Westford-Tyngsboro, Mass. Operated by MIT Lincoln Laboratory.

(f)   Eight mechanically-coupled 50ft paraboloids at Crimea, USSR. Operated by the Institute of Radio Engineering and Electronics.

(g)   Steerable paraboloids at Goldstone Lake, California. Operated by the Jet Propulsion Laboratory of the California Institute of Technology.

(h)   Bi-static configuration: 85ft transmitting; 210ft receiving. *210ft dish has a gain of 62dBi.

(i)   Hay-Stack Radio Observatory. Operated by MIT Lincoln Laboratory.

From the table, it can be seen that, between 1961 and 1967, the system noise temperature was reduced from 1000K at 408MHz to 5K at a frequency of 7.84GHz, such was the push to obtain better weak-signal results.

At low frequencies, the required noise temperature is not that low, due to the atmosphere generating considerable noise at these frequencies, plus the sky noise. At frequencies in the UHF and SHF regions, the atmospheric sky noise drops rapidly and the receiver can benefit from a lower system temperature. However, at increasing frequencies it becomes more difficult to achieve low noise performance from active devices.

and a consequent increase in echo amplitude. With knowledge of both of these pieces of information, a decision is made more easily.

In order to be able to detect targets both very far away and very close in, the problem arises that a manually-set IF gain system is no longer acceptable. For maximum range the gain needs to be high, for close-in targets the gain, if set too high, could cause blocking of the receiver because the echo is very strong. A system where the receiver can set the IF gain for each successive echo is required. The attack time of the AGC needs to be very fast, as does the recovery time. If the recovery time is too slow, a weak echo from a distant target could be missed. No practical AGC system can satisfy this requirement.

Limiting Amplifiers

A possible solution to this problem is to use IF amplifiers that give a limiting action to strong signals but operate near full gain for weaker echoes. This is similar to the IF amplifiers used in FM receivers. The process of limiting, however, removes all the amplitude information. Hence, all echoes above a certain level will appear to give the same amplitude output. Therefore target size information is lost. Limiting amplifiers can adjust their gain very quickly, in some cases in less than a few nanoseconds. What is required is a version of a limiting amplifier that can adjust its gain automatically, but still preserve the amplitude information. Because of this requirement, special IF amplifiers were developed. These are known as 'logarithmic amplifiers'.

Logarithmic Amplifiers

A logarithmic amplifier is a type of IF amplifier that adjusts its gain logarithmically, based on the level of the input signal. The typical gain of a log-amp might be approximately 10dB for very small signals. However, over a 10dB increase in signal level the gain falls to 0dB in a linear manner. The log-amp also contains a precision detector that produces a DC output voltage or current which is an exact measure of the gain ruling at any particular time. Hence, a log-amp might output zero volts when the gain is maximum, 0.5V when the gain is reduced to 5dB and 1V when the gain has fallen to zero dB. This would give a range of 100mVdB^{-1}. With this precision, it is much easier to see a very small change in input power level.

The 10dB range of a single log-amp is not of much use for a receiver IF, although it could be used to measure power very accurately in, say, a through-line power meter. By connecting several log-amp stages in series, the total gain rises in 10dB steps as each new amplifier stage is added and the dynamic range also increases by the same amount. A 'log amp strip' with three 10dB devices would give a maximum gain of 30dB and a dynamic range of the same value. Hence, it could accurately measure the signal level over a 30dB range with an accuracy of approx. 0.1dB.

For a typical long-range radar, the IF gain would need to be 100dB or more. This would require ten log-amps to be connected in series. However, a problem now arises for very strong echoes. When the input level exceeds the level to cause 0dB gain, the log-amp does not give any further increase in the DC detected output voltage or current.

The last log-amp stage in the series-connected chain will be the first to compress to 0dB as the signal level rises. The penultimate stage will then start to compress towards 0dB, and so on. This is known as 'successive detection'. When the total 100dB range has been used up the first stage will have fallen to 0dB, and hence the detected output will not increase any more no matter how much bigger the input signal becomes.

The basic problem with this scheme is that the final stage will almost certainly be in total compression due to the intrinsic receiver noise and will be giving full-detected output on just the noise. This means the output DC level will not extend to zero volts and leaves a DC offset in the system. This can be trimmed out in the succeeding post-detection processing amplifiers.

To extend the range any further by adding more log-amps in series is not a feasible scheme, because then the last two or more stages will be driven into compression on quiescent receiver noise, thus reducing the available dynamic range by a large amount. What is required is another approach.

Log Amp Lift Stages

If another short chain of series-connected log-amps are connected to the input in parallel with the first log-amp stage and these are fed from an attenuator to provide a level that will start the new parallel stage to begin compressing when the first stage has just reached compression, the parallel stage can carry on giving valid detector output information for a further 20dB if two stages are used in series.

This extends the 100dB range to at least 120dB. This technique is known as a 'lift stage' as it lifts the dynamic range a further amount. Fig 3.19 shows a log-amplifier chain. At the top is the normal chain, the lift stages are the two ICs below. These are fed with a resistive potential divider to attenuate the input to this stage. A typical log-amplifier with lift stages would use a parallel-connected stage of two or three devices.

Most log-amplifier ICs are inherently very wide-band devices. Typically, they utilise DC-coupled stages and can operate from DC to 900MHz for the most modern devices. If this extremely wide bandwidth was used, the SNR would be severely degraded as the noise power per unit of bandwidth is constant. It is normally necessary to insert one or more inter-stage noise filters to limit the bandwidth. The overall bandwidth of the receiver would normally be

Fig 3.19: Inter-stage noise filtering

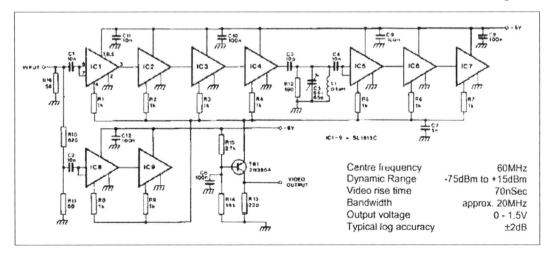

Centre frequency	60MHz
Dynamic Range	-75dBm to +15dBm
Video rise time	70nSec
Bandwidth	approx. 20MHz
Output voltage	0 - 1.5V
Typical log accuracy	±2dB

set by a band-pass filter after the receive mixer, but this does not help in the case of log-amplifiers. This is because the skirt selectivity of a typical crystal filter extends only to about 90dB; below this, the attenuation does not significantly increase

Also, many crystal filters, because of their multi-pole design, have spurious responses at frequencies removed from the centre frequency that can be as little as 70dB of the pass band attenuation. As the log-amp can have a dynamic range of some 30dB more than this, it causes a problem. In the previous diagram can be seen a single band-pass noise filter half-way down the first chain of ICs.

This filter needs to be carefully designed so that it does not upset the logarithmic law of the chain. In very high-quality log amplifiers, such as those used in spectrum analysers, a noise filter is often used between each stage to improve the SNR.

Detected Output

The detected output of a log-amp is a voltage that varies between zero volts and some maximum. If you look at the diagram the total dynamic range is from -75dBm to +15dBm, a total of 90dB. The detector output varies from zero to 1.5V for this range. Therefore a 90dB range is compressed into a 1.5V range. This gives a figure of 16.66mVdB^{-1}. Subsequent DC amplifiers can be used to expand this range. For example, if the DC amplifiers change the full-scale output to 5V, the figure becomes 55.55mVdB^{-1}. By scaling the DC output to suit the sensitivity of the display, the full dynamic range can be made to just fill the display vertical scale. The log-amplifier is the IF used in precision measurement instruments, for example, spectrum analysers and measuring receivers. It is the most accurate S-meter available. Normally the log-amplifier dynamic range is more than the displayed dynamic range. This is known as the 'on-screen' dynamic range. The 'off screen' dynamic range is often as much as 30dB more than the 'on-screen' range to allow for abnormally-large signals.

Receiver Muting

As the log amp is inherently free from blocking when a very large signal is received, such as the transmitted pulse, the IF can recover very quickly. A typical log-amp strip, although it will hard limit when the transmitter pulse occurs, can recover in a few hundred nanoseconds, and be ready to give a valid output very soon after the transmit pulse ceases. Hence, there is no requirement to mute the IF during transmit, only the receiver front end needs blanking to prevent burn-out damage.

A LOW COST LOG-AMPLIFIER

The circuit previously shown is for the Plessey SL-1613 series of log-amplifiers. Today, these are obsolete. However, another option is to use a more modern device. One such device is made by Analog Devices and is usable to 50MHz. This device is the AD-606 and features a log range of up to 90dB with a built in lift stage and video filtering. The block diagram of the AD-606 is shown here.

The log-amp output is a DC voltage which varies between 0.5V to approximately 4V for the 90dB range, 3.5V = 90dB or 38.88mVdB^{-1}. The response to a rapid pulse signal is good, as shown opposite.

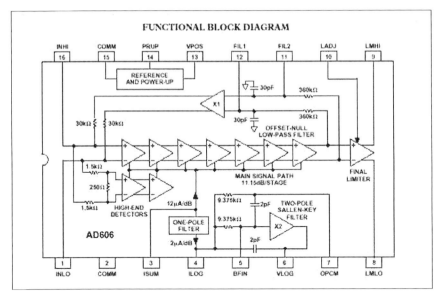

Fig 3.20: Analog Devices AD-606 block diagram. (Courtesy Analog Devices)

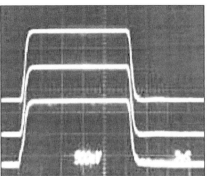

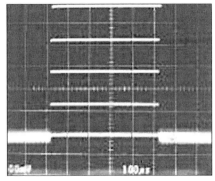

(left) Fig 3.21: V_{log} output for a pulsed 10.7MHz input. Top trace: -35dBm to +5dBm. Middle trace: -15dBm to -55dBm. Bottom trace: -35dBm to -75dBm

(right) Fig 3.22: V_{log} response to a 10.7MHz CW signal modulated by a 25µs-wide pulse with a 25kHz repetition rate using 200pF input coupling capacitors. The input signal goes from +5dBm to -75dBm in 20dB steps

A Lower Cost Approach

A line-up using log amplifiers is not the least expensive method of getting accurate amplitude information. Many of the modern ICs designed for wireless communication contains a similar type of measurement circuit.

In cellular telephone systems, the base station needs to know the level of received signal from a handset to allow it to adjust the transmitter power to reduce inter-modulation in its multi-channel output stages. Handsets situated close to the base station do not require as much base transmit power to attain a good SNR, and hence transmit power can be turned down. The handset also contains an IF amplifier with a signal-measuring device, which performs a similar function to adjust the handset transmitter power to conserve battery life and thus allows longer 'talk-time' between recharges. On the modern cellphone, the received signal level is displayed.

This method is known as RSSI (received signal strength indicator). Many of the FM integrated circuits today contain some sort of RSSI circuitry which, although not as accurate as a true log-amp, is adequate for most amateur applications.

A typical IC is the Philips NE 604/614. This is conventional FM IC and contains circuitry to drive a quadrature detector with a good RSSI circuit. For our

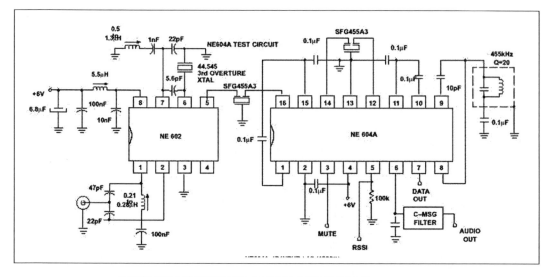

Fig 3.23: Application circuit for a double-conversion receiver.

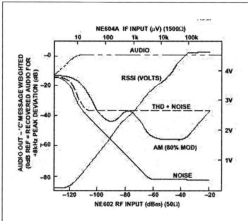

Fig 3.24: The RSSI response of a NE602 / NE604 combined receiver

application, the FM detection is not required only the RSSI, this covers a range of 90dB. The bandwidth of the NE604 is limited to about 1MHz so the best option is to use it with a 455kHz IF which is converted down from either 10.7MHz or 21.4MHz.

The application notes available from Philips detail the use as a measuring receiver and it has been used in several designs for an amateur spectrum analyser.

The response of the RSSI is fairly slow with the standard circuit but, if the NE624 version is substituted, it can be speeded up to approximately 2µs with suitable component substitution, and a low-pass post-detection filter to reduce the quiescent noise.

For full information on how to use the NE604, the reader is advised to look on the Philips website for application notes and data sheets. The NE604 is not the only suitable IC; Philips make a bewildering range of similar devices for receiver applications.

Another suitable device is the NE605 or NE615 which combines the IF and the NE602 mixer into one IC. There are many others from other manufacturers.

SPECIAL FILTERING TECHNIQUES

As we have seen, the optimum bandwidth for a radio telescope might be far greater than the types used for normal communications. As the use of a low IF allows easier filtering and high gains to be used, the industry has adopted certain frequencies for these applications. In a VHF receiver, we might use a first IF of 21.4MHz or 10.7MHz. These two frequencies are very popular and many filter manufacturers make a variety of filters with different bandwidths. Typically, the narrowest bandwidth is approximately 2.5kHz, which suits receivers using SSB; the widest filter available is approximately 30kHz. If filter bandwidths greater than this are required, we have to resort to other, more expensive technologies. One of these is the Surface Acoustic Wave filter, know as a SAW filter. With SAW devices, it is possible to make filters with bandwidths up to 10MHz wide when a centre frequency of 70 or 100MHz is used.

The lower frequency filters are normally available at 455kHz, 1.6MHz, 5MHz and 9MHz, and these use either quartz crystal technology for the higher frequencies and ceramic technology for the popular 455kHz types. In a typical amateur VHF receiver, the use of 10.7MHz and 455kHz are very common, as these filters are readily available at low cost. UHF receivers normally require a higher first IF due to the image filtering problems. Here, a popular choice is 45MHz, as this is a readily-available filter used in cellular telephones.

If we require a wider bandwidth filter and cannot tolerate the cost of a SAW filter, we need to resort to other methods. In the early days of communications receivers, the use of LC-coupled filters provided acceptable filtering if the IF was sufficiently low - perhaps as low as 100kHz in some designs. The reason is the limited Q that it is possible with conventional coils and capacitors. If the filter needs to have a low insertion loss and a steep cut-off, a high Q is essential. If the Q of the inductors is poor, the insertion loss increases and the skirt selectivity is also poor.

With practical inductors wound on ferrite coil formers or a ferrite toroid, the maximum Q is limited to approximately 250 at frequencies above about 10MHz. If we needed a filter with a bandwidth of 5kHz at 10.7MHz, the inductor Q needs to be greater than 5000. This is impossible and explains why crystals are used to construct these types.

But when we require wide bandwidth filters, such as is the case for a radio astronomy receiver, conventional inductors and capacitors can get the job done for a reasonable cost. The author has developed a technique for narrow-band filtering for a radio telescope receiver that required a bandwidth of 100kHz and good skirt selectivity. Normally that would require an expensive SAW filter which, once purchased, meant that he was stuck with that bandwidth unless another expensive filter is purchased. Although there are a number of ceramic filters manufactured for FM broadcast receivers using 10.7MHz as the IF, these have poor skirt selectivity. They are also quite wide, being typically 300kHz at the -3dB point.

Multiple Conversion Filtering

In a conventional superhet receiver, we might start with a first IF of 10.7MHz and then convert to 455kHz. The 10.7MHz filter does not need to be very narrow; approximately 500kHz is adequate and this can easily be achieved with LC

Fig 3.25: Block diagram of the down-up filter mixer

Fig 3.26: Frequency response of insertion loss and input return loss (VSWR) of the 1.35MHz band-pass filter

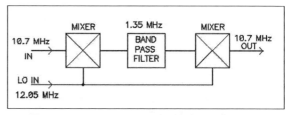

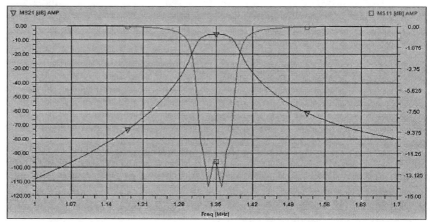

or ceramic filters. The main selectivity is obtained at 455kHz after the final mixing process.

In the author's case, this was not acceptable for a very good reason. The main IF uses a 10.7MHz log-amplifier. This is used for all frequencies and is essentially a wide-bandwidth amplifier strip with a bandwidth of 2MHz. To increase the sensitivity, we need to reduce the bandwidth. For optimum performance, we might settle on a 50kHz bandwidth to increase the noise power accepted from a distant radio star. The inductor Q required to construct such a narrow filter is much greater than that which is possible using conventional inductors if the insertion loss is going to be kept low. We can probably tolerate up to 10dB of insertion loss at this point in the receiver, as the front-end largely defines the ultimate sensitivity and the generation of 10dB of gain to make up for the filter loss is simple to achieve.

The technique used is a little unusual, but follows standard practice. If the 10.7MHz signal from the mixer is mixed down again to a low frequency, the filtering can be done at this low frequency. Having defined the IF bandwidth at this low frequency, the signal is mixed back up to 10.7MHz before passing to the main log IF module. The system requires a second LO, but this does not have to be very stable, as any drift will be cancelled out when the signal is mixed back up to 10.7MHz. In practice, this could be a free-running oscillator but, in the author's case, a suitable crystal was obtained from the junk box. This crystal is 12.050MHz and hence defines the second IF as being 12.05 - 10.7 = 1.35MHz.

Using the *ARRL Radio Designer* software package, a suitable filter was designed using ferrite toroid-wound inductors. It was determined using a Marconi Q-meter that the possible Q with the available toroidal cores was of the order of 150 at 1.4MHz. Hence, in the circuit simulation, a value of 100 was

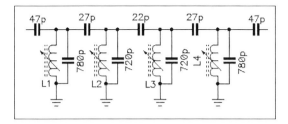

Fig 3.27: Circuit diagram of the 1.35MHz band-pass filter

Fig 3.28: Complete circuit diagram of the down-up filter mixer.

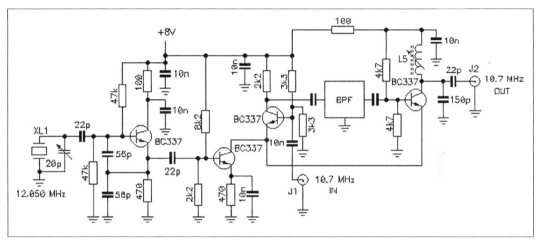

used to allow a little extra leeway. The circuit simulation file gave good results and the plot below shows the overall filter response.

The overall insertion loss mid-band is approximately 6dB, and the ultimate selectivity at 1MHz is over 100dB down. The upper frequency is slightly less because of the circuit topology used, but is still more than 80dB down. The bandwidth is 50kHz at the -3dB points and the filter has a Gaussian response, which is better at rejecting impulse interference from ignition and other man-made noise.

The filter design is basically a four-stage network with top coupling with low value capacitors; hence it tends to behave like a high-pass filter on the high-frequency side of the response. On the low-frequency side, it behaves like a low-pass filter and this is why the rejection is better at 1MHz than at 1.7MHz. During the optimisation process the capacitor values were constrained to E12 values for ease of manufacture. The filter circuit is shown below.

The resonating capacitors are made up from two parallel capacitors to obtain the required value and to maintain the higher Q possible with smaller capacitor values. Hence, the 780pF capacitors consist of two 390pF in parallel and the 720pF consist of a 390pF and a 330pF. All capacitors are ceramic plate types with a Q of greater than 2000 and are made by Philips.

The inductor values are as follows:

L1 & L4   16.74μH
L2 & L3   18.13μH

The overall schematic of the rest of the circuit is shown in Fig 3.28. The crystal oscillator uses an NPN transistor configured as a Colpitts oscillator with feedback provided by the tapped capacitors between base and emitter. Two high-value resistors to bias the base at one-half the positive rail voltage provide the base bias of the transistor. The output from the oscillator is capacitor-coupled to the bottom npn transistor in the modified Gilbert cell mixer. The 10.7MHz output from the filter/mixer is provided by a variable inductor resonated to 10.7MHz by the 150pF capacitor.

SYSTEM CALCULATIONS

In order to establish if the proposed receiver is able to fulfil the required parameters, we need to do some calculations using the various building blocks. Whereas it is quite simple to do these with a scientific calculator, the availability of analysis software makes the task less onerous and allows many different combinations to be examined in a short time. The author uses the program *SysCalc*.

Fig 3.29 shows a typical analysis for a proposed Hydrogen Line receiver at 1420MHz. This receiver requires a very low noise figure and an IF bandwidth of approximately 50kHz. Using a wide-band IF reduces the ultimate sensitivity, but allows more noise energy to be captured and a shorter integration time.

The various blocks are constructed with the gain or loss, noise figure and intermodulation parameters assigned. The system will consist of a two-stage PHEMT LNA mounted at the antenna, and the main receiver is situated remotely with a feeder cable connecting the two units. The relay connecting the LNA to the antenna is used as part of the Dicke switching to allow a load resistor or the antenna to be connected to the LNA; this was measured to have a loss of 0.1dB. This is a microwave changeover relay obtained from a scrap Hewlett-Packard piece of test equipment which covered 1 to 18GHz. As this precedes the LNA, this loss adds directly to the overall noise figure. The predicted noise figure of the LNA first stage is 0.18dB with a gain of 13dB; this design uses Agilent ATF-34143 PHEMT devices in a strip-line circuit. The first stage is optimised for the best noise figure and the second is optimised for best gain of 17dB consistent with obtaining a noise figure of 0.3dB. The overall LNA noise figure is 0.21dB and the gain is 30dB.

The input signal level assumed was -140dBm and so the power levels shown throughout the analysis results show how this level varies with the gains and losses of the various stages. At the output of the main receiver, prior to the detector, the level has risen to 72dBm because the overall gain is approximately 68dB.

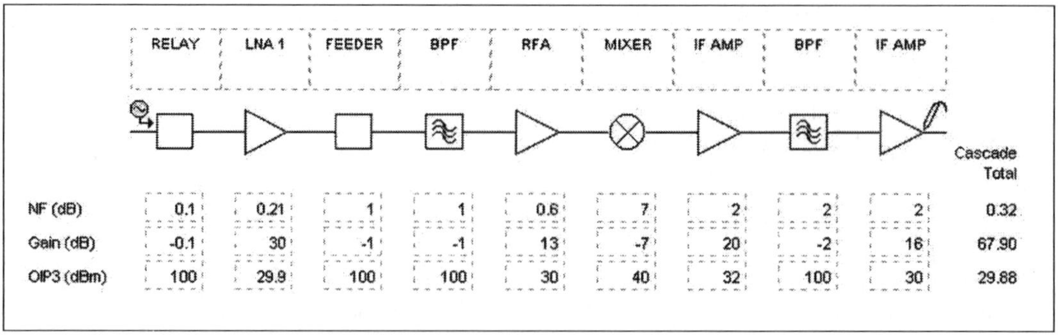

Fig 3.29: Analysis software output screen The detector is the AD606 log amplifier, which has an intercept point sensitivity of -88dBm and a useful input sensitivity of approx. -80dBm. Therefore the

	RELAY	LNA 1	FEEDER	BPF	RFA	MIXER	IF AMP	BPF	IF AMP	Cascade Total
NF (dB)	0.1	0.21	1	1	0.6	7	2	2	2	0.32
Gain (dB)	-0.1	30	-1	-1	13	-7	20	-2	16	67.90
OIP3 (dBm)	100	29.9	100	100	30	40	32	100	30	29.88

receiver system will be able to resolve signals much below -140dBm; by altering the input power level, we can see that the minimum discernible signal is -148dBm with the 50kHz bandwidth. If we choose to use a narrower IF bandwidth, say 10kHz, then the MSD level falls accordingly. However, a very narrow IF bandwidth would require the LO to be variable in frequency to correct for the expected Doppler shift from distant objects.

The main receiver consists of a band-pass image rejection filter at 1420MHz and then an LNA prior to the mixer stage. Connecting the LNA and the receiver is a length of low-loss feeder with a predicted loss of 1dB; this will be a piece of foam-filled microwave coax. It would be preferable to eliminate this extra loss by siting the receiver down-converter at the antenna, but environmental problems concerning weatherproofing and ambient temperature changes made this a difficult challenge. By changing the analysis file, we can see what advantage is likely to occur if we choose this route. In fact, there is no significant improvement, the overall noise figure remains the same; the only change is 1dB more output signal at the input to the log amplifier, so there is no need to go to all the trouble and inconvenience of mounting the receiver at the antenna. In fact, with 6dB of feeder loss, the overall noise figure rises only to 0.34dB, so the loss in this piece of cable is relatively insignificant.

The noise figure of the main receiver is approximately 2.7dB, being the band-pass filter loss and the noise figure of the receiver LNA stage and the following stages.

The other thing the *SysCalc* software is able to do is to analyse how large a signal is needed to paralyse the receiver. If the input signal is above a certain level, the later receiver stages will be driven into a non-linear region and will generate IMD products that will mask the wanted signal. With an input level of -140dBm, the spurious-free dynamic range (SFDR) is 59dB. So, as long as the input signal does not exceed 140 - 59 = -81dBm, the receiver will perform satisfactorily. If the input level is anticipated as being greater than -81dBm, it will be necessary to provide some form of manual gain control in the receiver, perhaps in the IF amplifiers following the mixer. The AD606 log amplifier can safely handle large input signals up to +10dBm without overload.

Calibrating the System

For the receiver output to have a meaningful result it is important to calibrate the receiving system. Professional radio telescopes have an elaborate system for this. This requires at least one very low loss coaxial relay with a low VSWR.

During the development of the DUT Indlebe project getting an accurate calibration occupied a considerable amount of time and effort, but the end result was worth all the effort.

In a conventional receiver sensitivity measurement we use a calibrated signal generator and a SINAD measuring meter. For radio telescopes this is not the best option. The signal levels we are dealing with are at least 30dB less and in some case much smaller. Although one can extend the lower end by fitting calibrated attenuators between the signal generator and the receiver the limitation is the amount of signal leakage from the signal generator oscillator.

Radio telescope receivers are calibrated in a different way. There are three measurements that need to be made. The first is the receiver output level with the antenna pointed to a quiet part of the sky, known as "Cold Sky". The second is with the LNA switched from the antenna to a precision load (50Ω) and the third is with an absorber material fitted to the feed horn to reduce the cold sky noise to close to zero. The microwave background radiation value for cold sky is still about 3K, so we have to factor this out in our calibration to get a starting point of 0K. To do this requires an absorber plug of microwave material that fits into the open end of the feed horn to exclude signals. (A good substitute is the black conducting anti-static foam that ICs are often shipped in. Several pieces are cut and stacked to increase the thickness to be a close fit in the mouth of the feed horn and then held in place with duct tape).

The signal level from the cold sky is an unknown at first. The signal level from the load resistor can be accurately calculated for the known ambient temperature of the resistor, using Boltzman's Constant. The final measurement with the absorber 'plug' measures the inherent LNA noise when perfectly terminated into the feed horn system. Note that because the LNA often needs to be operated in a mismatched mode to obtain the lowest noise figure it often present a poor match to an antenna. Removing the absorber plug allows the feed horn to now see the reflecting surface and the VSWR match to the LNA changes. This affects the measured cold sky value.

Fortunately many radio astronomy observatories have been through this calibration method and can offer advice. If one picks a strong object, such as Sagittarius-A, one can obtain accurate data of the flux density of the object in janskys at a particular frequency. The Radio Eyes software gives some data at spot frequencies for most objects. Hart RAO was able to accurately measure the flux level at the times the calibration was made and this allowed the team to calculate the absolute system parameters.

In the DUT Indlebe system the noise output from a load resistor was too small to make the calibration work and instead a precision noise source was added to give an accurate starting point. Two Hewlett Packard microwave changeover relays were to hand and these have an insertion loss of about 0.05dB at 1420MHz.

The VSWR of the relays was more than good enough not to introduce errors. These relays were designed for use up to 12GHz and gifted from a redundant microwave measurement system that was scrapped. The only downside was that they were latching relays and required a polarised 24V pulse to change the contacts over to the opposite state.

4

Antenna Parameters

In this chapter:

- Antenna directive gain
- Effective aperture equation
- Beamwidth vs antenna gain
- Front to back ratio
- Yagi and other beam antennas
- Yagi antenna design
- Angle problems
- VSWR and why it is a puzzle
- Coaxial stubs
- Practical method of building Yagis

- Measurement
- End-effect
- Baluns
- Myths about coaxial cable lengths
- Polarisation
- Parabolic antenna
- Special antenna configurations
- An interesting proposal
- Dipole arrays
- Six-element meteor radar array

It is obvious that the antenna directivity (gain) plays a very significant part in the receiver equation. In fact, it has been said that 'the best low noise amplifier is the antenna'. Whereas there is some element of truth in this statement, it should not be taken in the wrong context. Nevertheless, the antenna is one of the most important items in any radio communications system. The terms directivity and gain are somewhat interchangeable. An antenna with a small beamwidth inherently has a high gain; conversely an antenna with a low gain will have a wide beamwidth.

Antenna gain is also in direct proportion to the *effective aperture* size (capture area) of the antenna. It is relatively easy to see the connection between the physical size of a parabolic dish or dipole array and the apparent gain, but in the case of a Yagi or other types of antenna, it is not so obvious.

ANTENNA DIRECTIVE GAIN

The directive gain of a transmitting antenna (Gd) may be defined as

$$G_d = \frac{\text{Maximum radiation intensity}}{\text{Average radiation intensity}},$$

where the radiation intensity is the power per solid angle radiated in the direction (θ, ϕ) and is denoted $P(\theta, \phi)$. A plot of the radiation intensity as a function of the angular co-ordinates is called a radiation-intensity pattern, or polar diagram.

Since the average radiation intensity over a solid angle of 4π radians is equal to the total power divided by 4π, the directive gain can be written as

$$G_d = \frac{4\pi(\text{maximum power radiated per unit solid angle})}{\text{total power radiated}}.$$

The gain of the antenna, G, is defined as

$$G = \frac{\text{Maximum radiation intensity from antenna}}{\text{Intensity fom isotropic source of same power}}.$$

Accordingly, the gain of an antenna is related to that of an isotropic source, in dBi. Another way of expressing antenna gain is to refer it to a half-wave dipole at the same frequency, or dBd. Another means of comparing the apparent gain is to use a reference antenna such as the IEA dual-dipole over a ground plane; this, if correctly constructed, gives a gain of 7.7dB relative to a half-wave dipole.

Professional antennas, as used in radio astronomy, always quote gain in dBi. A dipole is semi directional, having two major lobes, or directions of radiated energy, and it has a gain over an isotropic source of 1.64 times expressed as a power ratio or 2.15dB when expressed in logarithmic terms.

ANTENNA EFFECTIVE APERTURE EQUATION

The effective aperture (capture area) of a parabolic antenna is expressed in terms of the area, A_{phys}, by

$$A_e = A_{phys} \times \eta,$$

where: A_e is the effective aperture area (m²),
   η is the aperture efficiency, and
   A_{phys} is the actual collecting area of the antenna (m²).

From this, antenna gain, G_{ant}, can be derived

$$G_{ant} = \frac{4\pi Ae}{\lambda^2},$$

where: A_e = effective aperture of the antenna (m²),
   G_{ant} = gain of the antenna as a power ratio, and
   λ = operating wavelength (m).

For a parabolic antenna

$$A_{phys} = \frac{\pi D^2}{4} = \pi r^2,$$

where: D is the diameter, and
   r is the radius (m).

For practical circular aperture antennas (parabolic dish, etc) the formula needs to take into account the efficiency of the antenna, and the formula becomes

$$G_{ant} = \left[\frac{\pi D^2}{\lambda}\right]^2 \times \eta,$$

Where η is the efficiency ($\eta = 1 = 100\%$).

To give some indication of the implication of the efficiency factor, most parabolic antennas have an efficiency factor of approximately 0.5 to 0.6. What this means is that although the dish may be, say, 1000 m^2 in actual surface area, if an efficiency factor of 1 (100%) was possible the dish would only need to be about 500 to 600 m^2 to achieve the same gain as the larger parabolic antenna.

Taking Jodrell Bank Mk1 as an example at 408 MHz:

Diameter = 250ft = 76.2m,
$A_{phys} = \pi r^2 = 4560$m^2,
$\eta = 0.5$,
$\lambda = 0.69$.m

$$G_{ant} = \frac{4\pi A_{phys}}{\lambda^2} \times \eta = 6.017 \times 10^4.$$

Therefore $G_{ant} = 10\log(6.017 \times 10^4) = 47.8$dBi.

Working out A_e from the gain of 47.8dBi = 2148m^2.

This is equivalent to a parabola of 52.3m in diameter (171ft). So, if it were possible to achieve an efficiency of 100% the saving in the parabolic size would be considerable. However, any improvement, even a few percent, is worth striving for.

BEAMWIDTH VERSUS ANTENNA GAIN

It is as well to appreciate that the apparent 'gain' of any antenna is solely due to confining the radiated power into a small conical beam area. An approximation of the antenna gain can be calculated from the half-power beamwidth (-3dB) of the antenna, derived from the formula of Dr John D Kraus, W8JK

$$G_{ant} = \frac{27000}{\theta.\Psi}$$

where θ and ψ are the horizontal and vertical components, or

$$G_{ant} = \frac{4\pi}{\theta.\psi},$$

if the beamwidths are in radians.

If the efficiency of the antenna is taken into account, due to the ohmic losses etc, the equation can be re-written as

$$G_{ant} = \frac{27000}{\theta.\psi} \times \eta,$$

for the beamwidth in degrees.

119

Note: The gain derived is expressed as a power-ratio.

For the gain of the antenna in dBi, the formula becomes:

$$G_{ant} = 10\log\left[\frac{27000}{\theta.\psi}\right] \times \eta \quad dBi.$$

Note: To express the gain relative to a half-wave dipole (dBd), subtract 2.15dB from the result.

However, Gunther Hoch, DL6WU, has warned about the assumptions and approximations made by Kraus, which may not be applicable in all cases. One of the limiting factors to the overall forward gain assumption is that the antenna vertical and horizontal beamwidths are much less than 40°, and there are no substantial side or rear lobes. In a Yagi antenna, this is often not the case, unlike a parabolic antenna that has superior rear lobe suppression by virtue of its mechanical design. Therefore, the actual gain could turn out to be several dB lower than calculated.

Example:

An antenna has vertical and horizontal -3dB beamwidths of 5°. The apparent gain is therefore approximately 30.33dBi, or 28.18dBd.

By comparison a 16-element Yagi will have a gain of approximately 18dBi or 15.8dBd.

One of the reasons the parabolic dish is such a popular antenna is due to its insensitivity to frequency. It performs equally well at audio frequencies as it does at microwave and light wave frequencies. However, the gain and beamwidth vary with frequency. By arranging several different feeds at the focal point, changes in frequency can be easily made. This is not possible with a large dipole array or types such as Yagi beam antenna.

Often in a radio telescope dish, two sets of dipoles are used per frequency band, one horizontally-polarised and the other vertically-polarised. This is to be able to determine the polarisation of the received signal. By utilising suitable phasing networks with two dipoles, the antenna pattern can be either horizontal plane, vertical plane, left-hand circular or right-hand circular and any degree of slant polarisation in between.

Fig 4.1: 327MHz crossed-dipole array and feed-trough reflector used at Jodrell Bank for receiving the Deuterium line. (Photograph: J Fielding 2004)

Many people have difficulty visualising how antenna aperture and gain are related. Two simple analogies can be used to illustrate the effect.

If you imagine the roof of your house and the rain gutters as the 'collecting area' and the downspout as the 'focusing mechanism', things become a lot clearer. For a large roof the amount of rain collected is also large and this is channelled via the gutters to the downspout - the focal point. Assuming the rainfall is uniform across the total roof area then doubling the roof area will result in twice as much rain being sent down the downspout in a given time.

In an optical telescope the aperture is also large in terms of wavelength and hence so is the gain or 'amplification ratio'. If you consider the Mount Wilson 200in reflector telescope, this has a diameter of about 5m. Because the wavelength of visible light is very short, being measured in nanometres, the gain can be calculated as being about 240dB. It is the very large collecting area focused onto a very small area (the eyepiece) which explains why the high signal amplification occurs that allows a very faint light source many light years distant to be seen with the human eye.

FRONT-TO-BACK RATIO (F/B)

A parameter often quoted for directional antennas is the front-to-back ratio. Some antenna manufacturers quote some unbelievable values for this parameter and the reader needs to appreciate what it actually means. As the F/B number gets bigger, the average amateur assumes this is a really superb antenna. Don't be fooled!

If F/B is, say 20dB, this means that the signal power received from a source at the rear of the antenna is 100th of that of the same source viewed from the front. Sounds good? However, an antenna with F/B of 20dB may have a forward gain of about 13dBd. Hence, the difference, in practice, is really only 7dB below a dipole. Front-to-back ratios need to be more like twice the forward gain to prevent strong signals causing interference. For a parabolic antenna, F/B is often as high as 50dB or more because of the construction. Yagi antennas do not have such good values of F/B; the best you can expect is about 30dB with a long-boom design. And this quickly falls to less than 15dB when the signal is at a point about 30° off the back of the array, due to side lobes in the polar pattern.

To put F/B into perspective, you need to consider the signal strength being received. If, for example, the signal received off the front of the antenna is S9 +40dB then when this same signal is received off the back with a F/B of 20dB the signal will be S9 +20dB, in other words it is still a very strong signal.

If we look at it another way, which is applicable for all forms of weak-signal reception, assume the wanted signal is equal to S1 and the interfering signal from the rear of the antenna is S9. With 6dB per S-unit this is a difference of 48dB. If F/B is 30dB, the interfering signal is still 18dB stronger than the signal we are trying to receive.

YAGI AND OTHER BEAM ANTENNAS

As a slight diversion, it is useful to explain how the aperture or 'collecting-area' of a Yagi or other beam antenna varies with gain. A very long Yagi - with many directors - will have a high forward gain. In order to achieve this, it confines the vertical and horizontal radiated pattern into a small area, or a narrow quasi-conical beam.

Hence, a Yagi with only a few elements will have a low gain, a wide beamwidth and hence a small aperture - expressed in m². A very high-gain Yagi will have a narrow beamwidth and hence a large aperture or effective signal collecting area, although the antenna physical dimensions can be much smaller than the apparent collecting area.

If you take a Yagi designed for 144MHz and scale it to make a 432MHz version, the forward gain should end up being the same. However, at the higher frequency, the collecting area or aperture is only 1/9 of that of the 144MHz antenna. To obtain the same level of signal power we would need to increase the gain by the same factor (nine in this case) of about 8dB.

Because of the factors constraining a Yagi or other beam antenna design, you cannot simply keep adding director elements to infinity. The elements further away from the feed-point have less and less effect as the director number increases.

There is a certain maximum number of directors beyond which each additional element contributes so little extra gain it becomes insignificant, and the mechanical problems with supporting a long slender boom become excessive. Consequently, a practical Yagi antenna is often limited to about 24 directors or less.

In experiments, it has been shown that, for a very long Yagi (>30 director elements), you can cut off the front third of the antenna and the gain only falls by about 1 to 2dB. If more gain is desired, it is mechanically better to stack two or more medium length antennas to constrain the vertical beamwidth to achieve extra gain.

Below is listed some experimental data obtained from various Yagi antennas obtained by Fishenden and Wiblin [1]

It is perhaps worthwhile pointing out the apparent incorrect name of the Yagi antenna. Uda, a professor at the Tohoku Imperial University in Japan, performed the original work. Uda published his paper [2] in Japanese and, because of this, very few antenna designers were aware of it for many years.

Subsequently Yagi, a colleague of Uda, in another paper written in English and published in an American journal, described the experiments performed by Uda.

Directors	Beamwidth (°)	Gain over $\lambda/2$ dipole	Gain per element
30	22		
20	26	21	0.95
13	31	15	1.00
9	37	13	1.18
4	46	8	1.33

Note: The beamwidths in the above table are measured at the -6dB points and not the more normal -3dB points.

Yagi's paper [3] covered not only Uda's work, but also several others items. It was published with the permission of Uda. Because the first knowledge by English speaking engineers was the Yagi paper, which was widely read, many people have erroneously credited Yagi with the original design work. This occurred despite the fact that Yagi was quite clear in his paper about the part played by Professor Uda. In view of the circumstances that prevailed after the publication of Yagi's paper, the adopted name for this type of directional antenna is now accepted as being the Yagi-Uda array.

Yagi Antenna Stacking Distance

The optimum stacking distance is, in reality, a function of boom length. For example, if two horizontally-polarised 6-element Yagis are stacked vertically, the distance required is approximately one wavelength, which is approximately the boom length.

If two 20-element Yagis are stacked vertically the distance required is approximately five wavelengths, which is also approximately the boom length. When four Yagis are stacked in a box configuration the vertical and horizontal stacking distances will often not be the same. This is because the vertical and horizontal beamwidths are usually not the same value. The exact distance required is that which just causes the individual antenna patterns to fringe at some far point.

If the separation is too small, the patterns overlap and, due to wave disturbance, the gain falls several dB. If the separation is too great, the patterns do not fringe correctly and the loss of gain is a little less, but can still amount to several dB. In order to calculate the optimum separations, we need to know with some accuracy what the vertical and horizontal beamwidths are at the 3dB points. Without this information, we cannot accurately determine the best distance.

The formula to calculate optimum vertical stacking for horizontally-polarised antennas is

$$D_v = \frac{1}{2\sin(\phi_v/2)}$$

= distance in wavelengths for vertical stacking.

The formula to calculate optimum horizontal stacking for horizontally-polarised antennas is

$$D_h = \frac{1}{2\sin(\phi_h/2)}$$

= distance in wavelengths for horizontal stacking.

ϕ_h and ϕ_v are the horizontal and vertical beamwidths -3dB values in degrees.

To convert to the distance in metres, multiply D_h and D_v by λ.

Note: The horizontal and vertical patterns are dependent on the attitude at which the antenna is mounted. If the antenna is mounted so the elements are vertical, the antenna is vertically-polarised, and the beamwidth in the azimuth direction will be the horizontal one. If the antenna is mounted so the elements are parallel to the ground, it is horizontally-polarised and the azimuth pattern will now be at 90° to the first case.

Example:

A 144MHz horizontally-polarised Yagi has horizontal and vertical -3dB beamwidths of 20° and 30° (a gain of 16.5dBi or 14.35dBd). If two such Yagis are stacked in a horizontally-polarised form, two antennas can be positioned one above to form a vertical bay. Alternatively, the two Yagis could also be stacked side by side to form a horizontal bay.

For the vertically-stacked case, you only need to know the vertical pattern beamwidth. For the side-by-side stacking, you only need to know the horizontal pattern beamwidth.

If four Yagis are stacked in a box configuration, this is now two sets of vertically-stacked and horizontally-stacked arrays, and both the vertical and horizontal pattern beamwidths are required.

The optimum distance in this example for vertical stacking is 4.3λ (8.9m) and the horizontal stacking distance is 6.4λ (13.3m). At 144MHz, λ = 2.083m.

Note: The distance is the boom centre-to-centre measurement. To calculate for vertically-polarised antennas, transpose the vertical and horizontal beamwidths in the above formulas.

If two horizontally-polarised Yagi antennas are optimally stacked, one above the other, the azimuth beamwidth does not change, but the vertical beamwidth is reduced to half. Hence, if the azimuth beamwidth remains the same, less of the power transmitted is sent skywards or into the ground and the gain only increases in the elevation plane. The signal is directed more towards the horizon.

If the antennas are horizontally polarised and stacked side by side the beamwidth in the azimuth direction will be reduced to half but not in the elevation direction.

For the case of vertical polarisation, these conditions are transposed, ie the side-by-side stacking will reduce the azimuth beamwidth to half, but not the vertical beamwidth. If the vertically-polarised antennas are stacked one above the other (vertical stacking), the azimuth pattern will not reduce but the vertical pattern will reduce to half the beamwidth.

All of these assumptions are based on the optimum stacking distances; if these are in error, the patterns can be skewed either in azimuth or elevation.

Since the maximum theoretical increase in gain with perfect stacking of two antennas is two (3dB), it can be seen that the correct stacking distance is critical. When four antennas are stacked, the maximum theoretical gain increase is four (6dB). In practice, the net gain will be lower due to imperfect stacking distances and the additional feed-line and the combiner losses. At best, we can expect 2.5dB for a two-stacked array and about 5dB for a 4-stack array.

When several antennas are stacked, the various feed-points need to be connected together with low-loss power combiners and feeder cables. The matching of impedance, amplitude and phase are extremely critical to achieve maximum gain. If the impedance, amplitude or the phase is in error, a loss occurs. If only the amplitude or phase is in error, as well as a loss of gain the antenna beam is skewed away from the boresight axis of the boom, causing a 'squint'. In severe cases, this also causes the horizontally-polarised antenna to become predominantly vertically polarised, and vice versa.

If you take an average Yagi designed for 144MHz and try to use it for a frequency some way off 144MHz, the squint becomes apparent. If, for example, the antenna squints to the left at, say, 130MHz, it means that to achieve maximum received signal you have to turn the antenna away to the right to make the signal peak. Similarly, if you try to receive a signal at, say, 160MHz the antenna will squint in the opposite direction, hence you need to turn the antenna towards the left to peak the signal. Try this out and see what the squint angle is for your 2m Yagi. You need to know the location of the two transmitters for the different frequencies.

This explains the often-observed fact that your 2m Yagi does not point exactly at the local 2m repeater but some way off. This is because the Yagi already has a squint because the elements are operating either above or below the optimum frequency.

One of the most important factors to consider before several antennas can be stacked is that they must all be identical. The impedance match and gain need to be as close as possible for all the antennas. Another point to watch out for is the connection to the driven elements. If one or more driven elements have the feed transposed, a severe loss of gain will result. Although each individual antenna might have the same gain within a fraction of a decibel, the phase will be 180° different if the driven element is connected incorrectly. If when you look at the driven element from, say, the rear and the centre lead of the coax goes to the right-hand side element, all the other antennas must be connected in the same way. Also, do not mount some of the antennas upside down unless the driven element is also connected correctly to compensate for this. In a four-stack array with two antennas one way up and two the other way up, the net gain will be 0dB. We will return to this problem a little later when we discuss various arrays using dipoles or Yagis.

Combiner and Cable Loss
Any practical power combiner will have some loss. Generally this is quite small for a well-designed and constructed unit. However, even 0.25dB is ~5% of the total power. The length of cable required from the power combiner to each antenna can end up being quite long and this introduces extra loss. It is necessary to use the lowest-loss cable possible for these connections. (Low-loss cable is, however, a large diameter and hence adds extra weight and may cause problems with sagging of the rear portion of the boom, necessitating additional bracing which, if of a metallic structure, can cause some interaction with the main array and a further loss of gain to occur.) The extra loss of the combiner and connecting cables may well be more than the extra gain achieved by stacking. Hence, a stacked Yagi array is not very suitable where the ultimate performance

is required, such as in radio astronomy. It also limits the radio telescope to a single narrow band of frequencies.

A further factor is that the simple Yagi is a plane-polarised antenna, and it is either mounted so that the predominant polarisation is horizontal or vertical. For radio astronomy, it is useful to be able to select many different types of polarisation so that the signal polarity may be ascertained.

Especially at low frequencies, this is essential due to variable Faraday rotation to which low-frequency signals are susceptible. This would require crossed-Yagis and consequent extra feed-lines, phasing networks and combiners. This then becomes a very big compromise and a somewhat self-defeating exercise.

However, for low frequencies, a relatively small plane-polarised Yagi array can develop more gain than a practical sized parabolic dish. As an example, the author's 23cm long-Yagi array of 26 elements x 4 is equivalent to a dish 4m in diameter.

The array occupies a frontal area of approximately $0.5m^2$. The 4m-diameter dish occupies $12.6m^2$ and hence has considerably more wind loading. For a 144MHz array of four 22-element Yagis with a nominal gain of 24dBi, the equivalent dish would need to be approximately 15m in diameter.

Antenna Bandwidth

One of the most misunderstood facts about the Yagi and other beam antennas is what is meant by bandwidth. Depending on the perception of the most important criteria changes the definition. Criteria for bandwidth might be gain, axial directivity, F/B, level of side lobes, squint level of vertical or horizontal polar diagram and impedance match. Most amateurs regard the bandwidth criteria as being solely the impedance matching.

An average long Yagi in practice will have a 2:1 VSWR bandwidth of about 1%, at 2m this is about 1.5MHz. This means if you have designed the antenna to have an optimum impedance match at the bottom of the band, when you attempt to use it in the satellite portion above 145.8MHz the VSWR is too high. Long Yagis behave very much like narrow-band filters; in fact they are narrow band filters!

However, VSWR is not the be-all and end-all of Yagi antenna design. With a flexible enough matching network you can match just about any antenna to 50Ω. What is more important is the gain-bandwidth product. If the constructor has had to modify element lengths to provide a low VSWR match, the chances are the antenna is no longer resonant on the design frequency.

Take the simple half-wave dipole as an example. When the element lengths are resonant, the feed impedance will be close to 75Ω non-reactive; in fact, the exact value is 73.1 +j0Ω..

If this dipole is connected to a 75Ω transmission line, the VSWR will be very close to 1:1. However, if it is connected to a 50Ω transmission-line, this will yield a VSWR of ~1.5:1. In actual fact, the antenna will radiate perfectly well whether the transmitter 'likes' the match or not. All the RF power entering the feed point will be radiated.

The portion of the RF power that is reflected back towards the transmitter will eventually return, because it will also be reflected back again by the output network in the transmitter.

This is because the output impedance of the transmitter is not 50Ω, but closer to 0Ω. The reflected RF power spends it time bouncing backwards and forwards at just below the speed of light (determined by the velocity factor of the coax) between the antenna and the transmitter. If the feed-line is low-loss then little will be wasted as heat and the vast majority will be radiated eventually.

To prove that the output impedance of a transmitter is not 50Ω, consider this:

If the output impedance were 50Ω it would mean that 50% of the RF power generated in the output stage would be dissipated as heat in the internal 50Ω. This means that, if this were the case, the maximum efficiency we could obtain would be 50%. However, it is quite easy to obtain efficiencies of well over 50%, therefore the output impedance cannot be 50Ω.

The same argument exists for audio amplifiers. They drive low impedance speakers, as low as 2Ω, but we know the output impedance is much less than 2Ω or else the amplifier would not be able to deliver the current into the load. Ideally the output impedance would be 0Ω.

In days gone by, before the through-line VSWR meter was invented, a different method was used. The transmitter used an aerial ammeter that showed the RF current being sent to the antenna. This was a much better indication; one simply tuned for maximum current. The output network in the valve transmitter could normally match over a wide range of impedance and, when maximum current was reached, the transmitter was putting out maximum power into the antenna. When the VSWR Bridge type of meter was invented, amateurs suddenly became aware of the mismatch that had always existed but did not limit the performance. We became obsessed with the VSWR reading; before, we were blissfully unaware of it and everyone was happy!

Many amateur conceptions about VSWR are wrong. One of the misconceptions is that if the antenna feed-line is open circuit, the voltage becomes very high and can cause arcing. This simply is not true and it can be shown that, under an open circuit condition, the voltage at the open end of the transmission line only increases to a value of twice that of a properly-matched line. Similarly, under a short circuit condition, the current can only rise to a value of twice the matched-line condition.

When you alter an antenna element length because you are obsessed by the VSWR, you change its resonant frequency. In many cases you can get a good VSWR match, but the antenna is now some way off its resonant frequency. Walter Maxwell, W2DU, in his book *Reflections*, gave a hint of how the antenna industry works. A junior engineer proudly presented to Maxwell a new, compact, wide VSWR bandwidth, spacecraft antenna he had designed, for his comments. Maxwell commented "I have an antenna in my drawer which no doubt radiates better than this one". He then produced a 50Ω dummy load!

Many dipole antennas used by scientists at radio observatories are not λ/2. Some use λ/4 dipoles, λ dipoles, or even 3λ/2 dipoles. The reason is that they exploit the different polar diagrams they give to direct the beam in a certain direction. Buckland Park MF meteor radar on 1.98MHz, operated by the University of Adelaide, Australia uses λ/4 dipoles operated over a ground plane for this very reason.

Very few amateurs, when they build a Yagi antenna, bother to do even basic tests with a field strength meter to determine the forward gain and side lobes. Even a rudimentary set up can be used to get an idea of the -3dB points and the gain relative to a dipole. Elements that have been radically altered in length, apart from reducing the gain at the expense of a VSWR improvement, usually exhibit a squint along the boresight of the antenna. This is because they are operating either above or below the correct frequency. This means the maximum gain is now at some angle to the centre line of the boom. Often it is the vertical component and, if the antenna is mounted so that it is horizontally-polarised, you will not be aware of this. It could mean that a good deal of your precious power is either being sent skywards or into the ground! This type of 'electrical steering' is used in many radar and radio telescope antennas to bend the beam in another direction without moving the antenna.

The author has also fallen into this trap from time to time. Many years ago, I built an impressive array of long Yagis for 23cm. I already had one of these Yagis I made as a prototype. Having mounted the new four-Yagi array on the mast next to the original one, I demonstrated the 'improved gain' by flicking a switch which operated a coax relay mounted at the antenna. In one position the local 23cm beacon was S8, with the switch in the other position it was over S9. Only many weeks later when I came to take the array down for a portable contest did I realise that the antenna giving the S9 result was the single Yagi. The reason was that I had changed the design slightly to obtain a better VSWR match and the antenna was no longer resonant on the desired frequency and had a severe squint. A very red face!

The bottom line is this. If you build an antenna to a published design and find the VSWR is not what it should be then the chances are that you have made a mistake somewhere and 'fudging' the element lengths is a poor way of correcting the problem. Alternatively the antenna was a poor design to start off with!

A higher-than-normal VSWR can be caused by many factors. The antenna impedance, as seen by the transmission line, is made up of two components, resistive and reactive. In practice, the resistive part also comprises two components. One is the radiation resistance of the antenna and the second is the ohmic loss due to non-perfect electrical conductors. The second component, the ohmic loss, is normally quite low, because we normally use high-conductance materials, such as aluminium, for the antenna, because it has a high strength-to-weight ratio, but any joints can be the cause of ohmic loss.

The radiation resistance is the transformation of the free-space impedance of approximately 377Ω to the antenna design impedance of, say, 50Ω. The antenna is thus an impedance transformer with a ratio of about 8:1. Any dimensional inaccuracies in element length or spacing will change the transformation ratio and cause a loss in coupling to the free-space impedance. If the ohmic losses are more than a small percentage of the radiation resistance, the gain falls.

The reactive components, in theory, cannot dissipate power and, therefore, are incapable of introducing loss. With high-Q matching components, either inductive or capacitive, the inherent losses are very small. The problem comes when you use less-than-perfect components for matching networks.

The author was once told a story by a colleague who had been based at the South African Antarctic scientific base (SAANI). He was a radio amateur and was recruited because of his expertise in communications. On arriving at the base, he was given the task of repairing and improving the antenna system. This consisted of several mono-band verticals fed by 1kW transmitters. He discovered the VSWRs of the antennas were far from perfect and started to experiment to sort out the problem. The basic problem was that the base was on ice, which was several kilometres thick, and so the ground resistance was very high. As most people know, the vertical quarter-wave Marconi antenna is really a dipole with the other half mirrored in the low-resistance ground. The radio link worked well, but no one was happy about the possible damage to the transmitters due to the high VSWR. He experimented with extra radials to lower the ground resistance. Having laid many thousands of metres of new radials, the VSWR improved considerably. The signal reports they now got were considerably weaker than before. The problem was that, although he had improved the VSWR by lowering the ground resistance, most of the energy was now being absorbed by the lossy ground and simply heating up the ice! The ohmic losses were higher than the radiation resistance, so the majority of the power was going to ground in the lossy ice.

Later investigation revealed that the problem could have been solved at much less effort by simply building impedance-matching networks to insert between the feed-lines and the antennas. The moral of the story is first to assess what the problem is before spending time and money.

If the antenna design requires an inductive element in the network to cancel out a capacitive reactance at the feed-point (for example a 'hairpin loop'), the inductor needs to have a very high Q. If the inductor has excessive loss, the overall result is that you are introducing resistive loss, and this can dissipate power.

Many amateurs are stumped when they come across a situation like this and, because they can't see the wood for the trees, start altering element lengths and/or spacings to try to find a solution. Professional antenna designers have access to complex test equipment such as vector network analysers and vector voltmeters to solve the problem. The vector network analyser displays impedance on a Smith Chart and the exact value of reactive and resistive components can be read off the chart. A Vector Network Analyser (VNA) on its own is not of much use, apart from displaying the impedance match. If a 50Ω load resistor were con-nected to a VNA, it would display a perfect match across a very wide frequency range. All the VNA is capable of doing is to show the designer how the imped-ance match varies with frequency and the phase relationship, ie capacitive or inductive; knowing this, the designer can alter the matching components to obtain the best match over the frequency range of operation.

Vector voltmeters measure the amplitude of the voltages and the phase angle separating them. If a two-element vector voltmeter is connected across the two outer ends of a dipole cut for a particular frequency, the voltages should be iden-tical and 180° out of phase. In many antenna designs, apart from narrow band dipoles, this is not always the case. In Yagi-Uda arrays, the alternate elements in the director string exhibit a phase change of approximately 90° as the vector voltmeter probe is run down one side of the dipole ends. As long as the other end of the element shows a 180° difference, the element length and spacing is correct. Amateurs do not normally have access to such luxuries. The crux of the problem is that the simple through-line VSWR meter cannot determine the actual antenna impedance seen by the feed-line.

YAGI ANTENNA DESIGN

It has been said that if you take a selection of aluminium tubes of varying lengths, and randomly distribute them along a boom, you will end up with a Yagi antenna. This is not far from the truth. However, to gain some insight of the constraints of the Yagi-Uda design, it is useful to read what Yuen T Lo of the University of Illinois has to say in Jasick's *Antenna Engineering Handbook* [5].

The analysis of a Yagi-Uda antenna with more than three elements is difficult, but there are a few general properties, which may be useful for experimental design.

1. The radiation pattern of a Yagi-Uda antenna is almost independent of the length of the driven element. Thus the length and the construction of the driven element are determined only by the impedance characteristics.

2. For the radiation patterns, close spacing will result in a higher F/B with a broader main beam. Wider spacing gives a sharper beam, but more and larger minor lobes. This is particularly true for the spacing of the director next to the driven dipole.

3. In order to allow for manufacturing tolerances, and for the effect of rain or snow on the antenna, it is preferable to choose directors slightly shorter and reflectors slightly longer than the optimum values.

4. Since the director length decreases very slowly with the increase of the number of directors, it is logical first to adjust the spacing every time a director is added and then to shorten all the lengths slightly.

5. Since a large Yagi antenna has too many parameters to be optimised, it is simpler to design two stacked Yagis, each with few elements, rather than a single Yagi of many elements.

Fig 4.2: Experimental data for five-element television Yagi antenna. (From Jasick's *Antenna Engineering Handbook* [5])

In television reception, the problem is to manufacture an antenna that can satisfy as many of the television channels as possible. For the low VHF channels, this involves 'broad-banding' the design. When this is done, the gain falls dramatically. As an example Yuen T Lo gives some experimental data for a five-element Yagi-Uda design that covers the American TV channels 2 to 6 (54 to 88MHz). In the diagram, we can see two examples: one design was optimised for a single channel (Ch 4, 66 to 72MHz); and a design that covers the whole band.

The single-channel design achieved a gain of approximately 9dBd and the broadband design only averaged 4dBd.

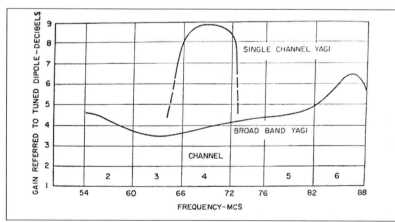

The single-channel design needs to cover approximately 5MHz to encompass the vision and sound carriers fully; the design shown covers 6MHz with a 1dB variation at band edges. By inference, we can see that, if the single-channel Yagi was made even more narrow-band, the gain should increase a little more and over 9dBd should be possible from a carefully-optimised version.

Skin Depth and Ohmic Loss

There is a general misconception amongst amateurs, and some professional engineers, as to what constitutes a good material for antennas and other conductors commonly used. The writer has seen some unsubstantiated comments made about unsuitable materials for low UHF and microwave antennas. One article stated that "... under no circumstance should brass tubing ever be used for a 23cm Yagi antenna because of the high skin-effect losses". This is simply not true and shows a basic misunderstanding about this topic.

> One company manufactured an HF dipole antenna made from stainless steel stranded wire. This immediately drew adverse comments from the 'experts' as likely to be very lossy. In actual fact, it worked quite well and the difference between it and an antenna made from traditional copper wire showed no measurable difference in operation. What the 'experts' overlooked was the skin effect and how it determines the overall resistance loss.

For all conducting materials, such as copper or aluminium, the resistivity is measured in Ω/cm. Copper and aluminium both have very low resistance figures; brass and stainless steel are somewhat higher. The skin depth at a particular frequency is a function of the resistivity. For a low-resistivity material, such as copper or aluminium, the skin depth is small, but for a higher-resistivity material the skin depth is much greater. Hence, although the material may have a higher resistivity, this is offset by having a greater skin depth and hence the overall ohmic loss can be similar or even lower, because there are more parallel paths for the current to flow in.

Skin depth really only becomes an issue when we get to the higher microwave bands; even brass, which has a poor resistivity figure compared to copper or aluminium, is quite acceptable, even in an unplated form, up to a few GHz. The original writer of the article was correct in condemning brass because of its stress fatigue characteristics under vibration and low temperatures. Brass, like copper, work hardens with repetitive bending, and stress fractures are likely to occur. This is especially a problem with sub-0°C temperatures. All common materials used for antenna construction suffer from this problem, some more than others. Aluminium is a common choice but, if the wrong grade is chosen, the fatigue stress can be a problem with constant buffeting by the wind.

As an aside, one of the companies I worked for manufactured UHF high-power solid-state amplifiers. These used coils made from silver-plated copper wire. It so happened that one day we somehow managed to run out of the silver-plated wire and a batch of amplifiers was halted in production due to this shortage. As the order was urgent, I decided to try normal tinned copper wire as a stopgap measure. The difference in performance between one using silver-plated wire and standard tinned copper wire was hardly measurable (about 0.05dB less gain with the tinned copper wire) and the amplifier met all the specifications. As the silver-plated wire was much more expensive and was imported, it raised the question as to why the design used it. It turned out that the engineer who designed it had some silver-plated wire given to him as a sample and used it in the prototype design. When it proved to be acceptable, it was written into the parts list, and no-one questioned the material. Had the engineer taken the trouble to try normal tinned copper wire, which was a standard stock item and used in many other products on the production line, it would have saved a considerable amount of money.

Complex Feed Impedance of Multi-element Arrays

When several antenna elements are mounted in close proximity to others, the mutual coupling existing between adjacent elements causes the feed-point impedance to change. The antenna design where this is most easily seen is the Yagi-Uda array. Here we have a driven element, often a simple half-wave dipole, a reflector element and several director elements. Calculating the exact feed-point impedance of the antenna is very difficult, because the lengths and spacings of the elements all interact.

If the driven element is considered in isolation, the feed-point impedance at resonance will be $73.1 +j0\Omega$, if the element is a half wave dipole made from two metal rods, tubes or wires of small diameter relative to the wavelength. When the reflector element is added, the spacing, as it is varied, causes the feed-point impedance to change. If the reflector is mounted so that it is in close proximity to the driven element, the feed-point impedance of the driven element will become lower. When the first director is added, this again changes the impedance, usually bringing it to a lower value. Additional director elements normally lower the feed-point impedance even more. In some instances, the feed-point impedance (with a half-wave dipole driven element) can fall to very low values, perhaps as low as 5Ω. If the chosen feed-line is 50Ω the VSWR now equates to 10:1 and is very difficult to match.

For example - a three-element Yagi with optimised element lengths and spacings for maximum forward gain, will have a feed-point impedance of approximately $26 +j59\Omega$. If we cancel the inductive reactance of 59Ω with an capacitive reactance of -59Ω, we end up with a resistive load of 26Ω. This will yield a VSWR to the 50Ω transmission line of ~2:1.

One way around this problem is to start with a higher impedance, as is offered by a folded dipole driven element. This type of element has a feed impedance of four times the same length simple dipole, or about 300Ω. Now, with the parasitic elements added, the feed-point would only fall to a value of four times the original design (approximately 120Ω when the capacitive reactance is resonated out). This makes the matching simpler, as the difference in the impedances is not as great.

To get some idea of how complex the Yagi-Uda array is, we can consider some experimental results of a 13-element array. Generally, the spacing between the driven element and the reflector is chosen to be ~$\lambda/4$, and the spacing between the first director and the driven element is chosen to be between $\lambda/4$ to $\lambda/2$. The director element lengths are usually tapered to achieve equal current amplitudes in successive directors, as per Uda's original paper.

Below is a table of experimental results for such a design. In this design, the director spacing is fixed at 0.34λ and the reflector is 0.5λ long. It can be seen that the spacing of the reflector has a profound effect on the feed-point impedance, as does the director length.

Reflector spacing (λ)	Feed impedance with director length 0.406	Feed impedance with director length 0.42
0.25	62	50
0.18	50	43
0.15	32	27
0.13	22	
0.10	12	

FEED-LINE IMPEDANCE

Today, the use of 50Ω coaxial cable is almost universal, but is it the best choice? If you examine the various properties of different impedance coaxial cables you might not spot the real story. To appreciate how we ended up with 50Ω cable requires a step back in time to WWII.

At the time, the coaxial transmission lines in common use were rigid and constructed from copper tubing. The inner tube was supported coaxially within the outer tube by thin insulating discs somewhat like a washer so, effectively, the major dielectric was air with a dielectric constant of unity. The spacing discs were placed approximately every 50mm. As the need was to make transmission lines quickly, in large volumes, the need was to select the impedance that could accommodate all users' requirements. The biggest user of transmission line was the US Navy, because the average warship contained many thousands of feet for all sorts of purposes. Consequently, a committee was formed in America to decide on the standard impedance. This consisted of engineers and scientists who deliberated on the ideal impedance.

One faction of this committee argued for the use of 75Ω. This, they claimed, would make the matching of the transmission line simpler as the predominant antenna feed was a half-wave dipole, an impedance of about 75Ω. In addition to this, they showed that 75Ω lines had the lowest attenuation per unit length, and this is why television feed-line still uses this today. Another faction favoured 60Ω; this was the standard impedance used by the Germans, arguing that the use of 60Ω would allow the use of captured German hardware to be turned against the enemy. (A similar situation existed with small-calibre ammunition, where the Germans had adopted 7.62mm and the allies used 0.303 inch, the difference between these is so small that either ammunition would work in both rifles).

Several other factions argued for other impedances, one being 93Ω, which has the lowest phase shift and hence is used today for data transmissions. The committee quickly reached a stalemate situation were none of the factions was prepared to concede that the other parties had a valid argument. In the end, 50Ω was chosen as a compromise, despite the fact that it had never been proposed as a possible choice. Quite why this occurred is very interesting.

An engineer who attended the many committee meetings, but hardly entered into the discussions, put forward the fact that, with the commonly-available copper water piping, it was possible to make a 52Ω transmission line in any required size. This was because of the way that American copper water tubing was graduated in size. So, because of a practical manufacturing factor, 52Ω became the standard impedance. When flexible transmission lines (coaxial cable) became practical to manufacture, it had to conform to the rigid transmission lines standard and hence was also 52Ω. Over time, as the manufacture of coaxial cables grew in volume, the impedance was revised to 50Ω, although there are still many of the older 52Ω cables manufactured today.

Television receivers still use 75Ω transmission lines and they are available in many sizes and can carry many kilowatts in the larger sizes. It is an excellent choice for low-loss antenna feed-line and one the author has used for many years. They are inherently better shielded than standard 50Ω type, as the problem with ghosting requires the use of a solid copper sheath or double shielding. Most of the popular low-loss connectors, such as the 'N' type, are available in 75Ω versions.

Some years ago, I purchased some 432MHz Yagis from the Jaybeam Company. I wanted to use 75Ω communal television distribution cable to feed the array of four Multibeam antennas, because I could buy this cheaper than 50Ω types. To save on transport costs, I arranged to collect the antennas from the Jaybeam factory. On arriving, I told them I had placed an order and was there to collect the antennas. A storeman showed me into the stockroom and asked which impedance I wanted. I told him I wanted 75Ω. He pulled four boxes off the shelves and took a felt tip pen from his pocket. On the end of each box was a label with 50 / 75 to denote the impedance. He crossed out the 50 on the labels. Puzzled by this I asked him if he was sure the antennas were really 75Ω. He said they weren't, they are all designed for 62Ω. He then went on to explain that 62Ω is the geometric mean of 50 and 75 and so will work perfectly on either impedance.

ANGLE PROBLEMS

In a vertically polarised antenna, such as a λ/4 whip, the radiation is approximately 30° to the vertical or 60° to the reflecting ground. Hence, the majority of the signal is launched skywards and little signal is projected towards the horizon.

With longer antennas such as 5λ/8, the radiation is tilted more towards the horizon but, in practice, it is still about 75°. For optimum long-distance communication in a terrestrial system, we would prefer the radiation to be closer to 90° to the vertical (or 0° elevation). In multi-element vertically-polarised collinear arrays, the angle is close to 0° and these give good omnidirectional coverage with considerable gain.

A former colleague recounted an interesting tale to me. A local municipality in Cape Town had installed its VHF repeater on top of Table Mountain, a 1000ft site which is about 5km from the city centre, which is at sea level. The communications were extremely poor close to the repeater but improved further afield. The installers, in an effort to correct the problem, changed the original repeater

λ/4 ground-plane to a 5λ/8 type. This made a slight improvement, but it was still patchy in the town centre, which was visible from the mountaintop. A test with the new antenna showed that reception at a distance of 50km was perfect.

My friend Jim was called in to help sort out the problem. Being an amateur, he helped, having played with antennas most of his life. He took one look at the mountain from the town centre and told the installers to give him the λ/4 ground-plane antenna. They protested and told him it was hopeless, as they had already tried everything to make it work. My friend took it anyway and got on board the cable-car up the mountain. An hour later he called and told then to try the system. It was perfect and had no weak spots. When he came back down the mountain they quizzed him on what he had done. He was obstinately silent and told them to go up the mountain and take a look for themselves.

When they got up the mountain they couldn't believe their eyes. The λ/4 ground plane antenna was mounted upside down! Then the penny dropped. The signal was now beaming down into the town instead of up to the heavens.

Incidentally, this also saved the municipality a bundle of money. Because of the patchy coverage, they had begun fitting 5λ/8 whips to all their vehicles. By changing back to λ/4 whips, the radiation angle threw the signal up towards the mountain so giving an improvement in signal level.

VSWR AND WHY IT IS A PUZZLE

The through-line VSWR meter only tells you one fact, the mismatch ratio between the transmission line and the antenna. Take the VSWR formula and examine it closely and you will see the problem.

$$\text{VSWR} = \frac{\text{Feed - line impedance}}{\text{Antenna impedance}} \quad \text{or} \quad \frac{\text{Antenna impedance}}{\text{Feed - line impedance}}.$$

(The two different formulæ are necessary because the antenna impedance can be higher or lower than the feed-line impedance. The fraction is always adjusted to give a value ≥ 1.)

If the antenna is different in impedance from the feed-line, the VSWR can be any value except 1:1.

Suppose the VSWR meter reads 2:1, what are the possible impedances the meter sees? If the antenna impedance is 25Ω, the VSWR is 2:1. The same holds for an antenna impedance of 100Ω. So how do we tell which way we need to go? 25 or 100Ω impedance can be made up from many different reactive and resistive values.

A simple way is to use some low-value non-inductive resistors. With a little power applied at the centre frequency of the antenna, we can place a low-value non-inductive (carbon composition) resistor with very short leads across the antenna feed-point and observe the change in VSWR. Let us suppose we have a VSWR of 2:1 and we place a 100Ω resistor in parallel with the feed-point. The VSWR now drops to close to 1:1. Hence, we can be sure the antenna Z was close to 100Ω. If the VSWR only changes very little with the resistor, we know the impedance is more likely to be near the 25Ω value, and to correct it we would need to insert a 25Ω resistor in series with the feed-line to correct the situation. However, this would dissipate half of the transmitter power!

We can do the same experiment with capacitors or inductors. Capacitors are more convenient as we can use a low-value high-Q air-variable capacitor connected across the feed-point. Suppose we leave the 100Ω resistor in position, which gives us a VSWR close to 1:1 and then connect a variable capacitor in parallel. By adjusting the capacitor we will see if the VSWR gets better or worse. Suppose it improves. We now know that the feed-point is still inductive and requires an equal capacitive reactance to tune it out. If the capacitor makes the VSWR worse, we know the impedance is already too capacitive and would need an inductive reactance to cancel it. In layman's terms, matching is a case of 'Two wrongs making a right'.

Although the feed-point impedance is inductive and requires a capacitor to correct the problem, we should be aware of the real cause. The driven element of a Yagi is composed of two λ/4 rods or tubes connected in series and fed in the centre. The total length should be an electrical λ/2.

One of the interesting characteristics of the λ/4 transmission line (which is what the element half actually is) is that it is an impedance inverter. If you take a section of coax which is cut to λ/4 and connect one end to an impedance measuring instrument such as a Vector Network Analyser or Impedance Bridge, and the other end is left open, the instrument reads a short circuit. Similarly, if the open end is now shorted the instrument sees an open circuit. But the λ/4 line also inverts reactance. If you place a capacitor across the open end with a reactance of 100Ω, the instrument will measure an inductive reactance of 100Ω.

This when performed with a different impedance line will give a different result. For example, a λ/4 line of 50Ω with a 100Ω reactance or impedance at one end will give 25Ω impedance at the other end.

So, although the feed-point requires additional capacitance to tune out the inductive reactance, the real reason is because the end of the element is actually capacitive, the element being an electrical λ/4 has inverted the reactance. An element that is capacitive at the open end is one that is too short electrically. To correct the problem the driven element length needs to be increased. The story below serves to highlight the problem. These very simple measurements tell us a lot more than the VSWR meter can ever do on its own.

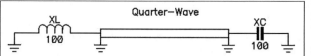

Fig 4.3: Impedance-inverting properties of a λ/4 line.

Fred's 'Magic Wand'

Many years ago, when I was mere novice, I was shown a trick by an old timer. I had built a small Yagi for 2m and could not get the VSWR right. Being unable to tell what was going on, I called for help, and Fred from the local radio club came to my assistance. Within 10 minutes, Fred had found the problem and told me how to fix it. You might imagine Fred brought along a truckload of equipment. In fact Fred arrived with nothing. When I asked him how he was going to solve my problem he told me he would use his 'Magic Wand'. He then told me to 'stuff some power into the Yagi and stand back whilst the magician does his work'. Fred then extended his right arm and theatrically waved his hand near the end of one half of the folded dipole driven element. The VSWR went up. He then repeated

continued opposite >

the trick on the other end of the dipole, the VSWR went down. Fred stepped back and told me the dipole was being driven asymmetrically. Amazed by this I asked him to explain how he deduced this fact. He repeated the action and I saw again that on one end of the driven element when he brought his hand close to it the VSWR went up and the other side it went down.

Fred explained that what he was doing was adding capacitance to each end by bringing his hand close. If the element was too short it would be capacitive already and the extra capacitance of his hand would cause the VSWR to go up. If the element was too long it would be inductive and his added capacitance should cause the VSWR to go down. As he could see the two halves of the dipole were about the same length this effect should occur on both ends of the dipole. Because it didn't, he knew the element length was about right but the phase balance was off.

Fred of course was right, I had made a stupid error when I calculated the 4:1 balun length, forgetting to allow for the velocity factor of the cable, and the phase balance was way off.

COAXIAL STUBS

The λ/4 stub can also be used for filtering. If we have an interfering signal at, say, the image frequency, we can eliminate it simply with a short piece of coax cable. Suppose the interfering signal occurs at 100MHz. If we make a λ/4 (electrical length, see later) stub cut for 100MHz and attach it in parallel with our receiver input, it appears as a short-circuit to signals at 100MHz, if the other end is left open-circuit. The insertion loss is practically zero. But there is another phenomenon with the λ/4 stub. At a frequency where the stub is a length of 3λ/4 or 5λ/4, and all other odd λ/4 lengths, it behaves in the same manner. So a stub cut for 100MHz will work at 300MHz and 500MHz, etc.

If we now short-circuit the inner and outer of the stub, the properties reverse. At 100MHz the stub appears as an open-circuit and at other frequencies it appears as a short-circuit to the signal. This will also occur at 300MHz and 500MHz.

The shorted λ/4 stub is a good way of protecting the front-end from lightning damage as the DC condition is a short. When cutting the stub, allowance must be made for the velocity factor of the coaxial cable used.

The same effect happens if we use a λ/2 stub. In this case, the impedances appearing at both ends are the same. So if we place a λ/2 stub across the receiver input and leave the far end open, it behaves as an open-circuit across the receiver at that frequency and a short circuit at other frequencies corresponding to when the coax is resembling λ/4 or odd multiples. If we short-circuit the far end, it appears as a short across the receiver input at the design frequency.

Fig 4.4: Simulation of a λ/4 shorted stub cut for 50MHz. At the operating frequency, the stub appears as an open circuit. At 150MHz, 250MHz and 350MHz, it behaves in a similar manner. At 100MHz, 200MHz, 300MHz and 400MHz, it appears as a short-circuit across the input

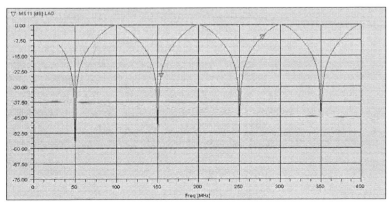

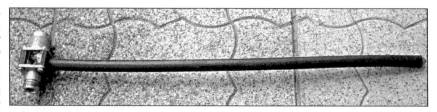

Fig 4.5: A short-circuit λ/4 stub for a 1kW 2m linear amplifier. The stub is made from a piece of RG-213/U cable 350mm long with N-type male and female connectors. The insertion loss at 144MHz is approximately 0.05dB and the 2nd harmonic rejection 40dB at 288MHz

Stubs as Harmonic Filters

Another useful property of the coaxial stub is that that it can perform as a harmonic filter with virtually zero loss. A common problem with 50MHz transmitters is the 2nd harmonic that falls in the FM broadcast band. By using a λ/4 stub cut for 50MHz with the far end shorted, the impedance the transmitter sees is an open circuit, so no power is lost. But at 100MHz, the stub behaves as λ/2 length and appears as a short circuit. In many 50MHz amplifiers using a π-tank network, the need exists for an RF choke across the output to blow the high voltage fuse should the anode blocking capacitor fail short circuit. The shorted stub can replace the normal RF choke and also provide additional harmonic suppression with less loss.

Coaxial Stubs as 'Metal Insulators'

In open-wire feeder systems, it is necessary to support the wires mechanically and to maintain the correct spacing for the impedance to be correct. Often this is performed by 'metal insulators'. These are two lengths of stout wire or tube that have one end connected by a shorting disc and the open ends connect to the parallel wires. If the length of the stub is such that it appears as an electrical length of λ/4, the open ends present an infinite impedance and can be connected across the wire lines with no ill effect. The shorting disc allows the bottom of the stub to be bolted to a supporting structure. By selecting different stub lengths, it can also be used for matching purposes. This technique was very popular in the days when open-wire feeders were the common method of transporting signals between the portions of a large dipole array. (See the Yagi array designed by Weiss later in this chapter.)

PRACTICAL METHOD OF BUILDING YAGIS

Today when I build a Yagi antenna from scratch, I have several other tricks to get the element lengths correct. I have a collection of aluminium tubing that I keep for use as temporary elements. Initially, I do not worry about the VSWR at all. I use a fairly long piece of coaxial cable with a fair loss to absorb the VSWR mismatch; the transmitter can safely work into about a 5:1 VSWR and the lossy coaxial cable behaves as a low value attenuator to protect the transmitter. I mount the antenna boom on a pair of tall wooden stepladders, so that it is at least one wavelength above the ground, with the boom pointing horizontally. I start by fixing the reflector and driven element at approximately the correct spacing, derived from calculations. At the feed-point, I mount a W2DU balun to convert the unbalanced coaxial line to a balanced feed. I have a sensitive field strength meter that has a large meter, and is fitted with a horizontal dipole on a wooden pole the same height as the antenna being constructed. (The wooden pole is guyed with thin nylon string to keep it vertical). I place this about 5λ away (or that distance where I obtain about 3/4 full-scale deflection) and directly in front of the Yagi. I feed the antenna with about 1W of RF and observe the meter through a pair of binoculars. I then adjust the element lengths and spacing for maximum reading on the meter. (For every adjustment it is necessary to move away from the antenna to prevent body capacitance from affecting the result.) Then I add the first director and adjust again for maximum reading. I continue adding each new director and adjusting the element length and spacing for the maximum reading on the meter. As the signal level goes up, I move the field strength meter further away, hence the need for binoculars! When the gain has increased and I run out of garden length, I then fit an attenuator between the search dipole and the field strength meter.

To assist in adjusting the element lengths I use several small telescopic pieces of aluminium tube that are a push fit into the element ends. By adjusting these I can make minor adjustments to the element lengths. When I have reached the final director and everything is adjusted for maximum field strength, I measure all element lengths and spacings and write these down for later reference. I then turn my attention to the impedance match.

To measure the VSWR, I mount a directional coupler hard up against the antenna feed-point with the shortest possible cable. (I normally use N-type connectors and the directional coupler is connected directly to the feed-point connector with a back-to-back coupler). I feed in a little RF and measure the reflected power. Minor adjustments of the driven element spacing to the reflector and driven element length are normally all that is required to find the biggest dip in reflected power. Finally I make new elements to replace the temporary ones.

MEASUREMENT

Measuring Beam Patterns

With the prototype antenna still mounted on the wooden stepladder I then move the field strength meter and dipole antenna to explore the polar pattern. I do this by using a long piece of string. I attach one end to the stepladder and run out a length to reach the field strength meter. I then pick up the meter and dipole mast and holding the string in one hand move in a constant radius until the meter indicates the reading has dropped to the 3dB point. (Fortunately I have a large garden approximately 40m in width and 75m in length without many trees or other obstructions. If space is a bit limited, and you are unable to move far in one direction, by turning the antenna over you can explore both halves by only walking in one direction.) Having found the point that corresponds to the -3dB, I mark the spot with a peg or stone. I then measure the distance from the antenna centre line to the sideways point and then work out the corresponding angle with trigonometry. I keep a piece of thin nylon rope with distances marked in metres by making a knot in the rope. This allows me to measure the two distances quickly without resorting to a long tape measure. It might not be very accurate, but the results give a reasonable idea of the actual polar diagram.

If I wish to examine the other polar pattern, I turn the antenna through 90° so that it is now vertically polarised and change the search dipole to vertical. I repeat the measurements with the string to find the -3dB points.

To measure the F/B, I use a similar technique. With the antenna pointing down the garden I select a suitable meter reading and mark the rope. I then turn the antenna so that the rear faces the meter. For more exact measurements, I run a long coax cable from the spectrum analyser to the search dipole. This can measure to within 1dB.

Gain Measurement

This is done by substituting a dipole for the prototype antenna. Again, the spectrum analyser is used to establish a reference point. Once this is set, the transmitter power must not be altered. I normally place a 10dB attenuator between the transmitter and the antenna to ensure the load is constant. The prototype antenna is then connected in place of the dipole and the difference in signal level read off the spectrum analyser screen. This allows measurement to within 1dB uncertainty. Although not in the same league as a professional antenna range it does allow some measurements and serves to confirm the anticipated gain.

Many years ago, the local amateurs were involved in experimenting with 23cm antennas and we would take our gear down to the local beach when the tide was out. This is an almost perfect antenna-measuring range and long distances of unobstructed area allowed accurate measurements to be made. We had an accurate measuring receiver and a 'Pip-Squeak' transmitter radiating into a dipole. (See Chapter 10 for details of signal sources for testing.) With a separation of about 100m between the signal source and the antenna, we got results very close to an expensive antenna test range.

END-EFFECT

Many radio amateurs have come across this effect when making a wire dipole for the lower frequency bands, such as 40m. The speed at which radio waves travel on a conducting material is somewhat slower than the free-space velocity of $3 \times 10^8 ms^{-1}$. This slower speed means that we have to shorten the dipole slightly to achieve resonance. This factor is, in round terms, about 98% of the calculated length, so for a 40m dipole we end up trimming about 1ft off the total length to achieve resonance. Alternatively, if the antenna is a bit short we can add capacity to the ends by suspending it as an inverted-V with the ends near the ground.

This is not just the case for HF antennas; the effect gets more pronounced as the frequency goes up. At 50MHz, the effect is very apparent, and at 144MHz it can really spoil your day. I was involved in building an EME array for 2m. Being poor I decided to copy a commercial antenna (what we call 'reverse engineering'), and build the required number from locally-available material. I had the good fortune of having a fellow amateur who owned a company that made antennas for the commercial market and so I was able to use many of his parts to assemble the antennas.

One of things we decided to do was to fit plastic bungs on the end of each element to stop the wind noise. Having made our first antenna and tested it to our satisfaction, we fitted the plastic bungs. The antenna was now hopeless. The gain dropped several dB and the VSWR match was awful. Scratching our heads we went and took a closer look at the original design to find it did not have element bungs. Then the penny dropped!

The fitting of the plastic bungs had effectively increased the element lengths by about 5% by adding capacitance. To cure the problem would mean recalculating all the element lengths and then making new elements. As we had four Yagis to make and had already cut all the available tubing to the correct lengths, we decided this was too much work and gave up on using the bungs. In some respects, this was a good thing because, not long after, I saw a convincing demonstration as to why plastic end caps are not a clever idea. A new high-power VHF broadcast transmitter used a commercial antenna that had similar plastic end caps. When the power was cranked up to 1kW, the end caps started to smoke and at 2kW they caught alight due to the very high voltage at the tips of the elements. Clearly the material used was quite lossy at VHF.

One thing I always do when I make elements is to chamfer and polish the ends to remove any sharp edges. These are stress risers for corona discharge and, ideally, any element should have a rounded end to prevent corona discharges. The writer's location is on top of a mountain nearly 900m above sea level and suffers from heavy mists during the winter months; in fact, at times, we are about 100m above the cloud base. Heavy mist or rain causes a Yagi antenna to detune.

Another way of looking at this is that if I end up with an element that is a little short sometimes I can correct the problem by fitting end caps!

BALUNS

Most beam antennas that are fed by an unbalanced coaxial transmission line will require some sort of balanced-to-unbalanced transformation. These are known as 'baluns', because they convert a balanced configuration, eg a dipole, to an unbalanced feeder such as coaxial cable. In many cases, the balun is part of the impedance-matching network between the driven element and the coax cable. Incidentally, a lot of people incorrectly pronounce the word balun - it is not pronounced 'baylen' but 'bal-lun'.

The importance of a balun should not be overlooked. The dipole or driven element in a beam antenna requires a 'push-pull' drive, with the two halves of the dipole being driven with signals of equal amplitude but opposite phase. If either the amplitude balance or the phase is incorrect, the gain will fall and the antenna will develop a squint away from its boresight axis.

Many baluns are lossy and contribute to the total ohmic losses. If you consider the 4:1 impedance step-up balun made from a half-wavelength of coaxial cable, it can be shown that this inherently will always give an amplitude imbalance. The reason is simple to see. The signal is delayed by 180° by travelling the extra half wavelength of coax between one half of the dipole and the other. As no coax has zero-loss, the small but measurable loss causes the amplitude imbalance.

A much better balun is the one described by W2DU. This is a 'choke-sleeve' balun which is a short length of coaxial cable with ferrite loading in the form of toroidal rings or sleeves on the outer sheath. This balun gives a 1:1 impedance transformation with perfect amplitude and phase balance. It is so simple that it is surprising that nobody had thought of it before. The author having tried one and confirmed its effectiveness with laboratory instruments has not used anything else since. It is virtually lossless, being only the loss caused by a few centimetres of cable, and the power handling capability is in the kW region. It can work from 1MHz to several GHz. A typical HF balun is approximately 300mm long and covers from 1MHz to 60MHz with perfect amplitude and phase balance. If the ferrite cores are a tight fit on the coaxial cable they don't need any additional fixing in most cases.

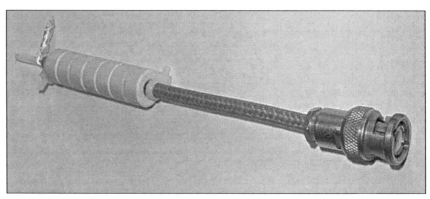

The W2DU Choke-sleeve Balun

Here is picture of a typical VHF choke-sleeve balun. The cores are a slightly loose fit and are held in place with nylon cable ties. The coax cable forming the balun is 150mm in total length, the ferrite rings occupy approximately 50mm and are suitable for 50MHz to 200MHz. The power rating is in excess of 1kW limited, not by the ferrite, but by the coaxial cable used.

VSWR Caused by Baluns

Some baluns do not correctly transform impedance or prevent the RF from flowing on the outside of the coaxial cable. If RF currents are able to flow on the outer of the coaxial cable sheath it will confuse the VSWR meter, this then gives an erroneous reading. Even if the antenna impedance is absolutely spot-on, the balun, because it cannot stop the backward flow of RF along the sheath, makes one believe the impedance match is faulty. The RF flowing on the outer of the coaxial sheath has nothing to do with the impedance mismatch. The mis-matched power would be reflected back down the coaxial cable on the inside and not the outside.

What the amateur is observing is that the antenna is in fact doing its job and radiating the RF. Some will be picked up on the coaxial outer sheath because the portion close to the radiating antenna also acts like an antenna, it is a low resistance conductor and RF is able to flow along it until it reaches the VSWR meter. When the RF gets to the VSWR meter, it cannot decide what is 'real reflected power' flowing in the inside of the coaxial cable and what is 'phantom-power' flowing on the outside, and it lumps the two together to give a high reflected power reading. To prove this factor, do this simple experiment. Transmit with a 10W HF transceiver into a dummy load with about 2m of RG-58 coax connecting the two and then hold a 2m handheld close to the coax and see what VSWR reading you get. You will be surprised to find the VSWR jump up when the 2m handheld is keyed! If the coaxial cable has rather loose weave to the sheath, the effect is made worse and the small gaps allow RF to pass through to the centre conductor. If you replace the coaxial cable with some semi-rigid solid copper sheath cable the effect is not as pronounced. Many cheap VSWR meters are not well shielded; some even have silly field strength connectors that accept a small whip antenna. If you have one of these, take it to pieces and disconnect the detector diode from the field strength portion. This led me a merry dance some years ago when I couldn't get a decent VSWR reading on a dummy load.

Any VSWR meter should have a coaxial shield 'blocking-choke' such as a W2DU choke-sleeve balun immediately before and after it to prevent 'phantom-power' getting into the meter. Even laboratory grade instruments, such as a Bird 'Thruline' wattmeter, normally require this modification.

Alternative Balun Designs

There are quite a few balun types in common use on the VHF/UHF and microwave bands. Several different types can achieve the basic concept of placing an open-circuit at the operating frequency. One of the earliest types was the Pawsey Stub, designed by an Australian radio astronomer, Dr J L Pawsey. This uses a section of $\lambda/4$ coax with one end shorted between the inner and outer and the other end open circuit. This is placed across the feed-point and the shorted end connected to the sheath of the main feed-line coax. When calculating the length of coax to form the $\lambda/4$ stub, the velocity factor of the coax needs to be taken into consideration. A variation of the original Pawsey stub is to use a short length of open wire feeder to replace the coaxial stub. In this version, the stub is a piece of tubing of similar diameter as the feed-line cable and it is spaced the required distance to make a balanced feeder with an impedance similar to that of the coaxial transmission line. The end of the stub closest to the antenna feed-point is connected to the centre of the coax feed-line and the other end is grounded with a low inductance shorting bar or strap to the jacket of the coaxial feed-line.

A derivation of the Pawsey Stub balun is often used for parabolic dish feeds with a simple dipole. In this, the $\lambda/4$ section is made as part of the main transmission line, which is often constructed of two pieces of copper or brass tubes. The centre of the coax is connected to the outer to form one half of the dipole. The outer tube is slotted to a length corresponding to $\lambda/4$. The second half of the dipole is connected to the outer tube.

Fig 4.9: Side view of dipole feed

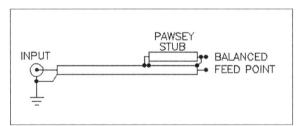

Fig 4.7: Pawsey stub balun

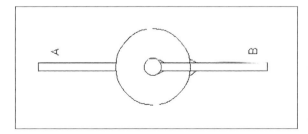

Fig 4.8: End view of dipole feed

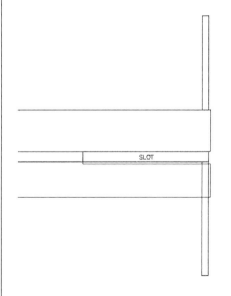

MYTHS ABOUT COAXIAL CABLE LENGTHS

Some amateurs still persist in the belief that an antenna should only be fed with a feed-line of an electrical length that is a multiple of $\lambda/2$. This is absolute non-sense and shows either a lack of understanding of the subject, or that the antenna is not correctly matched to the feed-line impedance. If the antenna presents the correct terminating impedance to the feed-line, the length of coaxial line required is completely immaterial. To prove that this is the case, it is simple to substitute the antenna for a resistive dummy load. If, with the dummy load connected, the addition of an arbitrary length of coaxial cable causes the VSWR to change, there is something very strange occurring. The only way the VSWR can be different from 1:1 is if there is an uncompensated reactive component.

The correct length of coaxial feed-line is the shortest length required between the equipment and the antenna feed-point. If the antenna matches the feed-line perfectly, altering the physical or electrical length of the feed-line should not cause the VSWR to change.

The only cases where the electrical length is critical is where the coaxial cable is used as an impedance-matching network or when lengths of cable are used with a power splitter to feed several antennas combined into an array. For this case, the feeder lengths do not need to be exact multiples of $\lambda/2$. Provided the electrical length of all of the phasing harness cables are the same, the same amplitude and phase will exist at each antenna feed-point. It may prove to be more convenient to make the lengths exact multiples of $\lambda/2$ from a measurement viewpoint, if the individual lengths are set up as a stub for measurement of the resonant frequency. For example, if the physical length required is, say, 2λ, the measurement frequency when the stub is connected as a $\lambda/2$ short circuit stub will be 1/4 of the operating frequency.

However, the velocity factor of commercially-available cable can vary by a significant amount along the reel or drum from the same batch of manufactured cable. (This was something the author found out when, as a student, he spent several days measuring to determine the variation to be expected.) For the more exotic cables, the variation is a lot less, but still measurable. For the types of cables typically used by amateurs (ie the cheaper varieties), it is beneficial to spending some time and effort in getting the cable lengths correct.

The way the author tackles this problem is firstly to make one piece of cable to fit neatly between the power splitter / combiner and one antenna. No consideration is given to the electrical length; quite simply, the cable needs to be just long enough to reach between the two points with adequate stress relief and support being catered for. Often an alternative mechanical routing can be achieved to shorten the cable, so reducing the ultimate power losses. When the shortest cable length has been found, the required coaxial plugs are then fitted to each end, and the piece of coax is then attached to a Vector Network Analyser (VNA) as an $\lambda/4$ open circuit stub. The VNA is set to sweep from 0Hz to some higher frequency, say 100MHz.

The VNA is set up to measure the input reflection coefficient (S_{11}). The frequency of the first dip in the response is recorded; let us assume it is 16.6MHz. This means the stub is behaving as $\lambda/4$ at this frequency. The remaining pieces of coax are then prepared by fitting a connector to one end and the length cut to be about 5% longer than the first piece. The connector on the first piece of cable is then removed and the new frequency ascertained where the first dip occurs. (If using N-type connectors, simply remove the outer front shell leaving the centre-pin in place; this will be a very small shift in frequency). Each new length is then adjusted in length to get the dip at the same frequency as the first piece. (This technique makes an allowance for the connector that is to be fitted.) When all the coaxial cables have been trimmed to length and the connectors fitted, each one is again measured on the analyser. Normally they are all within 0.5° electrical length, which is more than adequate.

This method gives excellent results if you have access to a VNA, but most amateurs will not be in this lucky situation. A signal generator and a receiver can also be used with equally good results. For this you will need a T-piece to fit between the receiver input and the signal generator matching the connector type to be used. The prototype stub is then connected in parallel across the signal line. If there is no need to make the cable an exact length and we can add a little to the length, we can calculate where the $\lambda/4$ open circuit stub notch should occur in frequency by measuring the cable and allowing for the velocity factor. This can bring the notch frequency within the measuring range of the receiver and signal generator.

Suppose the cable measures 3m in length physically, and we are using a cable with a nominal velocity factor of 0.66. This cable acts like a cable electrically 3m / 0.66 = 4.545m in length in free space where VF = 1.00. Calculating the wavelength of 4.545m gives us a frequency of 66MHz. The notch will therefore occur at 0.25 of this frequency (16.5MHz) if used as an $\lambda/4$ open circuit stub. At twice this frequency (33MHz) it will act like a $\lambda/2$ electrical length. If you have a signal generator and a general coverage HF and VHF receiver that covers this spectrum, you have all you need to trim the stubs to length. Ascertain the exact frequency where the deepest null in signal occurs and cut all the other pieces to the same frequency. For the 16.5MHz measuring frequency, leave the stub open at the far end; for 33MHz, short the stub end. An alternative to the receiver is a sensitive broad-band power meter. Simply connect the stub across the line and sweep the signal generator frequency until you find the largest dip in power level.

Because of the slight variation in the velocity factor along a reel of coaxial cable, you will not expect each piece to be exactly the same physical length. By using this technique, the variation in velocity factor is compensated, and the cables will all have the same electrical length, which is the important criterion.

POLARISATION

Plane Polarisation and Faraday Rotation

As has already been mentioned, Faraday rotation is caused by the signal passing through a variable propagation medium such as the ionosphere. The rotation of the wave can be more than 360°. If a horizontally polarised antenna is attempting to receive a pure vertically-polarised wave, the cross-polarisation signal loss can be as high as 20dB or more; in theory the loss is infinite. If the system fade margin is less than 20dB, which it often is for EME systems, the signal will be so weak that it will seem to disappear. Faraday Rotation is worst on the lower frequencies, up to approximately 200MHz; EME signals for 432MHz and higher do not suffer from the fading as much. The rotation can last for a few seconds or several minutes.

The angle of rotation is defined by the formula below.

$$\Omega = \frac{1.35 \times 10^6 \, N_e H \cos(\theta) l}{f^2} \text{ degrees,}$$

where: Ω is the angle through which the wave is rotated,
N_e is the number of electrons per cm^3,
H is the magnetic field in oersteds,
θ is the angle between the magnetic field and the path of the wave,
l is the path length in the medium in cm, and
f is the frequency of the radio wave in hertz.

If the case of EME is considered the angle Ω is doubled as the wave traverses the ionosphere twice.

From the above formula we can see that an EME signal at 432MHz will only suffer ~11% of the rotation of a 144MHz signal for the same ionospheric conditions.

An interesting fact, not generally known about polarisation effects, is that even when there is no Faraday rotation present, a station trying to receive an EME signal, even though the station parameters are sufficient may not hear anything. To understand why this is so needs some explanation.

Imagine a station in the UK, situated on the Greenwich meridian, transmitting a pure horizontally-polarised signal to the Moon. With no Faraday rotation, the signal will strike the Moon's surface still horizontally polarised. Assume also that the signal is reflected with no change in polarisation, ie it is still a pure horizontally-polarised wave and it arrived back at the UK station still horizontally polarised. Now consider a station situated in another country which is 90° to the East or West of the UK; the signal wave being received will be vertically polarised, ie rotated by +90° or -90°. So, in order to receive the signal, the listener would need to switch to a vertically-polarised antenna. If the station was situated 45° either East or West they would need to use a 45° or 135° slant-polarised antenna for best reception.

To get around this, the best method is for both stations to utilise circular-polarisation, which counteracts the Faraday rotation. However, one station needs to use left-hand circular and the other right-hand circular for this to work. If both used the same circular polarisation, the signal at the receiving station would be completely cancelled as the wave upon reflection from the Moon is reversed in rotation direction.

Even the professionals get this wrong sometimes. If you are old enough to remember the first television signal to be sent by a communications satellite between America and England you will recall that on the first attempt all we saw was a fuzzy picture of the American President who was supposed to send a message of greetings to the UK viewers. When the time, came the signal was so weak and indistinguishable, it was a major disappointment. The next evening all went according to plan. The reason was that there was a misunderstanding between the American and British technicians about antenna polarisation. The receiving station at Goonhilly Down had the opposite polarisation and so the signal was almost completely cancelled. Frantic work with a hacksaw the next morning converted the feed to the correct polarisation and all was restored.

Optimum Polarisation for a Radio Telescope

Often, when considering the factors to take into account before a radio telescope is constructed, one of the most vexing ones is what antenna polarisation to choose. We normally describe these as either horizontal or vertical in normal terms. These terms are meaningless unless the reference plane is also defined. Ordinarily these are accepted as being the surface of the Earth, but when an object is far out in space there is no such reference plane.

Many radio telescopes use at least two polarisation methods; these are often simple vertically- or horizontally-polarised feeds. Some types utilise circular polarisation, either right-hand or left-hand, and sometimes both are provided for. None of these polarisation types will be able to receive the full signal level because of errors in the polarisation.

A contributing factor is the polarisation of the signals arriving from a deep space object. From measurements made by many radio telescopes, there is no coherent polarisation in most cases. Therefore, all antennas suffer a loss in detectable signal power of 3dB because they cannot be configured to the actual polarisation of the radio waves from the distant object. Another contributing factor is any Faraday rotation that might be present, due to the signal travelling through the Earth's upper ionospheric regions. Dr John D Kraus. W8JK, at Ohio State University Observatory, spent a great deal of effort to establish the polarisation of many radio stars.

The weaker stars are difficult to resolve because of the high ambient noise in the galaxy. However, there are several radio stars that are very strong and allow fine details to be explored of their polarisation patterns. The brightest radio star is Cassiopeia-A; however, this is not the most powerful emitter of radio waves - this honour belongs to Cygnus-A which is a much greater distance away than Cassiopeia-A.

The power output of Cygnus-A must be enormous. It is situated some 550×10^6 light years away from Earth and is, in fact, not one star but two galaxies in collision with a 'black hole' at the centre. It is well to bear in mind what actually constitutes a light year; it is a distance of 6,000,000,000,000 miles (6×10^{12} miles, 6 trillion miles) or about 9.7×10^{12}km. So the Cygnus-A noise source is at a distance of 5.5×10^{15}km. Even when one takes into account the enormous path loss for such a large distance, the received signal level is quite high.

Using Cassiopeia-A as a reference, other radio stars can be evaluated in terms of signal level. The relative signal levels of some of the other stars are detailed below, including the average 'quiet sky' taken near the Galactic North Pole (GNP). The units used are the jansky (Jy), which is 1×10^{-26}Wm^{-2}Hz^{-1}.

Note: The jansky is not an ISO-recognised unit but is, however, recognised by URSI (Union Radio-Scientific Internationale), which is the body that coordinates the science of radio astronomy and consequently the shortened version is known as the Jy.

Cassiopeia-A	57 x 10-24Jy
Cygnus-A	38 x 10-24Jy
Taurus-A	8 x 10-24Jy
Virgo-A	6 x 10-24Jy
Sky near GNP	5 x 10-25Jy

Fig 4.10: Ohio State University recording of the Cygnus-A emission

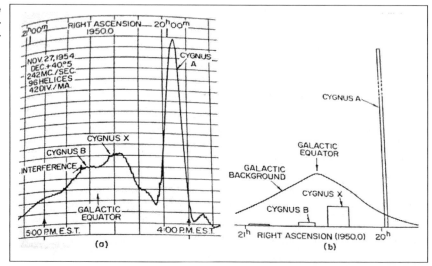

These signal levels were determined using the Ohio State University radio telescope at 250MHz. The actual levels measured are 0.5 of the above figures, because the polarisation loss incurs a 3dB factor. A radio telescope antenna, whether linearly- or circularly-polarised, will accept only half the radiated power.

PARABOLIC ANTENNA

Factors Affecting Efficiency

In order to achieve efficiency close to 100%, it is necessary to provide uniform illumination over the entire surface of the parabola. The radiating source needs to be positioned at the focal point of the parabola. This means that there should be equal power flux density over every unit area of the parabolic surface, but no power flux at the extreme outer surface (edge) of the dish. This is impossible to achieve with a practical feed mechanism. An ideal feed would radiate from an infinitesimal point source and hence provide uniform power density over the entire surface area, falling to zero at the outer edges. This feed would thus need to be an isotropic source, but it is practically impossible to make such an isotropic radiator at low frequencies.

> An isotopic source is an infinitesimal point source of RF energy that radiates uniformly over the volume of a sphere. You can imagine it as a very small ball placed at the centre of a large sphere. The energy striking the inner surface of the sphere would be uniform over each unit of area.

The consequence of illuminating more than the extreme outer surface area is that some energy will 'spill over' the edge and excessive side lobes will appear in the polar diagram, causing unwanted responses not under the control of the operator, and a loss of gain to occur. Consequently, the illumination of a parabola needs to be tapered to provide less illumination at the outer surface. Usually a power flux density of -10dB over the outer 10 to 15% of the surface is chosen to reduce the formation of side lobes. As the outer surface, for unit distance from the centre, has a far greater surface area than the surface nearer the centre, this causes a loss of efficiency and hence gain. In practice, the efficiency of a typical parabolic antenna will be between 50 and 60% at best.

Focal Length Considerations

Another compromising factor is the choice of focal length. In a parabolic reflector antenna the ratio of focal length to diameter is known as the f / D ratio, and is the ratio of the distance of the focal point from the centre of the parabola to its diameter. Typical terrestrial communication parabolic antennas use f / D ratios of between 0.6 to 0.8 and, consequently, the parabolas are very shallow. If the f / D ratio exceeds about 3 the dish, in effect, becomes a flat circular plate.

The longer the focal length the further out the feed is positioned and the easier it is to provide a more uniform illumination over the whole surface using a simple feed. A negative factor of a long focal length is that the feed is then positioned a long way from the centre of the parabola and three important factors come into play.

The first concerns the screening of the feed-point from noise sources from the side. In a deep dish, (short f / D ratio), the feed can be positioned at or just below the edge (rim) of the parabola as viewed from the side. This provides additional attenuation of noise sources from the earth, which often are many times stronger than the object under investigation. Where the feed is positioned in the plane of the lip (f / D ratio of 0.25), this is known as a focal-plane system. (The German Würzburg-Reise radar described in Chapter 1 used a quasi-focal plane dish for this reason.)

The second factor is a mechanical problem. If the focal point is positioned at a large f / D ratio, the leverage of the feed supporting structure on the parabola can be considerable. Husband, the civil engineer who designed Jodrell Bank Mk1, came across this problem. In order to reduce the deformation of the parabolic surface as the antenna was declined from the zenith towards the horizon, due to the out of balance leverage from the feed-point supporting tower, Husband and Lovell decided to use an extremely short f / D ratio of only 0.24 (a quasi-focal-plane dish). This saved a great deal of trouble and additional steelwork to counter-balance the leverage problem. In a small parabolic antenna, the problem is not as severe but, nonetheless, still present. In the case of the original Jodrell Bank Mk1 telescope, the feed tower was a four-cornered tapered lattice tower situated at the centre of the dish and rising 60ft (~20m) to the feed-point. This structure is constructed from heavily-braced angle sec-

Fig 4.11: Rear View of Jodrell Bank Mk1A, showing additional support steelwork to replace the original 'bicycle wheel'. Compare this with the picture of the 1957 version. (Photograph: J Fielding 2005)

tion steel and weighs some 20 tons. This weight needed to be counterbalanced by extra steel under the dish to prevent excessive over-turning moments. When the conversion to the Mk1A took place, the f / D ratio was increased and so the feed support tower needed to be increased in length. However, the addition of more structural supporting steelwork under the dish was also included to stiffen the bowl and this balanced the added leverage of the extended feed tower.

A further problem is that the supporting structure causes some obscuring of the surface, (aperture blocking); this, in most cases, is very small and can be neglected except in the case of a very high (GHz region) operating frequency. Here, it may be necessary to use special feed configurations, such as an offset-feed or a Cassegrain sub-reflector to prevent gain loss due to this effect.

In small microwave dishes, the feed supporting struts often terminate at the outer rim of the dish to avoid this problem. With a large dish, this is not a good method: mechanical and extra bracing needs to be used to prevent edge deformation. It was not a viable option on Jodrell Bank Mk1, due to the extra steel needed to make the rim stiff enough to bear the feed-point supporting load. Edge deformation causes the focal point to shift its position. The shifting in focal point causes the beam to deviate from the correct path and a pointing inaccuracy to occur. The Max Planck and Parkes dishes use an edge mounting method to support the focal point. However, this deforms the dish at certain elevation angles and computers correct the error by moving the feed-point to maintain optimum beamwidth and gain.

Incidentally this is how the large fixed dish at Arecibo is steered. The feed point is supported by three tall towers and a cable forming a delta shape. By a system of winches the feed can be positioned over a 20° range.

Fig 4.12: Arecibo 1000ft (300m) spherical dish with feed supports. Each of the towers is 180ft (60m) in height and the feed consists of a rotating structure weighing 600 tons. Winches position the feed at the focal point. By reeling in on one winch and paying out by the other two, the feed can be varied over 20°, so steering the beam

Fig 4.13: Parkes, Sydney, Australia 210ft (64m) antenna

Fig 4.14: Max Planck 100m antenna

The third factor concerns the additional length of feeder cable required in a long f / D ratio, causing degradation of the system noise figure. (If you look carefully at the picture of the Parkes dish, you will see the heavy coax running down the support leg closest to the observer and then across to the dish centre.) This can be overcome by using better cable, but this will be a larger diameter and hence weigh more so compounding the mechanical leverage problem. In practice, the LNA is normally positioned directly at the feed-point of the antenna and the length of coaxial cable required is very short. However, the coaxial cable from the feed-point LNA to the receiver is still a problem. In the Jodrell Bank Mk1 radio telescope, the signal from the receiver converters mounted at the feed-point are connected to the main control room and the receiver IF with a coaxial cable 200m in length.

As can be seen, the loss of efficiency causes, in a practical case, a loss of gain to occur. For an efficiency of 0.5 (50%), the gain will be 3dB less than the theoretical due to illumination deficiencies and other factors. Increasing the diameter slightly and hence the surface area can compensate this, if economic and mechanical factors allow.

> If the reader visits Jodrell Bank, there is a very useful demonstration of the focal length problem that the visitor can try. In the Science Park, very near to the Mk1A telescope, there are two small dishes that are fixed at ground level about 20m apart and point at each other. The two dishes have metal rings fixed at the focal points. One person places his mouth at one ring and talks to a second person with his ear at the ring of the other dish. One listener can hear the other, even if he whispers. By moving his ear away from the focal point, the sound diminishes.

Fig 4.15: Jodrell Bank acoustic dish. (Photograph: J Fielding 2005)

Surface Accuracy

A further potential loss of gain is the surface accuracy of the paraboloid. If the deviation from a perfect parabola exceed a certain amount (~10% of the wavelength) the loss of gain starts to become considerable, and this limits the maximum frequency at which the parabola can produce adequate gain. This, however needs to be put into context. This condition only holds true if the gross deviation occurs over a major portion of the dish surface, normally the outer third. Where the gross deviation is only over a relatively small percentage, the loss of gain is proportionately less.

For the case where surface inaccuracies occur, the amplitude and phase of the signal at each unit area of the surface will not be the same when focused at the feed, and so some amplitude and phase error will occur, hence some signal cancellation will exist. An approximation of the loss of gain due to surface inaccuracies was deduced from a study in which it was shown that surface irregularities of 0.25in (6mm) on a 85ft diameter dish produced a gain loss of 1dB at 1GHz. The total gain for such a dish is approximately 45dB, so the loss of gain at this frequency is relatively insignificant. As the operating frequency increases, and hence the wavelength decreases, the physical error becomes more significant until, at some high frequency, it would be possible to use a smaller dish with a more accurate surface profile than a large dish to produce the same gain. This was one of the contributing factors when Jodrell Bank constructed the Mk2 telescope, as it can operate at higher frequencies than the Mk1 and provide more gain, although it is only 10% of the size of the Mk1.

Deviations in the surface accuracy can be due to many factors, apart from the obvious physical dimensional errors during construction. The surface accuracy is also affected by wind loading, elevation angle and icing, which can cause variable deformation of the dish. In the case of Jodrell Bank Mk1, an elaborate drainage system was used to ensure rainwater did not collect in the dish when it was pointed upwards. The stowing position for Jodrell Bank Mk1A is in such a position and the weight of rainwater would cause an excessive load to be placed on the dish surface if the rainwater was allowed to collect.

Fig 4.16: Jodrell Bank Mk1A stowed for maintenance. (Photograph: J Fielding 2005)

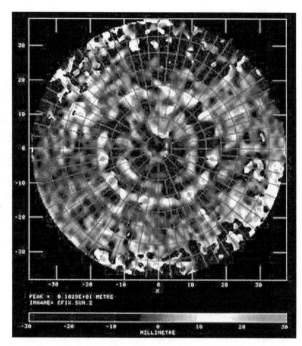

Fig 4.17: Holographic diagram of the surface inaccuracies of the Jodrell Bank Mk1A dish at 5GHz. The non-uniform illumination at this high frequency can be clearly seen. This prompted a modification to be made in 1999 to improve the dish surface with a better reflector. With the new skin, the dish is usable up to 10GHz. (Photograph by courtesy of University of Manchester Archives)

Electrical Conductivity

A perfect parabolic antenna would have a low resistance and a continuous, metallic surface. If cost were no object, the surface would be gold-plated to improve conductivity. Small microwave dishes are often made from fibreglass mats and resin with a layer of thin aluminium foil buried just below the surfaces to act as reflectors. In other small dishes, the entire dish is spun from a high-conductivity material such as magnesium alloy. The 50ft dish used at the US Naval Research Laboratory (NRL) was constructed by the Collins Radio Company and made from 50 aluminium castings, that were machined to a tolerance of 0.25mm, bolted together and capable of operating at up to 1cm wavelength (30GHz). The Arecibo dish uses a perforated aluminium mesh to provide adequate reflection up to several GHz.

In some cases, in an effort to reduce wind loading, the surface is constructed from mesh. This is only an effective reflector up to a certain frequency. Above the frequency that corresponds to $\lambda/8$ of the physical grid size of the mesh, more and more of the signal will be able to pass through the mesh and be lost, causing a loss of gain. This also has a side effect as it means that the feed is no longer screened from the rear of the dish and so interfering signals can pass through and become a problem if they emanate from the rear of the antenna.

Husband and Lovell, during the design and construction of Jodrell Bank Mk1, had originally planned to use a 100mm square wire mesh for the entire reflector, as the operating frequency was not expected to exceed 408MHz. During the construction, the discovery of the hydrogen-line emission at 21cm was made in 1955, and it was decided to use a smaller aperture mesh for the central 100ft portion of the dish, to allow acceptable operation on frequencies up to 1.5GHz. Initially this was 50mm x 100mm, later reduced to 50mm x 50mm and then 50mm x 25mm.

The presence of the Hydrogen Line emission at 1420MHz was first postulated during the war in 1944 by a Dutch scientist, van de Hulst, and subsequently confirmed by American scientists in the early 1950s, when equipment was built, but only released to the scientific community in 1955, some 4 years into the construction of the Jodrell Bank dish.

The change in design caused problems due to the weight of the additional structural steelwork to cater for this and the vast number of tie-points that would be needed to secure the mesh in place and maintain an accurate parabolic contour. A solid electrical connection would be needed between adjacent layers of mesh, which it was proposed to spot weld together. In the end, due to increasing mechanical, electrical, financial and logistical problems with sourcing suitable steel mesh and attaching the mesh to the framework, it was decided to abandon the idea and instead construct the surface from 1/8in (3mm) thick mild steel plates, welded together to form the parabolic shape. This required approximately 7100 metal plates to be welded in situ. This formed a stressed structure and was a major portion of the parabola's strength and contributed greatly to the overall rigidity of the antenna.

It must be realised that when the telescope construction was first started, the war had finished only six years previously, and the supply of much of the steel was still a rationed item and many steel works were still engaged in the supply of steel for reconstruction works to repair the ravages of the German bombing raids. Unlike the war years, when Lovell could get just about anything he wanted, within reason, by simply picking up the telephone and calling the Air Ministry, he now had to stand in line with all the other civilians to obtain supplies in great shortage. As it turned out, no manufacturer was willing or able to make the odd-sized mesh Lovell and Husband required within the allocated budget and so an alternative skin was devised.

The wind-loading tests performed by Husband on a scale model in a wind tunnel had assumed the worst-case condition where the mesh was completely filled due to icing and so the change to the solid surface was not out of keeping with Husband's calculations. Subsequent results during a freak hurricane in January 1976 vindicated the integrity of Husband's and Lovell's decision to use a solid steel surface. It certainly reduced the cost and added much needed stiffness to the dish structure, although not a very elegant solution with thousands of small metal plates to be aligned and then welded in place. Nevertheless, it proved to be a good substitute and one that would be used again when the Mk1 was upgraded to the Mk1A.

Modifications to Jodrell Bank Mk1 to convert it to the Mk1A involved constructing a new, shallower, mild steel dish above the original, thus increasing the f / D ratio. This was to improve the surface accuracy to allow operation on frequencies up to 3GHz and improve the side-lobe suppression. This double skin provided considerable extra stiffening to the whole structure. The accuracy of this new skin was a serious problem and each panel was aligned with a laser-surveying system to obtain a maximum deviation of not more than 5mm across the dish surface. Only when all the panels had been welded in place could measurements be made with the dish at various elevation angles. For the welding operation, which occupied a team of welders for nearly nine months, the dish was stowed pointing straight upwards to the zenith. When the scaffolding was removed, the dish was moved to 45° elevation and the laser surveying equipment used to measure the deformity of the surface. The results were very good considering the extra weight added to the structure. (With age, the new dish surface has relaxed and the 1999 measurement showed that as much as 30mm errors occurred at certain points. These points of stress are visible on the holographic image produced at 5GHz and are due to the supporting structure under the dish surface).

Tests performed with the dish pointed vertically upwards, before painting, showed that a coin could be thrown from the centre to the outer edge where it would roll around the dish in a circular manner, and its passage was observed to be like a ball in a roulette wheel. At each welded joint, the coin would skip and the worst points were noted and then ground down to obtain a near-perfect surface. This paid huge dividends as the overall gain rose a few decibels after the lengthy exercise. The steel had to be painted to slow down the corrosion. A microwave low-loss paint with low solar reflection was prohibitively expensive, and so good-quality enamel paint was used instead. The dielectric loss from this paint caused a few dB loss to the overall gain at 3GHz. The paint added several extra tons to the structure but this was acceptable. The conversion to the Mk1A added nearly 600 tons to the original structure, mostly extra stiffening and strengthening steelwork.

In the latest modification, which took place in phases between 1999 and 2002, the entire upper-dish surface was removed and replaced with a galvanised sheet steel covering. This was made up in 64 'petals' and fixed in place on top of the existing Mk1A structure with 100,000 stainless steel self-tapping screws. The older mild steel plates by then had started to show severe corrosion and the choice of galvanised sheeting was an attempt to slow down the corrosion and to provide a better reflecting surface.

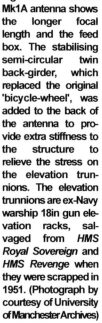

Fig 4.18: The modified Mk1A antenna shows the longer focal length and the feed box. The stabilising semi-circular twin back-girder, which replaced the original 'bicycle-wheel', was added to the back of the antenna to provide extra stiffness to the structure to relieve the stress on the elevation trunnions. The elevation trunnions are ex-Navy warship 18in gun elevation racks, salvaged from *HMS Royal Sovereign* and *HMS Revenge* when they were scrapped in 1951. (Photograph by courtesy of University of Manchester Archives)

Fig 4.19: Work on the new dish surface during 1999 to 2002 to fit a new galvanised steel reflector. The details of the feed supporting tower are clearly visible in this picture. (Photograph by courtesy of University of Manchester Archives)

Fig 4.20: Grinding off the old welds after a section of panel had been removed. (Photograph by courtesy of University of Manchester Archives)

Fig 4.21: An early trial piece of the new galvanised surface. Note the thousands of mild steel plates laid during the Mk1A conversion. The ladder to gain access to the feed box is visible running up the tower. Note the size of the man standing at the base of the tower and the size of the low-loss coax cable. (Photograph by courtesy of University of Manchester Archives)

Fig 4.22: Fitting a new galvanised steel panel to the Jodrell Bank surface. The new panel has a bed of waterproof mastic to prevent corrosion. Note the many stainless steel screws fixing each segment in place. (Photo by courtesy of University of Manchester Archives)

Fig 4.23: Progress at the end of 2001. (Photograph by courtesy of University of Manchester Archives)

Fig 4.24: Fitting the last screw. In traditional style, this one is a gold-plated one! (Photograph by courtesy of University of Manchester Archives)

The choice of galvanised steel sheeting was prompted by two factors. One was the cost and the second was the mechanical balance. If aluminium had been chosen, with its lighter weight, this would have entailed a similar reduction in the 'under-the-dish' mass to relieve the out-of balance-moments.

Note: The factor η in the antenna gain calculations quoted previously takes into account the losses due to surface irregularities, surface conductivity and any other losses, such as the dielectric loss of paint.

Feed Horn Choices

The feed is not part of the antenna, but the antenna cannot perform without the feed. Matching the feed to the parabolic antenna is a critical factor. The beamwidth of the feed needs to be such as to provide adequate illumination across the dish surface but with no spill over at the edges. Hence, the correct tapering of the illumination is a critical factor to reduce side lobes in the polar diagram. (As the feed confines the energy into the required beamwidth it has directivity and hence 'gain', a factor often overlooked by amateurs. Some feeds have a forward gain of as much as 16dBi).

Most parabolic antennas can utilise a circular waveguide feed. These are simpler to make from available circular tubing than square or rectangular waveguide. These are commonly known as 'coffee-can' or 'beer-can' feeds as originally they were made from tin plated steel cans in which coffee or beer is supplied. Variations on the basic design are the Kumar feed [6] (also covered by VE4MA in [7]), which uses a choke ring to improve the radiation pattern, and the Turrin (W2IMU) patented 'Dual Mode' feed [8]. See also [9].

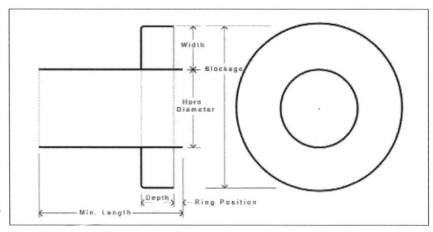

Fig 4.25: VE4MA (Kumar) feed

These belong to a family of feeds known as "prime feeds" or "direct feeds" as they are placed at the prime focal point of the dish positioned out from the vertex of the parabola and pointing at the dish surface.

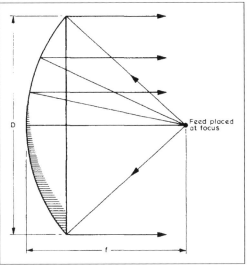

Fig 4.26: Geometry of direct feed system

An alternative system uses what are known as 'indirect feeds' and the Cassegrain feed is a common type used. These will be discussed later.

For all of these, some factors need to be kept in mind. These feeds can be plane polarised, circularly polarised or dual circular polarised giving "Right-Hand or Left-Hand Circular Polarisation' (RHCP or LHCP).

The simplest feed is shown below with a single monopole radiator giving a single plane polarised signal. The physical attitude of the monopole determines whether it is vertically or horizontally polarised. In the diagram it is shown as horizontally polarised.

Note: In a circularly polarised feed the polarity is reversed when the signal is reflected off the dish surface. If the polarisation required is RHCP then the prime feed needs to be selected to generate LHCP to give the correct polarisation.

Diameter of Guide

The circular waveguide needs to be a certain minimum diameter to propagate the TE11 mode, the larger the diameter the lower the frequency of waves that are able to pass from the antenna focal point to the monopole radiator placed near the closed off end. At higher frequencies (shorter wavelengths) the wave is able to propagate with virtually no loss along the waveguide [10]. Hence, the feed behaves like a high-pass filter. The minimum internal diameter is 0.58λ in free space and the optimum diameter is between 0.65 to 0.71λ for minimal loss.

Position of Monopole Radiator

The monopole radiator accepts the signal in the waveguide and converts it into a form suitable to send the signal to a coaxial cable. (In the transmitting mode

Fig 4.27: Circular horn feed

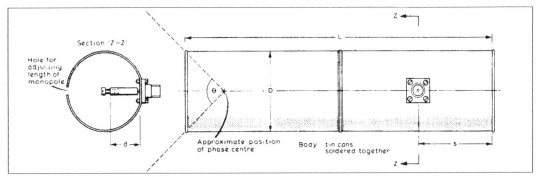

the monopole excites the waveguide and allows the wave to travel from the closed end towards the open end, where it is radiated). The monopole radiator needs to be $\lambda g / 4$ from the closed end, where λg (guide wavelength) is the physical length of the wavelength in the waveguide. (In a waveguide the velocity of the wave is slower than in free-space and so λg is physically longer for a particular frequency).

In the transmitting scenario the monopole radiates a signal both towards the open end and the closed end. The placing of the monopole $\lambda / 4$ from the closed end causes the radiation towards the rear to be reflected off the closed end, so reinforcing the forward wave. As antennas and feeds are considered to be reciprocal the opposite occurs in the receive mode.

Minimum Length of Feed Horn

The length of the waveguide largely determines the angle of radiation in the E and H planes. Long waveguide feeds spray the signal over a wider angle than short waveguides. This is also affected by the diameter of the waveguide; a waveguide only just large enough to propagate low frequencies becomes infinitely long. Above a certain length in wavelengths the signal will never reach the open end and the waveguide is said to be operating at 'beyond cut-off'. The minimum length of the feed is $\approx \lambda g$.

The E-plane and H-plane 3dB beamwidths in degrees are 29.4 L/D and 50 L/D, where L is the guide length and D is the diameter (both in the same unit of measurement, eg metres or λ) and hence they differ considerably. This makes even illumination of a parabolic antenna more difficult and hence why the Turrin dual-mode feed is a better performer for an antenna of about 0.55 f/D. In the example above, for an optimum internal diameter of 0.65λ with a guide length of 1λ, the E plane beamwidth is 45° and the H plane is 77°.

Image Rejection

Knowing these factors allows us to make certain important choices. The first is determined by the low frequency cut-off of the waveguide. As there is a certain minimum diameter to support propagation we can use this to help with the receiver image rejection.

The feed behaves the same as a "high-pass" filter, attenuating low frequency signals. Suppose we choose a waveguide diameter that rolls up at say, 1.2GHz. Below 1.2GHz little if any signal will be able to propagate from the focal point to the monopole radiator or vice versa. This helps to choose the local oscillator frequency. If the receiver is for the 21cm Hydrogen Line at 1.42GHz and the IF is 152MHz we have two choices of LO.

For low-side injection we need the LO to operate on $1420 - 152 = 1268$MHz and for high-side injection it is $1420 + 152 = 1572$MHz. Calculating the image frequencies for these two cases gives 1116MHz for low-side injection and 1724MHz for high-side injection.

In the case of high-side injection the image is very close to the GSM 2G spectrum of about 1.8GHz, if the IF bandwidth is wide enough the interfering signals may be a problem. In the case of low-side injection the image falls close to the band used by DME equipment fitted to aircraft and if an aircraft is within the antenna beam it may also be a problem, but it is simple to use a notch filter to reduce this type of interference.

Since the feed is operating as a 'waveguide beyond cut-off' for all frequencies below 1.2GHz, choosing the low-side injection option will usefully increase the image rejection but it will give zero image rejection for the high-side injection option. This means that the choice of low-side injection is the optimum choice and not as much image rejection filtering is required in the receiver front-end stages. Image rejection filtering using band pass filters inevitably incurs some loss and hence degradation of noise figure, using the feed horn to provide some additional image rejection incurs no additional loss.

A further plus factor relates to LO radiation. For the example above the high-side injection choice happens to fall into the GPS satellite band. If the LO signal leaks through the receiver and then is radiated by the feed this is not acceptable as it may cause interference to GPS receivers in the vicinity.

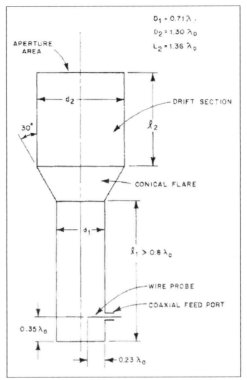

Fig 4.28: Turrin (W2IMU) original dual mode feed. The dimensions shown are for the 'free-space' wavelength. [source *ARRL UHF/Microwave Experimenters Manual*]

Dual Mode Feed

The dual mode feed is a patented design of Richard Turrin, W2IMU. This uses a launching section, the same as the coffeecan feed, and a conical flared section to a larger diameter. The smaller diameter section, which launches the wave along the guide, only allows propagation of one type of wave, the TE11 mode. The 30° conical flared section allows another form of propagation mode to exist. Having moved past the flared section into the larger 'drift section' a second mode (TM11) is allowed to propagate and the two modes are then combined with the correct phase relationship to give better illumination of the parabolic surface of f/D of greater than 0.5.

Fig 4.29: Kumar feed with additional choke ring on a coffee-can feed

When the two modes reach the open end of the drift section the relative phase and amplitude of both modes give zero fields at the periphery of the aperture resulting in very low rear and side radiation, and thus minimise noise pick-up. (The coffee-can feed has substantial 'edge currents' at the open end and these disrupt the polar diagram. The choke ring on the Kumar feed is an attempt to reduce the edge currents effect).

A later version of the W2IMU feed extended the smaller diameter in length to allow

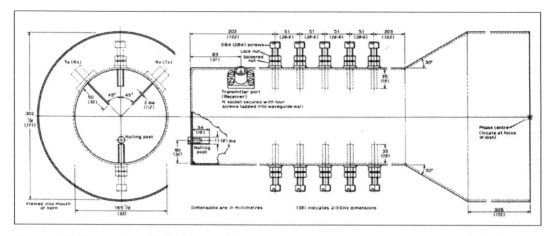

Fig 4.30: Turrin (W2IMU) dual mode feed modified for circularly polarity

From Turrin's notes in the Crawford Hill VHF Club newsletters the required phase shift (or delay) along the guide is 90°. The number of stages is a function of the spaces between the tuning screws. In the example in **Fig 4.30** with five tuning screws the spaces are four, so a phase shift of 22.5° occurs between each tuning screw. For different phase shifts the spacing between the screws varies.

polarising tuning screws to be included. This provided for circularly polarised waves.

Indirect Feeds

In the indirect feeds we have two types that are popular, the Cassegrain feed and the so-called "Splash-Plate" feed. The indirect feed system places the radiating feed near the vertex of the parabola and fires forwards to a 'sub-reflector' that intercepts the energy and illuminates the parabola.

One of the advantages of the indirect feed systems is that the feed does not need to placed a long way in front of the vertex of the dish, making adjustments when setting up simpler. The other main advantage of the indirect feed system is that the sub-reflector is normally a lower mass than a prime feed horn and so the supporting struts can be smaller giving less aperture blocking and bending moments to the dish structure. It also allows lower loss in the cable between the feed and the main receiver due to a shorter cable run.

Note: In the indirect feed system the signal is reflected twice, firstly off the sub-reflector and again off the dish surface. Hence, for a RHCP system the feed must provide a RHCP signal.

The sub-reflector is not a parabola, it is a hyperboloidal shape and this provides illumination across the prime dish surface. The limitations

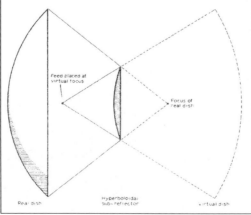

Fig 4.31: Cassegrain Feed system

of the Cassegrain feed is that the sub-reflector produces some aperture blocking of the prime surface and hence some loss of gain.

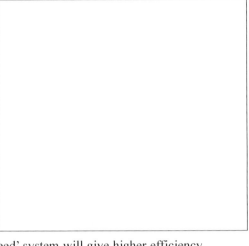

For a Cassegrain system to work with minimal aperture blocking the parabola diameter needs to be at least 50λ at the operating wavelength. For a 21cm wavelength antenna this is about 10.5m in diameter (34ft), hence it is not a viable option for low frequencies where the dish is small in terms of wavelength. A 'prime feed' system will give higher efficiency.

Another problem of the Cassegrain feed is generating an accurate sub-reflector with the correct f/D ratio. The sub-reflector needs to be at least 10λ in diameter and for 21cm this means a sub-reflector of 2.1m diameter. The 'splash-plate' feed is similar, instead of a hyperbolic sub-reflector it is a circular flat plate and hence easier to construct.

Again significant aperture blocking may arise if the operating frequency is less than optimum. Both of these feeds move the real parabola focus to a virtual focal point near the vertex of the dish, which corresponds with the phase-centre of the feed.

Focusing

In both the direct and indirect feed some means need to be provided to alter the position of the feed with respect to the dish vertex to place it at the correct focal point of the dish, and for the indirect feed the sub-reflector also needs to be adjustable. In the plain circular feed (coffee-can type) the phase centre can be inside the feed. In the Turrin dual mode feed the phase centre is at end of the drift section.

Further details of the W2IMU feed and other designs pertaining to parabolic antennae are available online in the Crawford Hill VHF Club notes edited by W2IMU [11].

Circular Waveguide Wall Thickness

A parameter not mentioned in many amateur publications (and others) concerns the wall thickness of the material used to construct the feed waveguide. The critical dimension for a circular feed is the internal diameter, but the wall thickness also has a considerable effect on the radiation angle. G L James and K J Greene of the CSIRO (Australia) in [12] discuss the wall thickness parameter and give some experimental data on how this affects the radiation angle of the feed. The original formula was based on calculations by Weinstein [13] where the wall thickness was considered to be close to zero; however in a practical feed this does not hold. The thicker the wall, relative to the operating wavelength, has an increasingly distorting effect on the radiation angle in the E and H fields. For a wall thicker than ≈ 0.01λ the effect becomes more pronounced. The wall thickness should be thick enough for mechanical rigidity but not thicker. For operational frequencies of about 1.4GHz (21cm) the wall should not be thicker than 2.1mm.

Near Field Effects

For transmitting antennas used at microwave frequencies we are aware of the dangers of high levels of RF (near field) strength in front of a parabolic dish. However, these near field effects can also cause degradation when the antenna is used for receiving. The near field can extend for a considerable distance from the antenna. This is given by the Rayleigh distance and is calculated from the formula:

Rayleigh distance = $2 (D^2) / \lambda$

where D is the diameter of the antenna and λ is the operating wavelength.

For a 10 metre diameter parabola operating at 23cm the Rayleigh distance is ≈ 0.87km. For the same antenna used at 13cm the distance increases to ≈ 1.5km.

In a paper by Haworth et al [14] the writer's point out that rain, cloud or ice particles within the Rayleigh distance may be a considerable contribution to additional attenuation of the signal. From the example quoted in the paper for a 6m diameter antenna operating at 30GHz ($\lambda = 10$mm) the Rayleigh distance extends to 7.2km. The other factor mentioned is that the rain or cloud can change the polarisation of the signal, in some cases dramatically. This is noticeable on satellite television reception as 'sparklies' or 'snow' on the signal. Hence, circular polarisation is the best option to counter this effect.

Construction of Parabolic Antennas

In some cases amateurs have been able to acquire surplus parabolic dishes designed for other applications. With the demise of the early C-band television satellite systems operating on about 4GHz there are many redundant dishes available. However, these are somewhat limited in diameter and often the decision is made to construct a larger dish.

The profile of a dish needs to be as near a perfect parabolic shape as possible to maximise the gain and hence directivity. Where this is not so important

then some shortcuts can be taken. One such method was designed for the reception of Meteosat weather satellite images at 1691MHz and it used a fabricated dish made from 'petals' cut from aluminium sheet that were fastened together by pop-rivets. This type of construction is adequate for dishes up to about 2m in diameter. The original details were contained in [15].

Fig 4.33: DC3NT 1.2m diameter parabolic antenna for Meteosat reception at 1.7GHz

Another method is to use aluminium T-shaped sections to form the ribs with gusset plates which are held together by self-tapping screws or pop-rivets. Each rib is built on a profiled jig to attain the correct parabolic curve and the various pieces attached to build up the final rib. For the home constructor this is a simple technique but somewhat labour intensive and time consuming.

A better method, if the equipment is available, is to use TIG welding. Modern construction of automobiles designed for the high-end market now utilises aluminium sections fabricated by bonding with epoxy adhesives. This method is a possibility as an alternative to welding to fabricate a parabola using aluminium. Colin Chapman of Lotus Cars was the first to utilise this radical approach to obtain an adequately stiff chassis weighing very little. The later Morgan cars also use this method to produce a very robust backbone onto which to assemble the car.

Wind loading of a large dish is a problem and often necessitates a move from a solid surface to one covered by a reflecting mesh to reduce the wind loading. The aperture of the mesh needs to be less than $\lambda/10$ in order to reduce gain loss and signal leakage.

Another approach to construct a near parabolic dish is the method used by Richard Knadle, K2RIW for a stressed parabola. This uses straight aluminium tubes attached to a central hub that are pulled by insulating ropes towards the feedhorn supporting central pipe. The feedhorn is attached to an insulating septum plate that fits in the mouth of the feedhorn. The tensioning ropes not only deform the ribs to a near parabolic curve but also serve to support the feedhorn

Fig 4.34: K2RIW stressed parabolic dish design

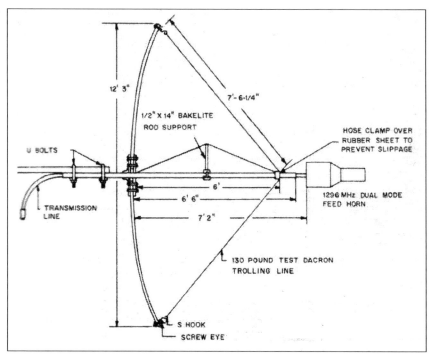

Fig 4.35: Side view of the stressed parabolic dish

pipe. The details for the design of a 3.7m (12ft) diameter dish originally appeared in [16] but have since been reprinted in a number of other ARRL books [17]. The reflecting surface is mosquito screen mesh laid over the ribs and fastened in place with ties.

During the design phase on the new Durban radio telescope it was intended to TIG weld the ribs from stock size aluminium tubing. An alternative suggestion made by one of the mechanical engineers was to use ribs that could be laser cut from ≈10mm thick flat sheet. The various bracing and stiffening gussets could be cut out in one operation leaving a completed rib. The disadvantage of this method is the large amount of material wasted, but some large aircraft components are made in this manner and the waste material sold back to the supplier for recycling

SPECIAL ANTENNA CONFIGURATIONS

The single greatest problem with radio astronomy is the limited angular resolving power of the antenna. Whereas any required narrow beamwidth is theoretically possible to achieve, provided that a very large antenna can be constructed, the angular beamwidth required is often less than one second of arc, and the antenna size then becomes measured in kilometres rather than metres. The beamwidth of the antenna gives the minimum resolving power to separate two distant radio stars; if the beamwidth is wide the star appears to have much greater angular size. Similarly, two stars very close in angular distance appear as one object.

The formula for antenna beamwidth can be converted into the formula below.

$$\phi = \frac{57.3\lambda}{D},$$

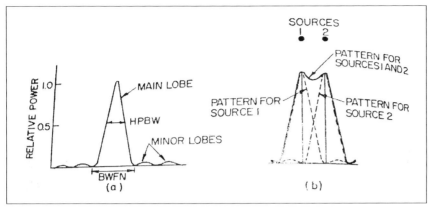

Fig 4.36: Antenna half-power beam-width and subsequent resolving ability to separate two closely-spaced objects. If the half-power bandwidth is more than the angular distance between the two objects, they appear to merge into one

where: φ is the 3dB beamwidth in degrees,
          λ is the wavelength in metres, and
          D is the diameter of the antenna in metres.

In the case of the Jodrell Bank Mk1A, the 3dB beamwidths are approximately

152MHz	1.4
408MHz	0.54
1.5GHz	0.15
3GHz	0.075

If the resolving accuracy of the unaided human eye is taken as the minimum required, this is a resolution of 0.05°. This is far from the required resolution to be able to separate, for example, two of the nearest radio noise sources in our nearest galaxy, the Milky Way, at a distance of 25,000 light years. If the wavelength used is 1.89m (152MHz), the diameter of the antenna required to produce a 3dB beamwidth of 0.05° would be 20km. This is impossible to realise in practice. However, if two antennas are connected together in an interferometer network, the required antenna sizes can be quite modest, and the resolving power is equivalent to a dish of diameter the same as the antenna separation, known as the baseline distance. It is necessary to point both antennas at the same point in the sky.

Fig 4.37: A simple interferometer network. (Courtesy of University of Manchester Jodrell Bank Observatory)

Interferometer Networks

The simplest version of an interferometer is known as the Michelson Interferometer. This consists of two half-wave dipoles connected in the manner shown in the diagram. Note that the two dipoles are connected in phase to produce the 'grating lobes', this is an analogy to the optical version. The dipoles could be replaced by Yagis to achieve more gain.

The lobes produced allow more precise angular resolution of a source. The formula to determine the position of the

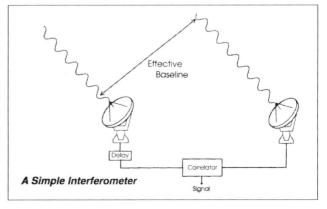

A Simple Interferometer

Fig 4.38: The Michelson Interferometer

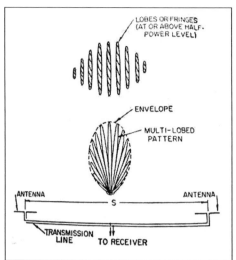

first nulls in the polar pattern is given by

$$\text{Null} = \frac{57.3}{S} \quad \text{degrees,}$$

Where: S = the distance in wavelengths (see diagram).

In order for the Michelson Interferometer to work correctly, the two antenna outputs need to be summed together into a common receiver input with zero phase error and minimal signal loss. If two lengths of coaxial cable were used to connect the antennas to a signal combiner, several problems arise. The first is the attenuation of the signals. Two antennas placed 20km apart would require a minimum of 20km of coaxial cable to connect them. Each antenna would be equipped with a cable 10km long and the signal combiner would be situated at a point midway between the two antennas. Not a very practical situation!

Ensuring a zero phase shift is extremely difficult to guarantee as the operating frequency changes. Techniques that have been used with antennas placed up to 200km apart have been to utilise microwave links to bring the two signals to a common receiver with adjustable phase shifting to synchronise the signals. A variation on the Michelson Interferometer is the Multi-Unit Interferometer shown below. This combines two Michelson elements to form a more powerful resolving antenna. (This technique was used by Watson-Watt in the GL2 anti-aircraft radar set to give accurate azimuth indication, described in Chapter 1).

The technique of using two or more antennas in an interferometer network has been developed over the last 50 years into a powerful technique. Dr (later Professor Sir) Martin Ryle, G3CY, at Cambridge, was the pioneer in this work and the later idea of aperture synthesis. The largest distance separating the antennas was the two-antenna interferometer set up between Virginia, USA and the Crimea, USSR which had a baseline of 6,500 miles (~10,000 km) in 1961. This had a resolving power of 0.001 seconds of arc, which is approximately twice as good as the resolving power of the best optical telescope. This became known as a Very-Long Baseline Interferometer (VLBI).

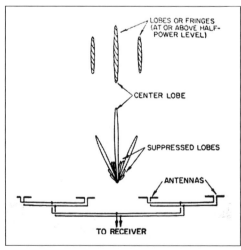

Fig 4.39: The Multi-Unit Interferometer

It was impossible to run this system in real-time, as it was impossible to connect via any reliable link. (At that time no satellites existed to link the two sites, today this is not a problem and satellites are regularly used for this purpose.) Consequently, an unusual technique was adopted.

The two signals were recorded on high quality videotape recorders and synchronised with atomic clocks. The two tapes were flown to a site such as Jodrell Bank, and the tapes played back together and adjusted so that they were correctly synchronised in time. The resulting signals were summed and digitised for analysis.

Using the formula above we can calculate what diameter antenna (or antenna separation in a two-element interferometer) is required for a particular resolving angle, or beamwidth.

$$\phi = \frac{57.3\lambda}{D},$$

where: ϕ is the 3dB beamwidth in degrees,
λ is the wavelength in metres, and
D is the diameter of the antenna in metres.

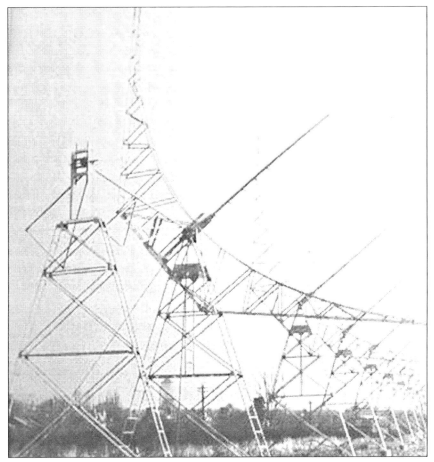

Fig 4.40: Cambridge University Interferometer by Martin Ryle, G3CY

For an antenna with a -3dB beamwidth of, say, 1° at 144MHz, we can find the antenna diameter. (At 144MHz, $\lambda = 2.083$m)

$$D = \frac{57.3\lambda}{\phi} = 119.37\text{m, or } 370\text{ft.}$$

Assuming an efficiency of 0.5 this gives an apparent gain of 43dBi or 40.85dBd. The difficulty of constructing a dish of over 100m is enormous; the difficulty of installing two small antennas at a separation of 120m is relatively trivial.

If the antenna beamwidth was, for example, 1°, the apparent angular size of a 'radio star' will appear to be the same. The human eye is considerably better at resolving a point source of light even without any optical magnification.

Apart from the impossibility of constructing an antenna of such enormous size as would be required, the problem of maintaining the antenna fixed on a radio source using a servo-controlled motor system would be extremely difficult. Even a gentle breeze would cause the dish to deform and hence the beam would shift enough to push it off-target. It is necessary to have some prior knowledge of the position of the source for this to be a viable technique. As radio telescopes, for a large percentage of their time, are used to explore unknown regions of the sky in order to identify new radio sources, having such a narrow beamwidth could be a severe disadvantage.

Multi-element Interferometer Systems

The interferometer technique is not limited to two antennas in close proximity. The UK MERLIN system (Multi-Element Radio-Linked Interferometer Network) uses up to seven antennas spread across the country to form a very high-resolution interferometer. The Australian radio observatory has up to 50 dish antennas linked in a complex multi-element system. Some of the dishes are on railway tracks so they can be moved to new positions to change the '3D picture' acquired. The largest example in use today is the Very Large Array (VLA) at Socorro, New Mexico, where 27 dishes of 25m in diameter are located on railway tracks. This allows a maximum separation of 36km between two dishes.

Fig 4.41: The Very Large Array (VLA) at Socorro, New Mexico. (Picture courtesy of NRAO, USA)

AN INTERESTING PROPOSAL

As has been previously noted that an antenna does not have 'gain' as such because it is a passive device. However, the concept of antenna gain due to confining the vertical and horizontal beamwidths gives an increase in transmitted or received signal over a single half-wave dipole. Now consider the case where the antenna has a low-noise amplifier mounted at the dipole feed-point.

Does the antenna now have more gain? The answer is yes, and this gain can be appreciable with modern low noise devices, perhaps consisting of two or more cascaded stages. The writer used this trick at an antenna gain-measuring contest for 2m antennas some years ago, where the maximum antenna size was limited to 2m boom-length by the rules. The reference antenna was a half-wave dipole and each antenna was measured with a precision measuring receiver and a constant power signal generator radiating into another dipole. A local school soccer field was used as the test site.

Consider the case where two such antennas are used in an interferometer system and separated by approximately 20 wavelengths. The angular resolution will be improved, as will the overall sensitivity of the receiver, by this technique. The lengths of coax connecting the two antennas will have little effect as the system noise figure is already kept to a low level by the masthead preamps. The power to each preamp is fed up the coax and the two coax cables connected to a zero degree power combiner.

Amateurs dedicated to meteor scatter originally employed this technique. A single transmit antenna is used and the two receive antennas are placed either side of the transmit antenna at right angles.

As the side lobe suppression of the antennas at right angles can be expected to be of the order of 30dB, and the distance between the transmitter and receiver antennas is large, the receiver can be run continuously without danger of burning out the preamps. The spaces between the slow Morse dots or dashes allow the operator to hear meteor reflections just like radar does. This is because the AGC in the transceiver when operated on CW has a fast attack and a fast decay.

For meteor scatter, the antennas all point to one part in the sky, usually with an elevation of 40° to 70° and, as this does not vary much, they can be fixed. The height of the receiver antennas can be as low as 5m if the 2m band is used. An experimental meteor scatter communications system, operated by the University of Natal, used such a system between the transmitter site in Pretoria and the receiving site in Kwa-Zulu Natal near Pietermaritzburg. The receiving antennas were mounted only 2m above the ground and elevated to 30°. This used a frequency just below the amateur 6m band.

In a later chapter, I will give construction details for a 50MHz meteor radar system for observation of meteor reflections.

DIPOLE ARRAYS

Many radio telescopes use a variety of dipole arrays to achieve high directivity and hence gain. The manner in which this is done is quite complex and can consist of hundreds or even thousands of dipoles fed with different phases to achieve beam steering. One of the popular varieties is the 'Mills Cross'. This was

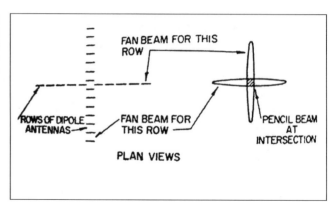

Fig 4.42: Mills Cross antenna shown in plan view, and the resulting two fan-shaped beams produced

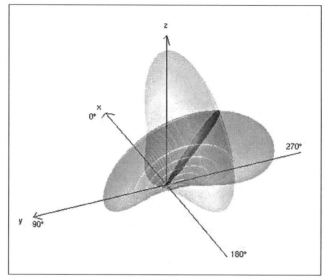

Fig 4.33: Dual fan-shaped beams produced by the Mills Cross array and the resulting pencil beam

invented by Dr B Y Mills and first used in Australia to make an 80MHz radio telescope. The beam of the Mills Cross can be steered over an angle of 80 degrees from the vertical; hence it can be tilted down to 10 degrees from the horizon.

Essentially the Mills Cross consists of two rows of dipoles which all point in the same direction. One set is normally aligned to run east - west and the second set is aligned to run north - south. A simplified diagram of the Mills Cross is shown in the diagram.

Each set of dipoles develops a fan-shaped beam that points vertically upwards when all the dipoles are fed in phase.

By varying the phases fed to the two sets of dipoles, the fan-shaped beam becomes a pencil beam. Typical half power beamwidths achieved are of the order of less than 1°. The greater the number of dipoles in each set, the greater the directivity becomes. The 80MHz Mills Cross erected near Sydney, Australia, had a beamwidth of about 0.1° (68dBi). Of course this type of array occupies a lot of land. Modern versions use arms of length 1.5km or more, so this type of array is not the sort of thing the average amateur is likely to construct.

Fig 4.44: **Mills Cross array at Molonglo, Australia. Each arm is 1500m in length**

However, the basic principle of the dipole array is quite simple and if, say, 16 dipoles are spaced the correct distance apart and fed with the correct phase relationship, it is possible to achieve a sizeable amount of gain - more than a 16-element Yagi.

Basic Dipole Phasing Technique

The polar plot of a half-wave dipole is shown in the diagram. The beam is bi-directional and radiates equally in two directions separated by an angle of 180°.

In order to confine the beam into one direction, we can place another dipole or reflector close to the dipole. The optimum spacing is approximately $\lambda/4$.

Consider the case where two identical half-wave dipoles are spaced $\lambda/4$ apart. To make the beam directional, the two dipoles need to be fed with the correct phases. If the two dipoles are connected to an open-wire feed-line which starts at dipole number one and connects to dipole number two, the feed-point of the second dipole needs to be reversed to get the correct phase relationship. This is because the spacing of two dipoles $\lambda/4$ apart introduces a 90° phase shift.

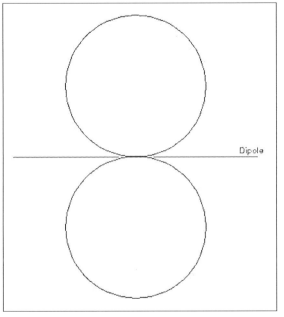

Fig 4.45: **Polar diagram of the half-wave dipole**

173

In practice, open-wire feed-line is by far the better option, rather than coax cable. The reason is that to make a transmission line with a 90° phase lead or lag requires the cable to be an exact number of quarter-wavelengths long. To produce a phase lead of 90° requires a $3\lambda/4$ cable. To produce a phase lag of 90° requires a cable length of $\lambda/4$. When using coax cable, we need to consider the velocity factor of the cable. Most amateurs know that cables such as RG-58 and RG-213 use a polyethylene dielectric that has a velocity factor of about 0.66. This means that to achieve an electrical quarter-wavelength, the cable ends up being only 66% of the physical quarter-wavelength. Hence, to try to connect two dipoles spaced a true quarter-wavelength apart is not possible if a quarter-wavelength of coax is used. The only way this scheme can work is if the piece of coax cable is made $5\lambda/4$ long. This is 1.25 wavelengths, and will introduce some additional loss. Although the phase might be correct, the amplitude of the signal at the second dipole will be slightly less than that of the first dipole, causing a slight loss in gain to occur. By using open-wire feed-line that has a velocity factor of about 0.98 means that only a slight reduction in the spacing of the two dipoles is required to make the wires reach between the feed-points.

Now assume we have many dipoles set out in a long line, each one a quarter-wavelength from its neighbour. To feed all the dipoles with the correct phases requires a lot of coax cable, each piece being electrically $5\lambda/4$ wavelengths long. Using open-wire lines simplifies the situation and reduces the transmission line losses considerably. All that is required is two parallel wires that run alongside the dipoles. The driving point needs to fitted with a balun to give the correct 180° phase difference between the two wires and a matching network to transform the total impedance to the feeder cable.

Going back to our original two dipoles - the phase of the second dipole needs to be reversed to get the correct phase relationship for maximum forward gain. Using an open-wire line, this can be done by simply reversing the feed to each successive dipole element. The case of just two dipoles is the basis of the W8JK beam, designed by Dr John Kraus. This is a popular two-element beam and features a gain of more than twice that of a single dipole, or about 6dB when correctly spaced and fed. It, however, has a two-lobed beam shape, the same as a

Fig 4.46: Multi-element dipole array with crossover feed-lines giving a bi-directional pattern

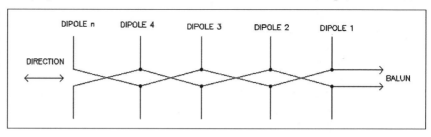

Fig 4.47: Multi-element dipole array without crossover feed-lines giving a unidirectional pattern

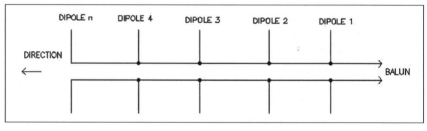

single dipole, which means the F/B is 0dB. By adding more dipole elements to the array, the directivity is increased. This is the basis of the Mills Cross array. To produce a unidirectional pattern, we need to change the array design. In the unidirectional array, all the dipoles are fed with a 90° phase difference between adjacent elements.

As you might have already worked out, the feed impedance of a two-element dipole array is going to be half that of a single dipole, or about 36Ω. If this is connected to a 75Ω feed-line, the VSWR will be 2:1. If we use a 50Ω feed-line the VSWR will be about 1.4:1. (If the dipoles are limited to six, the feed impedance will be approximately 12Ω which a 4:1 balun can transform back up to 50Ω).

The Yagi antenna behaves in almost the same manner, the current flowing in the driven element being parasitically coupled to adjacent elements, except that the currents flowing in the adjacent (unfed) elements are not of the same magnitude. As the elements get further away from the driven element, the current flowing drops off to a low level. This explains why adding more elements does not give the expected increase in gain. In the dipole array, the current in each dipole is substantially the same, and so it will deliver more gain for a given number of elements than a Yagi of the same element number.

With a distributed dipole array fed with open-wire, the theoretical gain increase, when the number of elements is doubled, is a factor of 2. In practice, it is slightly less but still worthwhile. The logical method is to keep on doubling the element count until the connection of more elements becomes too difficult. Therefore a dipole array would increase in size in the following logical manner 2, 4, 8, 16, 32 etc. The Mills Cross uses this method, except the large number of dipoles is split up into smaller groups, maybe as few as 64 dipoles to a group, and the individual groups are fed with separate feed-lines which can be adjusted in phase to steer the main beam.

Crossed-dipole Array

One of the common dipole arrays used is the crossed-dipole. This consists of two half wave radiators closely spaced but electrically isolated and mounted at 90°. The feed-points are connected by a section of coax cable that is an electrical length of 90°. This antenna, if mounted with the elements parallel to the ground, will produce a quasi-omnidirectional pattern with square corners. If the

Fig 4.48: Crossed-dipole array for 70 MHz

Fig 4.49: Crossed-dipole for the 4m band

array is mounted above a good reflecting screen made of either a solid metallic plate or a mesh reflector designed to represent a solid surface, the predominant radiation is upwards. Crossed-dipoles are popular horizontally-polarised antennas for such applications as beacons or mobile communication. Crossed-dipoles, like the Mills Cross, have a circular pattern when viewed in the vertical plane, as well as being omnidirectional when viewed in the azimuth plane.

In the pictures above, the array elements are connected with a $\lambda/4$ coax that is made from 75Ω cable (RG-59/U). The main feed-line is 50Ω coax with a W2DU coaxial sleeve balun made from ferrite sleeves.

Six-element Meteor Radar Array

One of the many antenna arrays that became popular in the early days of meteor radar is the type devised by Weiss in Adelaide, Australia. This array of six Yagis was based on the five-Yagi array originally used by Clegg at Jodrell Bank. The array of Yagis was fed with open-wire transmission lines of 470Ω impedance. The use of $\lambda/4$ metal insulators and stubs matched each pair of Yagi to the common feed-line. The beamwidth is $\pm3.5°$ in azimuth and $\pm4.5°$ in elevation.

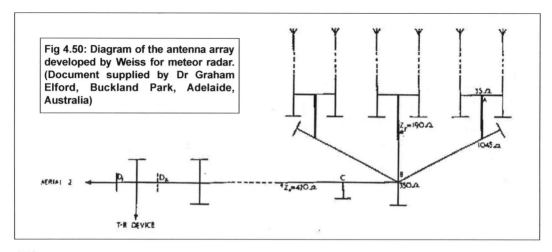

Fig 4.50: Diagram of the antenna array developed by Weiss for meteor radar. (Document supplied by Dr Graham Elford, Buckland Park, Adelaide, Australia)

Fig 4.51: Jodrell Bank VHF meteor Yagi array. (Photograph provided by Jodrell Bank Archives)

In Weiss's antenna he used two groups of six-element Yagis. The second set of Yagis is connected to the point marked 'Aerial 2' and is a copy of the first set of Yagis. A picture of a similar array used at Jodrell Bank is shown here.

REFERENCES

[1] Fishenden, R M, and Wiblin, E R, 1949, 'Design of Yagi Aerials', *Proc IEE* (London) part III, 96.

[2] Uda, S, March 1926, 'Wireless Beams of Short Electric Waves', *J IEE* (Japan), 452, pp273 - 82; ibid November 1927, 472, pp1209 - 18. Written in Japanese with English abstract.

[3] Yagi, H, June 1928, 'Beam Transmissions of Ultra-Short Waves', *Proc IRE*, 16, pp715 - 41.

[4] *Maxwell, M W, 1990, Reflections*, (ARRL), reprinted as *Reflections II* by WorldRadio.

[5] *Antenna Engineering Handbook*, McGraw-Hill, 1st edition, 1961.

[6] Kumar A, 'Reduce Cross-Polarization in Reflector-Type Antennas,' *Microwaves*, March 1978, pp48-51.

[7] Malowanchuk B W, VE4MA, 'VE4MA 3456MHz circular polarization feed horn', *North Texas Microwave Society Feedpoint*, Nov/Dec 1991.

[8] Turrin, R H, US Patent 3,413,631 'Dual Mode Antenna'.

[9] 'Dual Mode Small-Aperture Antennas', *IEEE Transactions on Antennas and Propagation*, AP-15, March 1967, pp. 307-308. (Reprinted in A W Love, *Electromagnetic Horn Antennas*, IEEE, 1976, pp. 214-215.)

[10] A British Post Office report in 1978 gave details of waveguide attenuation between 45 to 105GHz. In this the attenuation was measured as being <2dB/km on an experimental line of 250m in length. In amateur applications the greatest proportion of loss is probably due to imprecise conversions between waveguide to coaxial transitions.

[11]   *Crawford   Hill   VHF   Club   Notes,*   edited   by   W2IMU,
        http://www.ve1alq.com/W2IMU-K1RQG/w2imu_notes.html.
[12]   James G L and Greene K J, 'Effect of wall thickness on radiation from
        circular waveguides', *IEE Journal Electronic Letters*, 16 February 1978,
        Vol. 14 No.4 pp. 90 – 91.
[13]   Weinstein, L A, 'The theory of diffraction and the factorisation method',
        The Golem Press, Boulder, Colorado, 1969.
[14]   Haworth D P, McEwan N J and Watson P A, 'Effect of rain in the near
        field of an antenna', *IEE journal Electronic Letters*, 16 February 1978,
        Vol. 14, No. 4 pp. 94 – 96.
[15]   DC3NT in *VHF Communications* (edition 1979/3 pp 130-140).
[16]   *QST* (August 1972).
[17]   *The Antenna Handbook* (ARRL).

5

Early Low Noise Amplifiers

In this chapter:

- □ The noise performance of valves
- □ The tunnel diode amplifier
- □ Parametric amplifiers

- □ Strong signal handling factors
- □ Intermodulation performance
- □ Special techniques

T his chapter covers some of the historical aspects of radio astronomy receivers. A later chapter covers the more up-to-date devices now used.

As has been stated earlier, the first stages in a receiving system need to operate at a low noise figure for maximum sensitivity. Early receivers for radio telescopes used thermionic valves and consequently did not have very good noise figures by today's standards, but nevertheless, for the period, were considered state of the art.

THE NOISE PERFORMANCE OF VALVES

Noise induced in valves can be divided into several mechanisms.

Resistive Noise

This follows the kTB effect found in all resistive networks. Only when the resistive portion is reduced to absolute zero (-273.2°C) will the resistive noise cease. Thermionic valves operate at temperatures that are considerably higher than ambient, and so intuitively we can expect the valve to generate a considerable amount of kTB noise.

Shot Noise

Shot noise arises from the random movement of electrons. It gets the name as the noise it produces is similar to that which lead pellets (shot) make when falling on to a metal plate. In a valve, the main electron stream is from the cathode to the anode, and the slight perturbations in the current flow gives rise to shot noise.

There are two classifications of emission from the cathode of a valve, one being the saturated emission and the other the non-saturated emission. In the saturated emission case, and considering a simple diode with a tungsten filament, the temperature of the cathode directly controls the anode current. When at its permitted maximum, the anode will 'take up' all the electrons available from the cathode - there are no 'spares' drifting around. This mode is used by rectifier diodes.

Under the non-saturated emission condition, there is much more emission available than that which is being drawn by the anode. This gives rise to a space charge (reservoir of electrons) around the cathode, and this has the effect of smoothing out some of the fluctuations in anode current caused by the shot effect. Most valves are operated under space-charge-limited conditions, ie non-saturated emission, and the anode current fluctuations are much less than the saturated emission diode that is commonly used in rectifier diodes or noise generators.

Flicker Noise

This takes the form of large amplitude pulses, and is produced in most types of valves at low frequencies, being generally most troublesome in the range of 100Hz to 50kHz. The fact that these frequencies are in the audio spectrum does not mean that flicker noise has no effect at radio frequencies; quite the contrary, as the flicker noise causes amplitude modulation of the radio-frequency signal.

Partition Noise

In multi-grid valves, such as tetrodes and pentodes, the division of the total cathode current between the anode and the various other electrodes is subject to the fluctuations caused by shot effects. In turn, these additional electrodes will, by a process similar to modulation, cause increased random fluctuations in the anode current. From this, it will be appreciated that the fewer the electrodes in a valve, the better, and moreover, why it is that a triode will always have a lower noise figure than a pentode or other multi-electrode valve of similar characteristics.

Induced Grid Noise

The random fluctuations in the electron stream emitted from the cathode, in passing through the grid structure on the way to the anode, will induce a noise voltage on to the grid structure from the electrostatic charge carried by the electrons. The magnitude of this will depend on the frequency. At low and medium frequencies this noise will be self-neutralised as the charge on the electrons arriving at the grid will be cancelled by an equal and opposite charge on the electrons receding from the grid.

At high frequencies, the time taken for the electrons to pass through the grid structure will be an appreciable portion of the operating cycle, the fraction increasing with frequency. This transit time results in a difference in phase between the electrons approaching the grids and those receding from it. The result is that the cancellation is not perfect. As the frequency is raised the magnitude of the current induced in the grid also rises. This effect is normally termed transit time conductance and approximates to a resistive, high-temperature noise generator, the value of which is proportional to the square of the operating frequency. In order to assess the merit of a valve for receiver purposes, two parameters need to be considered. These are equivalent noise resistance and noise factor.

Equivalent Noise Resistance

This is defined as an ideal resistance which, when maintained at a normal operating temperature, would, if placed in the grid of a noiseless valve, produce anode current fluctuations equal to the shot and partition noise of an actual valve of similar characteristics. From this it can be seen that the lower the equivalent noise resistance, the better the valve will perform as a low-noise amplifier.

Noise Factor

Noise Factor, F, is a measure of how a signal passing through an amplifier is reduced in SNR. In a perfect amplifier device, the SNR at the output would be same as at that at the input. In other words, no additional noise is added to the signal. If the ideal case were achieved, the noise factor would be unity. In practice, all amplifiers add a small amount of noise to the signal, making the output SNR lower than the input SNR, and hence F will always be greater than 1.

Noise Factor, being a ratio, is a unitless measurement. Noise figure is the logarithmic value of the noise factor and is expressed in dB.

The measurement of noise factor (and hence noise figure) was conveniently carried out using a saturated noise diode as the noise source. A typical device commonly used was the A2027, although today it is obsolete. The noise performance of the A2027 was usable at frequencies up to 1GHz.

Transit Time Conductance And Induced Grid Noise

At high frequencies, the induced grid noise effects predominate, imposing a shunt conductance across the input circuit of the amplifier valve. In the case of the grounded-cathode circuit, the interaction of the valve and cathode lead inductance produces a conductance, Gc, placed across the amplifier input. To minimise the noise factor of an amplifier, the effects of the equivalent noise resistance and transit-time conductance, considered as noise sources, must be made as low as possible at the operating frequency.

Special Low Noise Valves - The Nuvistor

As the search for weaker radio noise sources gained pace, the radio astronomer had to find better thermionic valves than those currently available. One such breakthrough came from RCA when it released details of a new type of UHF valve. This was called the Nuvistor (an example is the 6CW4/8058) and promised exceptionally-low noise figures and high gain. Today, it is obsolete but, at the time, it served to bridge the gap between the then valves and the soon-to-come semiconductor devices.

THE TUNNEL DIODE AMPLIFIER

The tunnel diode amplifier was an idea that, at the time, seemed to be the perfect solution to low-noise amplification. A tunnel diode is a p-n junction with a high level of impurity doping. If the impurity content in a semiconductor is increased, the reverse voltage is reduced. If the impurity doping is made sufficiently high (2×10^{19} atoms cm^{-3} in Germanium), the reverse breakdown voltage is reduced to zero.

The degree of doping makes the tunnel diode an ordinary conductor in the reverse direction. It is said to make the semiconductor 'degenerate'. If degenerate p and n semiconductor materials are brought together under carefully-controlled conditions to make an extremely abrupt junction, of the order of 150Å (Ångstrom) in thickness, the forward characteristic is also affected. In effect, a negative-resistance junction occurs, so current can flow out of the junction and hence provide power and amplification gain. A typical tunnel diode can provide about 30dB of gain at 150MHz with, in theory, a noise factor of 1 (noise figure 0dB). In practice, the noise figure will be higher than this but will be typically 1.9dB at 400MHz with a gain of greater than 10dB. The tunnel diode shows shot noise (as does any resistance), but has a noise temperature of about 300K, which is far better than a valve and, at 400MHz in a practical circuit, exhibits a noise figure of approximately 3dB worst-case.

PARAMETRIC AMPLIFIERS

The parametric amplifier (paramp) utilises a similar technique to the tunnel diode. In this case, the amplification is performed by stored charge in a reactance, a variable capacitance diode (or varactor) diode. The varactor diode is used in a circuit that is driven by a high frequency power oscillator, referred to as the pump oscillator. The varactor diode stores the charge on one half cycle of the pump frequency and releases it on the other half cycle. As the source of the released charge is almost a pure reactance, with little or no resistive component, the circuit is theoretically noiseless. (Noise cannot be generated in a pure reactance, as it contains no resistive component.)

The signal to be amplified is connected from the antenna via a matching network (which needs to be of the highest possible Q to reduce resistive noise contribution) and the pump is injected into the diode via another matching network. The amplified signal is coupled out of the network via a selective matching network. Amplification of the order of 30dB or more is possible with a very low noise figure.

The stability of the network is heavily dependent on the amplitude of the pump oscillator and the gain is a function of the frequency ratio between the wanted signal and the pump signal. The greater the ratio of these two, the higher the gain and the lower the noise figure. A typical parametric amplifier for operation at 400MHz will require a pump oscillator capable of delivering 5 to 10mW at a frequency of about 10GHz.

On the face of it, parametric amplifiers are practically ideal for very low-noise amplification. The generation of the pump power is not difficult, as several low-power oscillator klystrons were available from wartime radar receivers with suitable power and frequency ranges. The frequency stability of the pump oscillator is not a concern and it has only to provide the correct amount of power. A design published in the *RSGB VHF Handbook* in the 1960s for a 432MHz LNA gave a noise figure of approximately 0.8dB and a gain of 25dB. This noise figure was only bettered in the late 1970s with a solid-state design, which only achieved 12dB of gain. The total cost of the paramp was less than the expensive microwave transistor used in the later design, as most of the components could be obtained on the surplus market after the war for next-to-nothing. In effect, the paramp was equal to a two-stage solid-state version for a fraction of the cost.

However, many engineers regard the parametric amplifier as a somewhat temperamental device because, if the antenna matching or the pump power vary, the amplifier (because it consists of a negative resistance with considerable power gain capabilities) can break into violent oscillation. This effect is also highly dependent on the operating temperature - if this varies over too wide a range, the amplifier can also oscillate.

Nevertheless, the parametric amplifier does provide a very low-noise amplifier with not too much equipment. A technique of maintaining a constant temperature and pump drive level is not too difficult to arrange, and the parametric amplifier, although by today's standards is something of a curiosity, is still in use in many radio telescopes around the world.

Once correctly set up, it will hold its tuning for long periods, the one disadvantage being that as it is inherently a narrow-band device and, if several radio astronomy frequencies are in use at a site, a paramp for each frequency will be required. This involves extra effort if frequent changes are required in the operating frequency.

Although, by today's standards, the noise figure is well short of what can be achieved by a modern solid-state device, the gain is still greater than that which a single modern solid-state device can achieve.

As an aside, the author some years ago made a parametric up-converter for 1296MHz. This was an experiment to see if the paramp could be used as the transmit converter for a solid-state 23cm transverter. The active device was a modified Microwave Modules 1296MHz varactor tripler. Normally, this used a 432MHz input, and multiplied the signal to 1296MHz with an efficiency of 60%. For an input power of 10W at 432MHz, an output power of 6W was normally possible. The input matching networks were modified to accept a 144MHz SSB drive signal of 1W and a 5W local oscillator (pump) of 1152MHz was used. Several extra idler circuits were required to notch out the various mixing products. Finally, an output of 2W at 1296MHz was achieved; this was a gain of 3dB. The intermodulation performance was excellent and far exceeded the normal solid-state designs then in use. The output power was sufficient to drive a single grounded-grid triode to about 30W output.

STRONG-SIGNAL HANDLING FACTORS

A secondary factor concerns the signal-handling capabilities. In a typical low-noise, high-gain amplifier, the ability to handle an interfering signal off-frequency with a considerable input level is highly dependent on the power being dissipated in the device. A low-noise solid-state device will not be drawing a large current and so the power handling will be poor. A device that has a reasonable anode, collector or drain current will be more able to tolerate a large interfering signal.

Inherently low-noise amplifiers have relatively poor large signal handling capabilities due to the lack of signal filtering before the active device (signal selectivity inevitably introduces losses which degrade the noise figure), and a large interfering signal removed from the operating frequency by, say, 10% can cause gain compression and desensing (desensitisation) to occur. The paramp, because it is being pumped by a large signal and has some inherent selectivity provided by the antenna input matching circuit, has a considerably better large-signal-handling capability, in a practical circuit some 20 to 30dB better than a bipolar transistor with a comparable noise figure.

So although a solid-state device can provide a better noise performance in the absence of an interfering signal, the paramp will continue working with a large interfering signal and produce a better noise figure than an equivalent solid-state device. Today, the margin is becoming very slight and modern GaAsFET and HEMT transistors can better the paramp in most applications.

INTERMODULATION PERFORMANCE

Allied to the strong signal-handling performance is the intermodulation performance of the low-noise amplifier. This is caused by the same mechanism that causes gain compression discussed above. When two or more signals are applied to an active device, the non-linearity inherent in the device operates on the signals in the same way as a mixer, generating new frequency products.

The effect is that if two signals, far-removed from the input signal and separated by a frequency which corresponds to either the input signal, the image frequency or the IF of the receiver, are of sufficient amplitude, they will generate spurious signals which fall in-band. These intermodulation products are extremely destructive and will cause severe interference to the wanted signal. The stage in the receiver that is the most susceptible to intermodulation generation is the receiver mixer. This needs to be a highly non-linear stage to act as an efficient mixer.

It is not difficult to appreciate that, as the radio telescope is usually trying to receive an extremely weak signal, it does not need a very large interfering signal to obliterate the wanted signal. In the real world, there are not just two strong out of band signals but possibly thousands that can have the correct frequency separation to cause intermodulation products. Admittedly, the radio telescope antenna can give an appreciable amount of suppression to these interfering signals by virtue of its frequency selectivity and directivity but, nevertheless, the problem exists.

As mentioned in the previous section, the strong signal-handling characteristics of the low-noise amplifier are of paramount importance. In an extreme case, it will be necessary either to include some filtering (with its inevitable loss) to notch out the interfering signal, or to use an amplifier with a superior signal-handling performance. Unfortunately, amplifiers with strong signal-handling are generally not of such low-noise performance.

SPECIAL TECHNIQUES

As the advances made in radio telescope receivers were always for greater sensitivity, it was obvious that the devices in use left much to be desired in terms of weak-signal performance. The noise factor is closely related to the ambient temperature of the LNA. Often we see the LNA fitted at the focal point of the radio telescope dish so as to eliminate as much as possible the losses in the coaxial cable between the antenna and the LNA. Thermal shielding is nearly always required. If one considers that the radio telescope dish is equally capable of focusing the sun's rays at the feed-point, it is possible for very high temperatures to exist. (This is used in third world countries for cooking - the solar cooker uses a polished parabola to focus the sun's rays onto a cooking pot.) Without special precautions, the LNA would most certainly be degraded if not totally destroyed.

As the ambient temperature plays a significant part in the noise performance it became normal to use some sort of refrigeration (cryogenics) to lower the temperature of the LNA. Cooling by liquid nitrogen or helium is commonly used for radio telescope front-end amplifiers and, whereas this raises some very special engineering problems, the end result is very beneficial. Reductions in the noise temperature by several orders of magnitude become possible and most radio telescopes today use some form of cryogenic cooling for the LNA and associated components. (See Fig 3.14 for more information)

Jodrell Bank, on the occasion of the last visit by the author in 2005, was still using liquid helium cooling for the feed-point LNAs and was expected to do so for the foreseeable future.

Today the LNAs used at Jodrell Bank are state-of-the-art HEMT devices (high-electron-mobility-transistors) which are capable of noise temperatures of 15K at up to 45GHz. This is achieved by liquid helium cooling.

Many of the special components required for a radio telescope are not 'off-the-shelf' items. This is not normally a huge problem, as the major radio telescopes throughout the world are operated by academic institutes who have allied departments that can design and manufacture one-off solutions as the need arises. The University of Manchester, which operates Jodrell Bank, is a typical academic institution that has some of the best brains in the world in the microwave semiconductor field. Many projects undertaken by degree students as part of their studies are to develop new components or techniques. Closely allied to this is the support of many large industrial concerns that fund research studies into new and emerging technologies. The spin-off is that these are available to Jodrell Bank, and other radio telescopes, when the need arises.

Many research students choose to stay on after graduating as technical experts working on newer and better equipment, funded by industrial bursaries. If you trace back to the start of the history of radio astronomy, you will note that the pioneers were nearly always engineers with a particular expertise in radio design or implementation and academics as a secondary factor. Funding for the newer developing technologies has often been lacking from governments, except where it was in the national interest. This often means military research often gets first bite at any surplus capital and the pure sciences only get the scraps left over.

6

Assembling a Station

In this chapter:

- ☐ Basic receiver components
- ☐ Choice of frequency band
- ☐ Some basic receiver requirements
- ☐ Permanent recording techniques
- ☐ Feed line considerations
- ☐ System budget calculations

- ☐ Antenna positioning co-ordinates
- ☐ North and South Pole correction
- ☐ A simple C-band radio telescope
- ☐ What you will be able to observe
- ☐ Radio object catalogues
- ☐ Besselian and Julian years
- ☐ Object naming system

I f the reader has digested the various sections prior to this, it should be relatively simple for him to work out what is required to assemble a station to meet his needs. Before we can specify the parameters of the various components, we need to decide on what the station is going to be capable of and the types of objects it will be able observe. It could be that an alternative use for the station is to be able to work EME, in which case the system could be designed to be dual-purpose with little extra expense.

BASIC RECEIVER COMPONENTS

In any station we will need certain items; these we can largely break down into logical parts.

- ● An antenna of some type,
- ● a low noise amplifier,
- ● a length of feeder between the antenna and the receiver,
- ● a receiver,
- ● some means of recording the received signals in a permanent way.

CHOICE OF FREQUENCY BAND

It is as well to be aware of the 'radio window' limits before choosing a suitable frequency band. The portion of spectrum from approximately 50m (6MHz) to about 1mm wavelength (300GHz) is the width of the window, therefore it would be pointless to attempt measurements on, say, the 80m band, as the radio waves would be unable to penetrate the ionosphere, except for limited periods during the night. The exact upper frequency is difficult to fix at present, but up to 1mm (300GHz) has been used and the likely upper limit may be higher than this.

The requirements for each type of system will rely heavily on certain factors. For example, if the desire is to receive meteor trail signals, we can state that the antenna needs to have a fairly broad beamwidth. Hence, it will be a limited-gain antenna. The frequency needs to be fairly low, not exceeding about 300MHz, and the receiver needs to have a high gain with a fairly narrow IF bandwidth.

Because the amateur VHF bands are somewhat harmonically-related and limited, we are left with three choices for the frequency band. Of these, 50MHz (6m) is a popular choice, but the antenna size is quite large for a reasonable amount of gain. The next available band, but not in all countries, is 70MHz (4m), where the antenna size is a little smaller. The final choice would be 144MHz (2m) where the antenna size is even smaller than the other two. In some countries, amateurs are able to use 220MHz, but this is starting to get a little high for reliable meteor-trail reflections.

The type of reflection to expect also varies with frequency. At 6m and 4m, the majority of reflections are from under-dense trails, and the reflections last for a fairly long time, often being many pings occurring one after another in rapid succession, and then they are often referred to as 'bursts'. The length of a burst can be several seconds under favourable conditions, allowing SSB operation. At 2m and above, the predominant mode is from over-dense trails and then the bursts are much shorter and more like discrete pings. At 70cm, the success rate drops to less than 10% of that of 2m, so 70cm is much more difficult in this respect.

The next factor depends very much on physical location. In an ideal situation, the station would be situated in a remote part of the countryside away from other dwellings, heavy industry and overhead power lines. Few amateurs are in this fortunate position. If you live in an urban environment with a lot of other properties close by, the level of man-made noise is likely to be high. Hence, 50MHz or 70MHz would not be as good a choice as 144 MHz.

In the author's case, the almost-ideal situation exists, at least on paper. The station is situated on top of a mountain in a rural environment with almost a 360-degree horizon.

When I was looking for a new property, this was an important point because of the amateur radio hobby. However, this is not ideal. Although the clear take-off in most directions is very good for VHF DX working, it is also a disadvantage due to other factors. It is a region of Kwa-Zulu Natal known as the 'Valley of a Thousand Hills'; there are more than 1000 hills in fact.

Nearby hills are densely populated with cell-phone, two-way radio, television and FM broadcasting stations. Because of this, the level of RF pollution is quite high and limits the ultimate sensitivity of any receiving system. Intermodulation products from the nearby TV and FM broadcast transmitters cause in-band signals to appear in 2m.

After the move from my previous location, it was found that the LNA used for the 2m EME station was suffering excessive overload because of the strong local signals. This required the design and construction of a new LNA that had better signal-handling and notch filters to eliminate the problem. However, the inter-modulation signals from the broadcast transmitters could not be eliminated, as they were generated in the transmitters.

For radio astronomy, we need a clear view of the sky, but not at the horizon in most cases. In order to screen the antenna from interfering signals, it is often beneficial to mount the antenna low down. In the case of meteor trail propagation, we need an antenna mounted only a few metres above ground level and pointed up at an angle of about 40° to 70°. It is necessary to be able to alter both the azimuth and elevation from time to time, but this can be a manual operation and, with the antenna close to the ground, is not difficult.

If the intention were to receive signals from deep-space objects (eg Sagittarius in the Milky Way), a higher frequency would be an advantage. The antenna would need to be fully steerable in azimuth and elevation, and a precise knowledge of where in the sky to point the antenna. This could be done with computer software or from celestial charts. In many cases, due to cloud, the sky will not be visible (occluded) so a visual sighting cannot be relied upon.

Suitable frequency bands would be 144, 432, 1296 or 2300MHz. The higher the frequency, the narrower beamwidth it is possible to achieve with a reasonably-sized antenna. Either a Yagi array or a small parabolic reflector would be suitable for 432MHz upwards. For 144MHz we are stuck with using Yagi-type antennas, due to size constraints. An advantage of a higher over a lower frequency is the sky-noise due to the atmosphere. At high frequencies it falls to low values and makes weak radio-star detection easier.

The disadvantage of choosing a higher band is the extra path-loss attenuation suffered by the higher frequencies, both from atmospheric attenuation and normal free-space loss, and the difficulty of obtaining a sufficiently-low system noise figure, due to limitations in available low-cost amplifier devices. A good compromise would be either 432 or 1296MHz, as here it is relatively easy to construct low-noise amplifiers with suitable noise figures. It should be obvious that we need to choose a portion of the band where no activity normally takes place; it is a bit pointless trying to listen on a repeater output channel or a beacon frequency!

SOME BASIC RECEIVER REQUIREMENTS

The receiver needs to be carefully considered. By placing a suitable low-noise amplifier at the antenna, we can effectively determine the system noise figure so the average commercial multi-mode transceiver is probably adequate. It may well be that you already have a VHF or UHF transceiver that covers the band selected. This is not always the best option as the IF filter fitted may be too narrow a bandwidth for the type of sensitivity we require. Often the best option is a low-noise crystal-controlled down-converter and a tunable HF receiver with a variety of IF filter bandwidths. It is easier to modify an HF receiver than a complex multi-mode VHF/UHF transceiver. FM transceivers are not at all suitable unless the IF can be replaced with an amplitude detector. In many cases, an older type communication receiver can be purchased at a reasonable cost. The modifications are not difficult to perform and many articles have appeared in various publications detailing these.

Another factor is that we do not want automatic gain control (AGC). The receiver gain needs to controlled manually for the best results. It is as well to appreciate that the signal level variation between not seeing a radio star and seeing a strong radio star will only be of the order of a few decibels at best. The task of detecting a weak source is difficult, even with sensitive equipment. If the AGC is continuously changing the receiver gain, because of small bursts of man-made noise, the chances of seeing a small increase in noise from a distant radio star are well-nigh impossible. The human ear is not a good detector for small changes in signal level. Often, even with a well-trained operator, it is difficult to detect less than a 3dB change in audio level. The detection needs to be done visually, with an oscilloscope, meter or a pen recorder. The receiver S-meter is virtually useless for this task, as it is far too insensitive to very small signal-level changes. In most receivers, when manual gain is selected, the S-meter ceases to work.

One technique used by meteor scatter operators to determine meteor activity, is to listen on the frequency of a distant beacon. At most times this will be either just on the noise floor or below it. To resolve a weak carrier requires a beat-frequency oscillator (BFO), which turns the received carrier into an audible tone. When a meteor trail occurs the beacon signal reflected off the trail is much stronger in level and the receiver outputs a strong audio tone while the trail is acting as a reflector. The duration of most meteor trail echoes is only a fraction of a second in most cases, and this causes the signal to sound like a 'ping'. By counting the number of pings occurring in a minute, you get a good idea of the meteor shower intensity. Low-intensity sporadic showers, which occur throughout the year, give ping rates of one or two in five minutes. In intense showers the pings can be as high as 1000 in a minute, making an almost continuous means of propagation which can be used for two-way contacts - meteor scatter (MS).

The receiver bandwidth required is the same as for CW; approximately 300Hz or narrower can be used. The narrower the IF the better, and often extra external signal processing will give good rewards. In the author's case, an external 40Hz bandwidth active audio filter is used which gives about 10dB SNR improvement on weak signals, such as EME.

PERMANENT RECORDING TECHNIQUES

For the sake of accurate data collection, some type of automated system is the best option. Whereas most people are capable of keeping notes of activity in a notebook, the events often occur too quickly for an accurate account to be made. It is a good idea to get into the habit of having a notebook as a rough record as sometimes systems crash and you would be left with no data in such an event.

In the case of meteor trail reflections one of the simplest and lowest cost, is a cassette recorder. If the receiver audio is fed into a cassette recorder, the pings can be recorded and later played back to count the number of pings in a given time. Today, with the advent of computers, another method is to use a .wav file to record the data via the computer's soundcard. This has the advantage that, with suitable software, the pings can also be displayed graphically at a later time for more precise analysis and time stamped by the computer real-time clock. Another benefit is that recordings can last for days and only rely on the size of disk storage available. The downside is that computers can generate broad-band interference, which can degrade the receiver performance.

If the resources run to it, a chart recorder is a nice way to capture data. It has the advantage that, with a long enough piece of paper, the records can represent several days with a slow enough rollout of the paper. (Professional chart recorders have a variable speed drive.) The chart recorder paper is normally incremented with divisions and vital information, such as start and stop times, and can be annotated manually. The author used this technique when studying signal enhancement at 1GHz during sunrise and sunset, to explore the path loss between two distant sites. At sunrise and sunset, the signals showed substantial improvements over the average recorded during the daytime or nighttime. This knowledge allowed the author to set a new personal best record during a contest on 23cm.

FEED-LINE CONSIDERATIONS

As with most sensitive receiving systems, you can never have too good a coax cable for the feed-line. In practice, as long as the masthead pre-amp is of sufficiently low noise figure and has adequate gain, more modest types of cable can be used. Often a type such as RG-213/U will suffice. It is preferable to use a type of cable that is double-shielded (RG-214/U) to prevent any interfering signals from leaking into the receiver. You will need to do the system calculations based on the cable length and predicted loss to establish if the cable loss is acceptable for the overall system

SYSTEM BUDGET CALCULATIONS

Some years ago, the author wrote a computer program in BASIC for calculating the path losses and overall SNR for EME (see box overleaf). Using this, and changing various system parameters, it was easy to see where the weak links in the proposed system were.

An Example of EME System Requirements

Using the software, consider a couple of system permutations to see where the weak points are. We will assume that 2m EME is the requirement and we have a 100W transmitter with average feed-line cable.

The basic system parameters are

Transmit power	100W
Transmit feed-line	1dB loss
Receive feed-line	1dB loss (the same cable is used for Tx and Rx)
Transmit antenna gain (dBd)	22dB - 4 x 16-element Yagis
Receive antenna gain (dBd)	22dB (the same antenna is used for Tx/Rx)
Antenna noise temperature	300K (pointed at a quiet part of the sky)
Receiver noise figure 3dB	(no masthead LNA)
Receiver bandwidth	300Hz (normal CW filter)

The calculated SNR is -10dB.

We will not hear our own echoes under these circumstances. The antenna is about the maximum we can erect, so we have to make alterations elsewhere. The sky temperature we have no control over and we have to accept this value. An obvious solution is to run more transmit power, this is an expensive option, but justifiable. So let us spend some money on a bigger amplifier to increase the transmit power to 400W and leave everything else the same.

The new calculated SNR ratio is -4.0dB (an improvement of 6dB, which is what you would expect with four times the power). This is a big improvement, but we will not expect to hear our own echoes. Stations such as W5UN will be able to hear us, and we will be able to hear them, because their system is making up for the deficiencies in ours.

Now let us invest in a masthead LNA with a 1dB noise figure and spend some more cash on some low-loss transmit feed-line with a 0.5dB loss. That is about all we can achieve in that department.

The new calculated SNR is -2.5dB. We are still a long way short of hearing our own echoes, but should be able to work some more of the bigger stations.

So we spend some more money and invest in an even bigger amplifier, this one is rated at 750W *[Be careful not to exceed the maximum power level permitted by your licence]*. This gets us down to -0.2dB. We might be lucky and hear our own echoes but it is doubtful.

We are scratching for fractions of a dB now. There is very little else to do but look at the receiver in more detail. One thing we can do cheaply is to use an external audio filter to reduce the system bandwidth. Let us build an external audio filter with a bandwidth of 40Hz. This probably costs the least of all we have spent so far. (The author's audio filter cost the equivalent of a few pounds Sterling to build).

The calculated SNR is now +8.9dB. So we should hear our own echoes if no Faraday rotation occurs. The outlay of very little cash on the audio filter gave us the 'biggest bang for our buck' - almost 10dB improvement.

Of course we could go on trying different system parameters, such as higher power, lower loss cable and a better noise figure, and see the possible improvements. The single most difficult part in a system such as this is the antenna gain. Four 16-element optimised long-Yagis are about the limit for a system like this for the average amateur. But you should not lose sight of the fact that the cheapest addition to the system, the home-brewed audio filter, bought us the biggest improvement. Doing these system calculations on a computer before we start spending money on hardware is the most economic option, we could have saved ourselves a lot of money!

As a comparison take a look at what W5UN is using for 2m EME using CW.

Antenna	~36dBd - 64 x 17-element long-Yagis
Feed-line	~0.5dB loss - large diameter hard-line
Transmit power	~1500W
Receiver Noise Figure	~0.6dB
System Bandwidth	~50Hz

Plugging these figures into the software yields an SNR of 41dB. This is about S7. When running SSB, W5UN's signals are ~25dB SNR, or about S4, because the filter in the receiver has a bandwidth of 2500Hz.

Now consider an EME system for 23cm using CW.

The system parameters listed below are quite practical and can be attained by the average amateur constructor. This is what the author is using.

Transmit power	250W - single water-cooled 2C39 - N6CA design
Antenna gain	32dBd - 4 x 26 element quad-loops - ~4m dish
Tx cable loss	0.5dB - 5/8in hard-line coax cable
Receiver Noise Figure	0.6dB - 0.45dB NF GaAsFET ant-mounted LNA
Antenna temperature	25K - cold sky
Receiver bandwidth	40Hz - audio filter

Listing for EME BASIC program

```
10   CLS : COLOR 11,1: CLS: PRINT : PRINT
20  PRINT' EME SYSTEM CALCULATOR':PRINT
30  PRINT' WRITTEN BY ZS5JF':PRINT:COLOR 14,1
40  PRINT' ASSUMED 1) ANTENNA IS COMMON TO TRANSMIT AND
     RECEIVE'
50  PRINT' 2) ANTENNA GAIN IS QUOTED IN dBd.'
60  PRINT:COLOR 15,1
70  INPUT' FREQUENCY (MHz) ';F
80  PL=-262-20*LOG(F/432)/LOG(10)
90  INPUT'     TRANSMIT     POWER     (WATTS)';PT    :
     PT=10*LOG(PT)/LOG(10)+30
100 INPUT' ANTENNA GAIN (dBd) ';G:GT = G + 2.14:GR = GT
110 INPUT' TRANSMIT FEED LINE LOSS (dB) ';LT
120 INPUT' RECEIVE FEED LINE LOSS (dB) ';LR : RL=10^(LR/10)
130 INPUT' ANTENNA NOISE TEMPERATURE -K ';TA
140 INPUT' RECEIVER NOISE FIGURE (dB) ';NF
150 NF=10^(NF/10) : TR=(NF-1)*290
160 INPUT' SYSTEM BANDWIDTH (HERTZ) ';B
170 TS=TA+(RL-1)*290+RL*TR        :        NP=10*LOG(1.38E-
     20*B*TS)/LOG(10)
180 SN=PT-LT+GT+PL+GR-NP : PRINT : PRINT:COLOR 14,1
190 PRINT ' SIGNAL TO NOISE RATIO = ';SN;' dB'
200 PRINT : PRINT:COLOR 11,1
210 PRINT ' CHANGE 1) FREQUENCY 4) TX FEED LINE 7) NOISE
     FIGURE '
220 PRINT ' 2) TX POWER 5) RX FEED LINE 8) BANDWIDTH '
230 PRINT ' 3) ANTENNA GAIN 6) ANTENNA TEMP '
240 INPUT 'ENTER OPTION (1-8, 0 TO END) ';Q$
250 IF Q$ = '0' THEN 440
260 IF Q$ = '1' THEN 340
270 IF Q$ = '2' THEN 350
280 IF Q$ = '3' THEN 370
290 IF Q$ = '4' THEN 380
300 IF Q$ = '5' THEN 390
310 IF Q$ = '6' THEN 400
320 IF Q$ = '7' THEN 410
330 IF Q$ = '8' THEN 430
340 INPUT    'FREQUENCY    (MHz)    ';F   :   PL=-262-
     20*LOG(F/432)/LOG(10): GOTO 170
350 PRINT:INPUT    'TRANSMIT    POWER    (WATTS)    ';PT:
     PT=10*LOG(PT)/LOG(10)+30
360 GOTO 170
370 INPUT 'ANTENNA GAIN (dBd) ';G: GT = G + 2.14: GOTO 170
380 INPUT 'TRANSMIT FEED LINE LOSS (dB) ';LT : GOTO 170
390 INPUT 'RECEIVE FEED LINE LOSS (dB) ';LR : RL=10^(LR/10)
     : GOTO 170
400 INPUT 'ANTENNA NOISE TEMPERATURE (KELVINS) ';TA : GOTO
     170
410 INPUT 'RECEIVER NOISE FIGURE (dB) ';NF:NF=10^(NF/10):
     TR=(NF-1)*290
420 GOTO 170
430 INPUT 'SYSTEM BANDWIDTH (HERTZ) ';B : GOTO 170
440 END
```

This gives an SNR of +14.5dB - an easy-to-copy signal with a fairly modest station. The biggest contributors are the lower sky temperature and the increased antenna gain possible in a small array. Despite the greater path loss, it is far easier to get reliable echoes at 23cm than at 2m. The cost of this system is about 1/3 of the 2m system and occupies a lot less area.

Finally let us look at an EME system for 432MHz.

Transmit power	400W - K2RIW amplifier with 2 x 4CX250B
Antenna gain	26dBd - 2 x 26 element quad-loops
Tx cable loss	0.5dB - 5/8in hard-line coax cable
Receiver Noise Figure	0.5dB - 0.4dB NF GaAsFET ant-mounted LNA
Antenna temperature	50K - cold sky
Receiver bandwidth	40Hz - audio filter

This system gives an SNR of +13dB and will therefore give reliable echoes.

Important note: The path loss assumed in the program is the average of the observed losses at 432MHz, and is optimum at perigee; at other times, the losses can be several decibels higher. For frequencies other than 432MHz, a correction factor is applied to give the approximate path loss. As the path loss can vary by several decibels, it is as well to include a few spare decibels in the system budget to ensure you are not disappointed. This program makes no allowance for Faraday rotation and its consequent extra losses. Similarly, the antenna efficiency is assumed to be 100%, which is not normally the case. It is prudent to subtract a few decibels from the antenna gain figure to allow for this.

Note: The receiver feed-line loss does not have to be the same as that of the transmit feed-line. If the system uses an antenna-mounted LNA, the feed-line loss is effectively zero and this value needs to be input. If the system does not use a masthead LNA, the receiver uses the same feed-line as the transmitter, and this value should be used. As this is a 'double-loss', it makes a significant difference to the results.

Fig 6.1: Diagram of the celestial co-ordinates

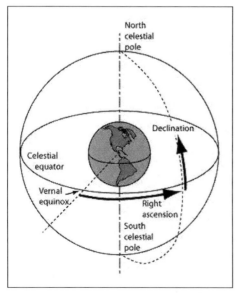

ANTENNA POSITIONING CO-ORDINATES

Amateurs are familiar with the azimuth and elevation system for antenna pointing, but are probably not too familiar with the system used in astronomy. Here a different system is used and the terminology is a little harder to grasp. The two main co-ordinates are known as Right Ascension (RA) and Declination (Dec). These are referred to an imaginary point on the equator known as the Vernal Equinox. Figure 6.1 shows the basic parameters. Right Ascension is measured in time from a common point and is given in hours, minutes and seconds. Declination is measured in degrees from the celestial equator. The celestial equator is a circle drawn around the Earth from the equator and at right angles to a line drawn through the North and South poles. The reference point for Right Ascension is the point on the celestial equator where a line drawn from it intersects the Earth and this point is the Vernal Equinox. The derivation of the Vernal Equinox is explained a little later.

A complication is that the Earth is inclined on its axis by an angle of approximately 23.5°. This can be shown by redrawing the celestial co-ordinates as illustrated in Fig 6.2. From this can be drawn the 'ecliptic plane' which is the apparent path traced by the Sun as the Earth rotates during a sidereal day. From this can be seen the derivation of the point on the celestial equator known as the vernal equinox, Commonly known as the 'First Point of Aries'. This is the point where the ecliptic plane and the celestial equator intersect. (On the Earth this is similar to the zero degree longitude reference point taken as being Greenwich).

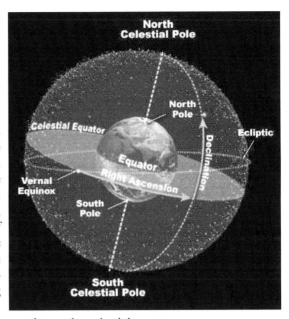

Fig 6.2: Celestial Sphere showing the Earth's inclination and the ecliptic plane

A measurement made from the vernal equinox point on the celestial equator eastwards is called Right Ascension; this is conventionally expressed in hours and minutes. On Earth the other coordinate is the latitude, measured along another meridian as degrees north or south of the equator. The equivalent measurement on the celestial sphere is Declination, measured again in degrees along another meridian north or south of the celestial equator. It is the convention to use + for objects North and - for objects South of the equator.

Right Ascension can also be expressed in degrees. Because the Earth takes ≈24 hours to complete one rotation one hour is equivalent to 15°. So, for example, a right ascension of 36° could be expressed as 1/10 of a day, ie 2.4 hours or a right ascension of 2hr 24minutes. Note that RA is always measured eastwards along the celestial equator from the vernal equinox reference point.

Converting from the RA and Declination can be done using standard formula but a much simpler method is to utilise one of the many software packages available at low cost. The writer uses a package called *Radio-Eyes* written by Jim Sky. This software gives a view of the sky from the observer's location and converts the RA and Dec of an object to antenna azimuth and elevation. (Because the view is looking down from space to the observer's location the azimuth is reversed to the normal. If you imagine looking up from the observer's point the azimuth is then correct).

When an object's apparent position in the sky is given in astronomical tables it is important to state the exact date and time this was established. This is called the 'epoch'. Hence, this epoch time is always appended to the data.

For example, Vega would be given as "5hr 24m, 38° 45'N (1950.00)". This means the exact time was 00h 00m on 1 January 1950, or it has been corrected back to that time.

(The alternative way of writing this would be "5hr 24m, +38° 45' (1950), because the declination is North and the 1950 assumes the first minute of 1 January 1950).

NORTH AND SOUTH POLE CORRECTION

Using a compass to find North or South involves an error due to the Earth's magnetic field variations. These not only vary depending where on the Earth's surface you are located but also vary on an annual basis. In South Africa it can be as much as 23° variation. So setting up an antenna azimuth North reference point can be difficult. A far better method is to use the 'True North' setting by determining where the Sun is at a particular time. Using software such as *Radio-Eyes* or a satellite-tracking program such as *Instant-Track* will give accuracy to within 0.5°. With a dish antenna, a simple method is to replace the feed with a plate with a small hole in the centre, so that it behaves like a pinhole camera. The antenna is then positioned so that the Sun is within the beam and the antenna adjusted so the spot of light is exactly at the centre of the dish. By running the software we can find the exact azimuth of the Sun at that time and hence calibrate the azimuth readout. Elevation is calibrated in the same manner.

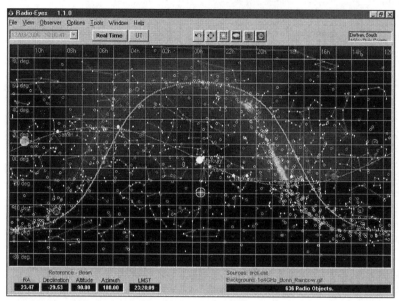

Fig 6.3: Screen dump of the *Radio-Eyes* software

The picture shown in Fig 6.3 is taken from the *Radio-Eyes* software. The Sun is in the middle of the screen and directly below is the position of the antenna, which is pointed to the zenith. The dotted line the Sun is on is the ecliptic plane. The moon is shown to the extreme left and is below the observer's horizon. The various constellations are also shown, but these can be turned off for easier

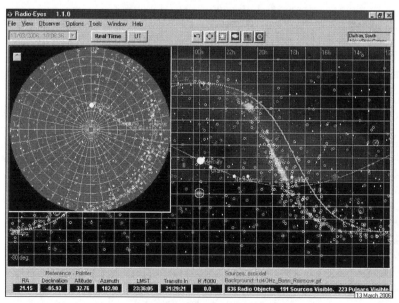

Fig 6.4: *Radio-Eyes* screen with superimposed 'Dome-View'

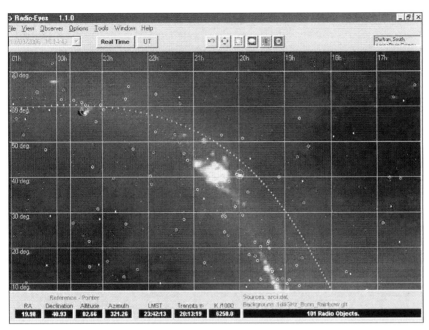

Fig 6.5: Close up of Cygnus-A (circled)

viewing. The bright band on the right hand side is the plane of the Milky Way and shows the hydrogen concentration. The inverted U shape is the visual horizon of the solar system as seen from the observer's location.

Another feature of the software is the 'Dome-View' which is a view looking down on the observer's location. This is shown in Fig 6.4. The centre of the dome is the observer's location. The Sun is seen running along the ecliptic plane.

By zooming in we can select one of the radio stars. In Fig 6.5 we have zoomed in on Cygnus-A. This is about 2.7° above the observer's horizon and at an

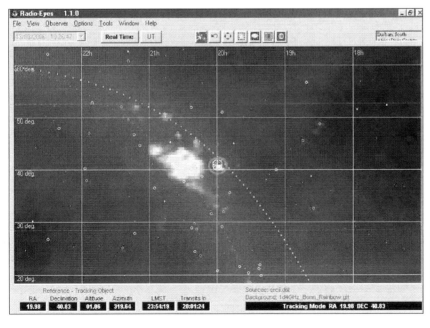

Fig 6.6: Radio Eyes software with antenna beam of 3 tracking Cygnus-A. The larger object to the left is Cygnus-X and 3C416.2

azimuth of 321°, the dotted line close to Cygnus-A is the observer's horizon. Currently *Radio-Eyes* is not able to control azimuth and elevation drives but this feature is being addressed and it is expected that it will soon be available. Hence it will become fully automatic tracking software. The latest version released in 2010 now includes fully automated control of popular rotators and elevators but requires a suitable interface between the computer and the rotator.

Fig 6.6 shows the antenna beam placed on a radio star and the tracking switched on.

A SIMPLE C-BAND RADIO TELESCOPE

Many amateurs are unable to erect a large parabolic antenna in their property but can manage something smaller. Today there are a large number of redundant C-band TVRO dishes (television receive only) as satellite television reception has mostly migrated to the 11GHz region. The system that follows was constructed by two amateurs, one in Spain and the other in Belgium and shows what can be done for little outlay in money.

The story began in about 1999 when Miguel A Vallejo, EA4EOZ, near Madrid was experimenting with satellite television tuners and the associated LNB (low noise block) containing the LNA, mixer and LO. The LNB was an Arabsat model that was used without any modification; it has about 800MHz bandwidth.

EA4EOZ originally used a Philips television tuner as the main receiver and took the AGC signal via an A/D converter to drive a computer that then plotted the signal strength. This was a transit telescope system and whilst EA4EOZ could detect the Sun that was about the limit as the system was not sensitive enough for weaker objects. During the experiments EA4EOZ happened to con-

tact another amateur, Jean Marie Polard, ON4EU who was also thinking along the same lines. Miguel was unable to erect a dish permanently in his property but ON4EU had a large garden and offered to host the radio telescope.

Subsequently after many further experiments EA4EOZ learnt about the 'Satellite Finder' which drove a signal strength meter from the LNB for setting up a television satellite dish. This little add-on has a wide bandwidth sensitive receiver built in that normally drives the S-meter and it was able to detect quite weak signals. Following further experiments and modifications they had a working system that was shipped to Belgium for installation, ON4EU meanwhile installed the dish and LNB.

Fig 6.7: ON4EU with the 1.5m C-band dish transit telescope

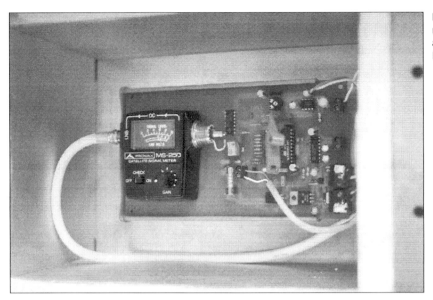

Fig 6.8: The C-band receiver (Sat-Finder) and A/D converter board

The one limitation of such a simple system is that it cannot tolerate being pointed at the equatorial plane, the so-called Clarke Belt, where all the television satellites orbit and which can cause interfering signals to overload the receiver, as some TVRO systems still use C-band. However, this still leaves a lot of sky to observe.

The back-end receiver is contained in a housing lined with polystyrene foam in an attempt to reduce the ambient temperature variations from affecting the baseline gain variations.

For a small diameter dish it would be beneficial to work on a higher frequency to obtain better resolution (narrower beamwidth) but experiments with 11-GHz LNBs as used for TVRO were not successful due to interference, so about 4-GHz was chosen instead. Many redundant LNBs are on the second hand market and can be bought for little outlay; they are also simple to use.

The results obtained with such a simple system are quite remarkable and some of the plots EA4EOZ and ON4EU sent me are reproduced here. (Note: ON4EU is now F5VLB.)

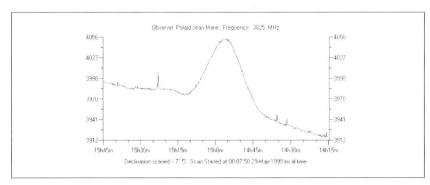

Fig 6.9: This is an early plot of the moon transit at ON4EU (see also the picture opposite)

Fig 6.10: Another early plot of the moon transit at ON4EU

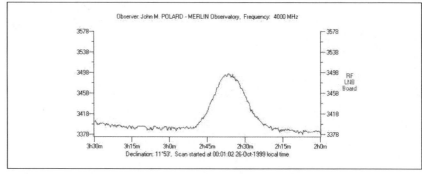

Fig 6.11: A plot of the moon and the various objects around the galactic plane

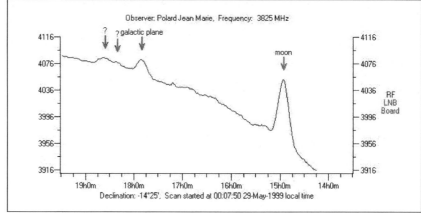

Fig 6.12: Another plot around the galactic plane

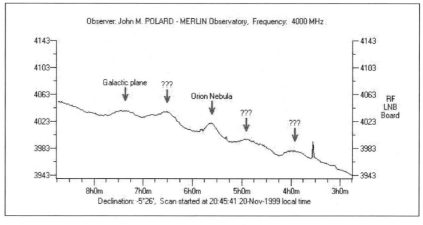

One of the problems discovered was a variation in gain with ambient temperature, which caused a variation in the baseline. This is particularly a problem in the summer, as at high ambient temperatures the LNB has a higher noise figure and a slightly lower gain. In winter, at low ambient temperatures, the LNB gain is higher and the noise figure is slightly better, but the problem can be ignored for the stronger sources. (In TVRO duty this gain variation is taken care of by the television AGC, but for radio astronomy this isn't practical).

Experiments with temperature sensors to adjust the gain to compensate produced somewhat better results but caused the baseline to exhibit steps. In the end it was disabled. With the antenna pointing at the Sun the Sat-Finder gain had to be reduced to prevent over-driving the A/D converter, but for weaker sources the gain could be run at maximum. Another problem was interference from altimeters on aircraft flying through the antenna beam; the spike on the last plot is probably this type of interference. The system was modified to allow the operator to hear the pulses on a loudspeaker so they could be identified.

Of interest is that when EA4EOZ contacted me I mentioned the book by William Lonc [1]. In this a similar set up was shown but EA4EOZ was not aware of this until I mentioned it.

WHAT YOU WILL BE ABLE TO OBSERVE

What is within your field of view will depend on whereabouts in the world you live. Here in South Africa we have a very limited observing time of objects such as Cass-A and Cygnus-A. Cass-A only shows itself above the horizon for a short time and at best attains about 1.5 degrees elevation at due North when it transits. This makes it difficult to confirm the object is in the antenna beam as the man-made background noise is high at low elevations. Cygnus-A is a little better as it

Fig 6.13: The elevation system used is simple using a jackscrew popular with TVRO dishes. The mount is a simple wooden framework, not sure if the bird feeder adds anything to the gain!

rises to about 19.5 degrees above the horizon when it transits. Objects such as Sag-A and Vela-X are much easier to see. Sag-A daily transits through due North at 89.1° elevation and Vela-X at 73.9° elevation due South at Durban. These are our two 'calibration sources' we use at the Durban University Indlebe radio telescope to check the system is performing as expected (the current transit telescope has a limited elevation angle and can only vary the elevation by about 30° either side of zenith). Sag-A is a huge signal, about 20dB above the cold sky noise value. (Durban is about 30° south of the equator and about 30° east of the Greenwich meridian line).

If you live in the Northern Hemisphere then Cass-A and Cygnus-A will rise higher in the sky and Sag-A and Vela-X may be below your horizon.

RADIO OBJECT CATALOGUES

From the beginning of the science of radio astronomy many different new objects were discovered, many could not initially be associated with visible stars due the inter-stellar dust obscuring them from earth. As new objects were discovered, a need arose to give their position in a useful coordinate system. It was logical to adopt the method used by optical astronomers of defining the position by Right Ascension and Declination, so they could be understood without ambiguity. One of the pioneers in this field was the Cambridge Observatory and they began to publish details of objects discovered in the *Cambridge Catalogue*. The first catalogue was known as 1C.

The 1C catalogue listed about 50 radio sources, detected at 3.7m (81.5MHz) with a fixed meridian interferometer. According to researchers at the Special Astrophysical Observatory, most of the sources from 1C were later recognised to be the effect of confusion; ie they were not real objects.

The survey was produced using the Long Michelson Interferometer at the Old Rifle Range in Cambridge in 1950. This device operated primarily at a wavelength of 3.7 metres, and was operated using Dr Martin Ryle's phase switching technique. F Graham Smith also used the interferometer to measure the electron density in the ionosphere. The catalogue from this survey is only informally known as the 1C catalogue.

The *Second Cambridge Catalogue of Radio Sources* (2C) was published in 1955 by John R Shakeshaft and colleagues. It comprised a list of 1936 sources between declination -38° and +83°, giving their right ascension and declination, both in '1950.0 co-ordinates' (see later) and flux density. The observations were also made with the Cambridge Interferometer, at 81.5MHz.

The *Third Cambridge Catalogue of Radio Sources* (3C) is an astronomical catalogue of celestial radio sources detected originally at 159 MHz, and subsequently at 178MHz. It was published in 1959 by members of the Radio Astronomy Group of the University of Cambridge. References to entries in this catalogue in the scientific literature use the prefix 3C followed by the entry number, with a space, eg 3C 273. The catalogue was produced using the Cambridge Interferometer on the west side of Cambridge. The interferometer had previously been used for the 2C survey, published in 1955.

The *Fourth Cambridge Survey* (4C) is an astronomical catalogue of celestial radio sources as measured at 178MHz using the 4C Array. It was published in two parts, in 1965 (for declinations +20° to +40°) and 1967 (declinations -7° to

+20° and +40° to +80°), by the Radio Astronomy Group of the University of Cambridge. References to entries in this catalogue use the prefix 4C followed by the declination in degrees, followed by a period, and then followed by the source number on that declination strip, eg 4C-06.23 or 4C+20.06. The 4C Array, which used the technique of aperture synthesis, could reliably position sources of less than 2 Jy, to within about 0.35 arc-min in right ascension and 2.5 arc-min in declination.

The *5C Survey of Radio Sources* (5C) is an astronomical catalogue of celestial radio sources as measured at 408MHz and 1407MHz. The Radio Astronomy Group of the University of Cambridge published it in a number of parts between 1975 and 1995. The One-Mile Telescope was used to produce this catalogue and it had an angular resolutions of 80 arc-seconds and 23 arc-seconds at 408MHz and 1407MHz respectively, and catalogued radio sources as faint as 2 milli-Jy, considerably fainter than any previously catalogued radio source.

References to entries in this catalogue use the prefix 5C followed by the catalogue part, "." and then the entry number, with no space, eg 5C12.311 is the 311th entry in part 12 of the 5C catalogue.

The most recent Cambridge Catalogue is 9C. These catalogues, although very precise, have to be available so the observer can look up the exact position in right ascension and declination. The later 'J and B prefixed' objects, although less exact, at least give an indication of the objects position. If more precise data were needed then a catalogue could be obtained.

BESSELIAN YEAR

Objects prefixed B are based on the Besselian year calculation, the most recent epoch time being January 1st 1950 (designated as '1950.0'). A Besselian year is named after the German mathematician and astronomer Friedrich Wilhelm Bessel (1784 - 1846). He also derived the Bessel Functions and in 1838 made the first accurate measurement of the distance of a star.

The beginning of a Besselian year is the moment at which the mean longitude of the Sun, including the effect of aberration and measured from the mean equinox of the date, is exactly 280°. This moment falls near the beginning of the corresponding Gregorian year. Unfortunately, the orbit of the Earth around the Sun is not entirely fixed, so the length of the Besselian year according to this definition is not constant. This makes Besselian years somewhat difficult to work with.

The prefix B is followed by the right ascension value and the declination, for example Pulsar B0904-74 is at right ascension 9 hours and 4 minutes and declination -74°. For the early discoveries the antenna beamwidth was relatively wide so a more precise method was not possible or necessary. With the advent of interferometers more exact positions could be obtained, but for most it is academic, as the narrow beamwidth cannot normally be obtained with a single antenna.

JULIAN YEAR

Objects prefixed by J are based on the Julian year method and the most recent epoch time as a reference is January 1st 2000. (Julius Caesar changed the world's calendar in 46 BC to change the time for one year to 365.25 days).

OBJECT NAMING SYSTEM

Many objects have but a single designation, but some have two or more designations. For example, Cygnus-A is known as 3C 405 and is object number 405 in the third Cambridge catalogue. Cassiopeia-A is 3C 461. Centaurus-A has three different designations, CTA 59, NGC 5128 and J1325-4303.

NGC is short for *New General Catalogue* and it is object number 5128, and the J prefix denotes the Julian year method, based on the January 2000 epoch time. The numbers that follow the J are the right ascension in hours and minutes and the declination in degrees and minutes (the seconds are not used). In the case of Centaurus-A the minus sign preceding the declination number means that it lies in the southern part of the sky when viewed from the celestial equator. If the number were positive, denoted by '+' before the number, it is in the northern part.

There is another common naming system based on the Messier catalogue of 1771. This is for visible objects. This catalogue does not include stars but galaxies, constellations and other objects such as nebulae and supernovas. For example, the first object in the catalogue, M1, is the Crab Nebula (Taurus-A, also known as 3C 144, CTA 36 at RA 05.34.30 and Dec +22.00.57).

The word nebula means a mist or misty patch, and was at one time used to refer to any such object.

Fig 6.14: 3C 144 The Crab Nebula (Taurus-A) [Hubble space telescope image]

This strong radio source is the result of a supernova explosion that occurred in July 1054 AD and observed by Chinese astronomers. During the month following the sighting of the initial explosion, many celestial observers saw the "new star" shine as brightly as Venus. Through an optical telescope the Crab Nebula appears as a knot of twisted filaments of hydrogen gas. Though its optical brightness has faded greatly, The Crab still shines brightly at radio and x-ray frequencies.

Taurus-A is home to a pulsar with a pulse rate of about 30 times per second. This pulsar is the spinning neutron star left behind by the supernova of 1054 AD. The Crab pulsar is rather weak, and was first detected by the large (now defunct) 300-foot NRAO telescope in Green Bank, West Virginia, USA and by the Arecibo dish in Puerto Rico in 1968.

The Crab pulsar is travelling through the cloud of nebular gas that surrounds it at about 125km/s. Wisps of gas can be observed ahead of the pulsar suggesting a shock wave effect. The energy radiated by the Crab Nebula originates with the pulsar itself. The rotating magnetic field produced by the rapidly spinning neutron star imparts photons into the nebula by the synchrotron mechanism.

There is another cataloguing system for supernovas, prefixed by SN and the four-digit number that follows is the year it was first discovered. Hence, supernova SN1986 was discovered in 1986. (If more than one supernova were detected in a particular year the second would be suffixed "A", the third "B" etc).

Optical astronomy was originally known as Astrology, as the ancient observers used the changing positions of the constellations in the night sky as a precursor or indicator of an event that would happen later. Astrology today is regarded as a means of predicting future events, but the "ology" part is in fact the correct name for a type of science, eg archaeology, biology etc.

The use of alphabetical letters after an object, such as Taurus-A, is a convention used by optical astronomers. The letters used are based on the Greek alphabet, Alpha, Beta, Gamma etc. Where there are several stars closely associated in an object the brightest star is given the suffix A, the next brightest B etc. The same convention is used by radio astronomers; except for "brightness" it implies the strongest radio source in the associated group. It is incorrect to assume that the brightest optical star is also the strongest radio source. Some of the very strong radio stars are not visible optically because of the dense dust clouds obscuring them to an observer on Earth.

The Horsehead Nebula (also known as Barnard 33 in bright nebula IC 434) is a dark nebula in the constellation Orion. The nebula is located just below (to the south of) Alnitak, the star farthest left on Orion's Belt, and is part of the much larger Orion Molecular Cloud Complex. It is approximately 1500 light years from Earth. It is one of the most identifiable nebulae because of the shape of its swirling cloud of dark dust and gases, which is similar to that of a horse's head. The shape was first noticed in 1888 by Williamina Fleming on photographic plate B2312 taken at the Harvard College Observatory.

The red glow originates from hydrogen gas predominantly behind the nebula, ionised by the nearby bright star Sigma Orionis. The darkness of the Horsehead is caused mostly by thick dust, although the lower part of the Horsehead's neck casts a shadow to the left. Streams of gas leaving the nebula are funnelled by a

Fig 6.15: The Horsehead Nebula [Hubble space telescope image]

strong magnetic field. Bright spots in the Horsehead Nebula's base are young stars just in the process of forming.

Johann Bayer used the Greek alphabet around the year 1600 to name the brighter stars. The basic rule was to name them in order of brightness, but the rule is more often than not violated, the designations commonly also depending on the position of the stars within their constellations and other factors known only to Bayer. To the Greek letter is appended the Latin possessive form of the constellation name, Vega, the Alpha star of Lyra, becoming Alpha Lyrae, and so on.

Bayer is most famous for his star atlas *Uranometria*, published in 1603, which was the first atlas to cover the entire celestial sphere. It introduced a new system of star designation, which has become known as the Bayer designation. It introduced twelve new constellations to fill in the far south of the sky, which

Johann Bayer (1572 - 1625) was a German lawyer and uranographer (celestial cartographer). He was born in Rain, Bavaria in 1572. Bayer began his study of philosophy in Ingolstadt in 1592, and moved later to Augsburg to begin work as a lawyer. He grew interested in astronomy during his time in Augsburg. He ultimately became legal advisor to the Augsburg city council in 1612 and died on 7 March, 1625.

was unknown to ancient Greece and Rome. The crater Bayer on the Moon is named after him.

The stars that appear as a group in common constellations are in many cases at vastly different distances from an observer on earth. This is purely an optical illusion. If we were able to view the constellation from a different point in space the pattern they form would appear to be very different.

Another fact to be aware of is that an object outside of our solar system, such as Sagittarius-A, will transit at a fixed location 3 minutes and 56 seconds earlier each day. For the object to transit at exactly the same time again it takes a complete year for this to occur, since the Earth is orbiting the Sun and completes an orbit in an Earth year of 365.25 days (3m 56s x 365.25 = 24 hours).

During its annual orbit of the Sun, the Earth travels slightly less than 1-billion km (9.42×10^8km) and is moving at a speed of just over 100,000 km/hr (about 30km/s).

Our nearest 'star' is the Sun, a rather insignificant object when compared to other stars, with about half its life run. In about 4.5 billion years it will have used up its reserves and it will become a 'red-dwarf', it is too small to become a supernova. The closest 'real star' is regarded as being Proxima Centauri, which is about 4.2 light-years from Earth.

If the Sun were to extinguish now it would be about 8 minutes before we saw the lights go out, for Proxima Centauri it would take about 4.2 years for the same result. Many stars are thousands if not millions or billions of light-years distant. The optical signals as well as the radio signals we detect on Earth are what happened that number of light-years ago. This is known as the 'look-back time' as we are looking at history, not present day events.

Today the furthest distance we can look-back is about 12.7 billion light-years, as anything after that is now receding away from Earth at close to the speed of light.

Astronomers do not like the use of light-years as a measurement of distance, rather they use the measurement unit of 'parsecs' where a parsec is 3.26 light-years. The name parsec is from the measurement of parallax angle of 1-arc second, which an object would subtend at a distance of 1AU.

They also prefer to use the 'Astronomical Unit' (AU) which is the distance between Earth and the Sun, being approximately 150 million km, as a gauge of distances between objects. Mercury, the closest object to the Sun in our solar system, orbits the Sun at an average distance of about 58 million km, hence this is ≈0.4AU. Being so close to the Sun, Mercury has a surface temperature of 400°C. Earth is the "third rock from the Sun".

REFERENCES

[1]   *Radio Astronomy Projects* 3rd Edition by William Lonc. Radio-Sky #B062. http://www.radiosky.com/booksra.html.

7

50MHz Meteor Radar System

T he author is involved with the study of the Southern Hemisphere sporadic meteor showers. These occur randomly throughout the year at low rates. In order to study them, it was necessary to modify some of the station equipment and build some new receiving equipment. The initial study is being carried out at 6m; at a later date it will be extended to 4m and 2m. The intention is eventually to have two systems running in parallel to assess the reflections on two widely-separated frequencies and try to correlate the results.

Amongst the author's old equipment was a dual-band linear amplifier for 2m and 6m built many years back that uses two QQVO6-40 valves. This was one of many 'doppelganger' types made by local amateurs to reduce the bench space and power supply requirements when operating on the lower VHF bands. The amplifier can operate on either 6m or 2m using a common power supply, but only one band at a time. This was mothballed when better equipment was constructed. The 6m section of the amplifier uses a QQVO3-10 as a driver stage, as the home brew 6m solid-state transverter used at the time produced only approximately 250mW. The fully-saturated output power is about 250W. This amplifier uses the author's screen and grid solid-state stabilisers published some years ago. With minor modifications, the 6m amplifier will also work on 70MHz. The author's newer 144MHz EME amplifier uses a pair of 4CX250Bs, which are capable of 1500W output, if needed.

As it wasn't necessary to build everything from scratch this saved a lot of time and effort.

The system calculations were performed with an RF simulation software package, where the gain, noise figure and intercept point for each stage are entered to identify the critical areas in the design. Having settled on a practical receiver and transmitter line-up, design and construction began of the new items. These were:

- Transmitter oscillator and switching circuits
- Transmitter control and pulse-shaping circuits
- Receiver front end and mixer
- IF amplifier, filter stages and detector
- Post-detection filtering and display driver
- Antennas
- LNA for receive antennas

LOW POWER TRANSMITTER STAGES

The transmitter uses valves for all the stages. A solid-state design is possible but involves a lot more effort. As the writer had a good stock of valves it was decided to use these. Another factor favouring valves is that high gain and high power are easy to obtain. The transmitter consists of just three valves to develop an output power of over 300W PEP. A further valve is used in the modulator stage.

The biggest problem with a design such as this is that the transmitter oscillator has to run all the time, it is impractical to switch off the oscillator during the receiving period. If the oscillator runs at the final output frequency, it will cause an interfering signal that the receiver will pick up and see as a constant signal. Therefore, it was decided to use a low-frequency crystal oscillator that was then multiplied to the final frequency. In the 6m version, a crystal at 0.25 of the final frequency is used. The oscillator (exciter) stages are built on a chassis separate from the main power amplifier and are contained in a well-shielded box to prevent radiation of interfering signals.

The oscillator consists of a Colpitts oscillator using a fundamental frequency crystal with a 30pF load capacitance. The exact frequency will depend on the final frequency required. In the author's system, a 12.675MHz crystal was ordered. The valve used is a 12AT7, which is a twin-triode. Other valves are also suitable, E88CC, 6J6 etc, or even two separate triode or pentodes. The anode circuit of the oscillator has a tuned circuit resonant at twice the crystal frequency (~25MHz). This is then loosely coupled via a 22pF capacitor to the grid of the multiplier half of the valve. The voltage developed across the multiplier grid is approximately 2 to 3Vp-p. This is adequate to drive the multiplier to full output. The multiplier also has a resonant anode circuit that is tuned to the output frequency of 50MHz. The two stages act as a doubler-doubler circuit with good filtering of unwanted oscillator products. The 12MHz products are more than 60dB below the carrier and are further attenuated in the following power amplifier stages to more than 80dB. A possible option is to use a crystal at 1/3 of the final frequency; the oscillator anode circuit would then be resonant at the crystal frequency, and the multiplier would then act as a tripler stage. The output from the multiplier is link coupled to 50Ω and fed via a coaxial cable to the power amplifier chassis. The anode supply of the oscillator is derived from the main 300V supply with two 75V, 1W Zener diodes connected in series to give a stable 150V supply for good frequency stability.

The multiplier stage is fed with a pulsed HT supply that is provided by the modulator stages. This voltage is only applied when the transmitter is required to provide an output, hence the drive to the following stages is on only when a pulse is required.

If the multiplier stage was fed with a continuous supply a problem arises. This is the generation of a strong carrier during the receive period which would effectively mask any echoes.

If the driver stage only has a limited attenuation when its screen supply is turned off, there would be a small constant signal driving the final stage. This causes a 'spacer carrier' which is very difficult to get rid of, and would block the receiver.

In practice, the final stage acting as a pulse modulator has an attenuation range of approximately 30dB because of capacitive feed-through in the valve. By switching off the multiplier and driver during the receiving period, the attenuation increases to the order of about 80dB. With adequate attenuation between the transmitter and receiver, this is acceptable.

When viewed on the spectrum analyser, the carrier suppression during receiving periods is over 90dB. The multiplier stage gives approximately 30dB suppression; the driver also gives the same sort of suppression, and the PA supplies about 20dB of suppression.

Because valves are used with high-Q tuned circuits, the unwanted products from the multiplier are well suppressed. The following power amplifier stages also have considerable discrimination to 'off frequency' products. The only significant products detectable at the output of the final stage are harmonics of the 50MHz signal.

All other products are more than 80dB down. To achieve this with transistors would be much more difficult and would require a greater number of stages. Valves are also far more tolerant to mismatch caused by antenna VSWR, and cope with over driving more easily.

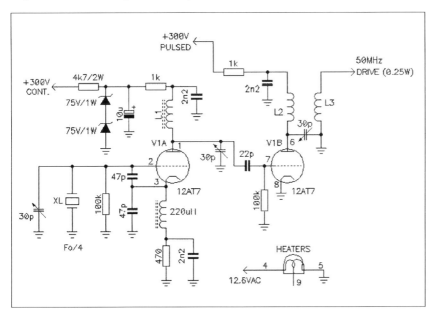

Fig 7.1: 6m meteor radar low-power transmitter stages

The inductor, L1, in the anode of the oscillator is wound on a toroidal ferrite core and is resonated with a 30pF trimmer to 25MHz. The inductor, L2, in the anode of the multiplier anode is an air-wound coil wound on an 8mm mandrel and also tuned with a 30pF trimmer. In the author's case these trimmers were Philips 'beehive' types rescued from old two-way radio transmitters. The 30pF trimmer across the crystal sets the exact operating frequency.

The choice of transmit frequency was so as to place it far away from the normal communications portion of the band. Depending on which band plan you follow will determine what frequency is suitable. In the author's case, the frequency of 50.7MHz was chosen because no activity normally occurs there. (In South Africa the amateur portion of the 50MHz spectrum extends from 50MHz to 54MHz, but only the bottom 2MHz is exclusively allocated to the amateur service. The portion between 52MHz and 54MHz is shared with commercial users.)

POWER AMPLIFIER

The dual band amplifier follows standard designs to be found in many amateur publications. Some pictures of the amplifier are shown here. The double-tetrode stages are operated in push pull to achieve low second harmonic generation. An external low-pass harmonic filter is used. If the driver is not required, the grid-input power required is approximately 6W for Class-C. This could be provided by a 10W transistor stage.

POWER SUPPLY

An old Yaesu FT-200 HF transceiver power supply is used to power the amplifier. This has HT taps for up to 850V. For this application, it is quite safe to use as much as 1200V for the PA stage anode supply as the duty cycle is low. The FT-200 PSU also supplies +350V, +175V, control grid supply of -100V and the heater supply of 12.6VAC.

GRID BIAS

For best efficiency in Class-C, the control grid of the QQVO6-40 needs to be supplied with a voltage sufficient to cut off the valve when no drive is applied. For the more normal Class-AB1 operation, the grid bias is adjusted to provide approximately 35mA of standing anode current with no drive applied. This normally requires a grid voltage of -35V to -45V, depending on the anode and screen voltage and the emission of the valve. Older valves have lower emissions and hence the grid voltage will be

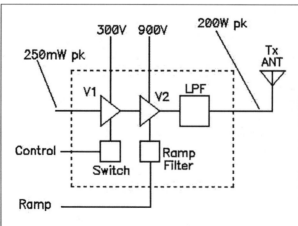

Fig 7.2: 6m meteor radar power amplifier

Fig 7.3: Rear view of the 6m and 2m dual-band power amplifier. The 6m portion is on the left. The QQVO3-10 driver valve is located behind the QQVO6-40 final stage. The cooling fan draws air from above the chassis and pressurises the lower portion of the chassis. The air is forced over the glass envelopes of the valves via the cut-outs for each valve base

closer to -35V than the higher value. For Class-C, the grid voltage is higher. The amplifier anode current is adjusted with the bias control, with no drive applied, until the anode current just shows zero. With approximately 850V on the anode and 300V on the screen grid, this will be a grid voltage of -50V for a good valve.

Another important factor about the grid bias, which is largely misunderstood by many amateurs, is that it must be a very 'stiff' supply. If the application of drive causes the grid voltage to vary, the operating point of a triode or tetrode will also vary - poor results being the outcome.

The sort of stiffness required is very high - in an SSB linear, the variation of the grid bias causes severe inter-modulation products to be introduced. A variation of only 1V is sufficient to shift the operating curve into a more non-linear region.

> Only one band can be used at any time because the screen and grid regulators are common to the two valves, as is the metering. The 6m section uses a lumped anode network: the 2m section uses a 'linear line' anode network. The 2m section develops approximately 150W PEP and has been used to contact W5UN on EME.

The pictures of the amplifier overleaf show it with the outer covers removed. The top cover is a U-shaped aluminium folded section. The bottom cover is a flat aluminium plate, as is the back plate. These covers make it reasonably 'RF tight', except for the necessary cooling air slots punched in the top and back cover.

TRANSMITTER CONTROL CIRCUITS

The transmit control circuitry is driven by the main Control Generator and part of it controls the screen supply to the driver valve and the anode of the multiplier valve. During receive, this supply is switched off.

Fig 7.5: Close-up view of the 6m output network in the dual-band amplifier

Fig 7.4: Underneath view of the dual-band amplifier. The 6m section is at the top

The drive signal is the blanking pulse that also switches off the receiver IF during transmit. Transistor TR1 and TR2 can be almost any low-power npn transistors such as a BC107 or 2N2222. TR3 is a low-power pnp such as a BC327 or 2N2907. The totem-pole stage consisting of TR2 and TR3 ensure rapid switching of the high gate capacity MosFETs. TR4 and TR5 need to be high-voltage MosFETs; IRF-840s rated at 500V were used mounted on a small heatsink.

Note: The diodes between the MosFET gates and ground must not be omitted, as they prevent damaging negative voltage spikes generated by the fast switching of the high voltage. The supply voltage must be greater than 10V and up to 15V maximum.

The pulse driving this circuit is twice the length of the final transmit pulse, because the shaping circuit delays the high voltage supply to the PA valve screen grid. This can be seen in the next diagram.

FINAL STAGE PULSE SHAPING

The remainder of the control circuitry performs the pulse shaping for the screen voltage that feeds the output valve. The low-pass filter needs to be a linear-phase type to prevent the distortion of the pulse. Butterworth or Chebyshev filters do not have the correct response to a step impulse, and the pulse will over-

Fig 7.6: Circuit for the switching supply to the multiplier and driver stage screen grid

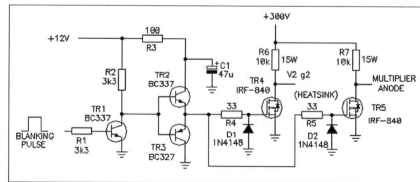

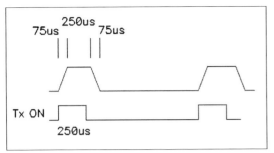

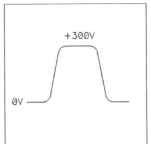

(left) Fig 7.7: The rise and fall times of the final shaped pulse is offset by 75µs

Fig 7.8: The ideal shape of the screen grid voltage

shoot and take too long to settle if these types of low-pass filters are used. The pulse shaping is performed in two separate stages.

The transmit pulse shaping circuit uses a dual op-amp and a passive low-pass filter to control the shunt modulator valves. Any decoupling capacitors on the screen grid of the PA valve need to be taken into account as these will add some extra time constant (=RC); in general, these capacitors will be low values as they are needed for RF decoupling only. An electrolytic capacitor of approximately 10µF should be connected across the +350V supply point if the screen supply is not well regulated. (The Yaesu FT-200 PSU gives about 380V when the 350V supply is lightly loaded.)

The Op-Amp is a non-inverting stage with a gain of 2.5 in order to be able to swing to approximately +20V. The input is the inverted +8V transmit pulse from the Control Generator. The rise and fall time of the pulse is approximately 75µs, which confines the transmit spectrum. The op-amp positive supply pin is fed from a +24V stabilised rail provided by a 1W Zener diode connected to the cathode of the modulator valve. The op-amp type shown can swing within 0.25V of ground and up to within 2V of the supply rail. Because of this, it is necessary to supply the op-amp with a negative supply to allow it to swing to below ground. This is provided by a negative supply derived from the 12VAC heater centre-tap and a Zener diode to clamp the negative supply to about 5V. (If the power supply only has a 6VAC winding, both halves of the heater can be strapped in parallel and the negative supply taken directly from the 6VAC).

The op-amp was chosen because it is a fairly slow device. The pulse-shaping is partially performed by the limited slew-rate of the LM358 op-amp, which

Many readers may wonder why I resorted to valves for the modulator. The answer is quite simple. After many attempts to construct the modulator with solid-state devices, it became apparent that no solid-state device had the necessary parameters. The output voltage needs to swing between, ideally, 0V and +300V. The collector-emitter and collector-base breakdown voltage of bipolar transistors do not lend themselves to this duty. Also, the control terminal needs to be very high impedance so that a low voltage device can control it. Whereas there are many bipolar or MOSFET devices that can sustain up to 400V, none can swing the output to ground without introducing a discontinuity. MOSFETs are particularly poor as the large drain-gate capacitance when swinging high voltages, causing a nasty condition called 'phantom-turn-on'. Early experiments with a MOSFET shunt regulator obtained the correct pulse fidelity on the falling edge but severely clipped the rising edge. Hence, the author had to resort to old-fashioned technology.

Fig 7.9: The shunt modulator stage. All resistors, except those marked, are 0.5W

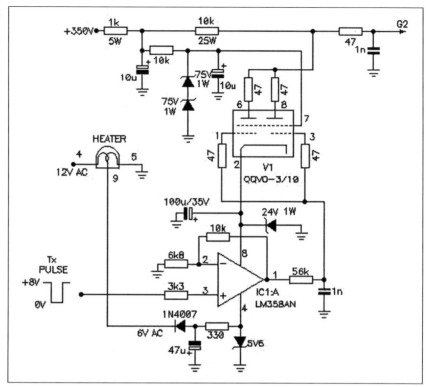

Fig 7.9: The shunt modulator stage. All resistors, except those marked, are 0.5W

provides about 30μs when configured as a gain stage of 2.5. The remainder of the shaping is performed by the RC low-pass pole feeding the grids of the shunt modulator valves; this gives the necessary linear phase filtering.

The partially-shaped pulse from the op-amp stage is applied to the low-pass filter RC section consisting of the 56k resistor and the 1nF capacitor. This finishes off the pulse shaping and the final signal is connected to the paralleled grids of the shunt modulator valve. This is a QQVO3-10 twin tetrode, the same as used for the RF driver stage, simply because I had several spare valves. This being a VHF tetrode, with considerable gain, it required the fitting of parasitic stopper resistors in the grid and anode. These are 47Ω 0.5W carbon resistors. The screen grid is fed from a +150V stabilised supply by two series-connected 75V 1W Zener diodes fed from the main 350V rail. Without the stabilised screen supply, the pulse fidelity is compromised because the modulator valve screen grid draws current when the anode current increases, lowering the screen voltage at a critical moment.

The screen grid and cathode are common to both halves of the valve. The cathode is biased to 24V above ground by a 1W Zener diode. This drives the valves into cut off with no signal applied and the anode voltage is pulled up to the 350V rail with a high-wattage resistor. To swing the anode voltage to ground, the grids need to be driven positive with respect to the cathode. Because we do not need very much current through the anode load resistor, it is satisfactory to swing the grids only to within 2V or so of the zero-bias condition. Perusal of the anode current curves of the QQVO3-10 shows that, with -2V on the grids, the anode current will peak to approximately 50mA, which is suffi-

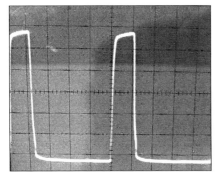 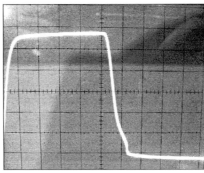

(left) Fig 7.10: Shunt modulator output signal. The voltage swings between +30V and approx +330V

Fig 7.11: Close-in view of one screen voltage pulse, showing the nicely-rounded rise and fall edges. The display in both pictures is 50V / division

cient to swing the anode voltage to within a few volts of the cathode. As the cathode is clamped to 24V above ground, the anode voltage will fall to close to this and swing up to the supply rail. In measurements, the anode swung down to about +30V, ie to within 6V of the cathode, the cathode being 'jacked-up' by the 24V Zener diode. Suitable alternatives for the QQVO3-10 are EL84, 6AQ5, 6L6, 5B254M or 6146 etc.

For RF valves such as the QQVO6-40, the maximum screen grid voltage should not need to be much more than +300V. If the supply voltage feeding the modulator is too low, the RF valves will be driven into a non-linear region and the crest of the pulse will develop a flat top. This will cause spectral spreading and is to be avoided.

A clock generator circuit using CMOS ICs provides the transmit pulse input and this circuit is operated from a +8V supply with a LM7808 1A-regulator fed with +12V.

Note: The circuit must be very well shielded to prevent the pulse of RF generated in the PA from getting into the low-power circuitry. If RF gets into the low-power stages it will cause the circuit to become unstable and 'howl' will occur.

GRID BIAS STABILISER

When operating a triode or tetrode valve as an RF amplifier, the grid bias is a very important parameter. If the grid bias is derived from a potential divider, the grid voltage will be driven more negative as the drive is applied. This pushes the valve harder into Class-C and creates a loss of gain, power output, steepening of the pulse slope, and an increase in the third-order intermodulation products, and hence an increase in the adjacent-channel splatter.

Some years ago, the author published screen-grid and control grid stabiliser circuits which eliminate this problem. They are both based on a shunt stabiliser. Without the grid stabiliser, the grid voltage on a QQVO6-40 valve increases from the quiescent point of about -35V to as much as -100V, pushing the valve hard into Class-C; the splatter generated, when transmitting SSB, is very bad.

With the shunt stabiliser, the grid current can safely flow without increasing the grid voltage. This yields in most cases an increase of output power of as much as 100%. A typical QQVO6-40 on 2m would only provide 75W of power when fully driven; with the new grid stabiliser, the power increased to over 150W with good linearity.

Fig 7.12: A shunt stabiliser for a triode or tetrode control grid

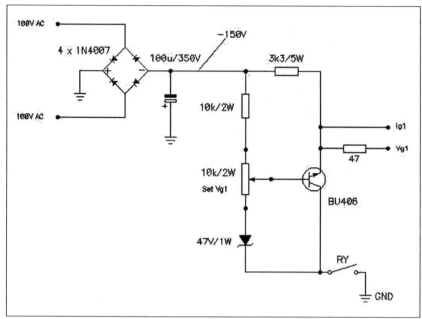

The circuit of the grid stabiliser is shown here.

Note: The resistor between the shunt stabiliser and the control grid must be very low in value to prevent the grid voltage 'hunting' as the drive level varies. A maximum value of 100Ω is recommended. The 47Ω resistor shown is for grid current metering. The high voltage transistor (BU406) should be mounted on a heatsink with an insulator to prevent the grid voltage being shorted out. When in standby mode, the relay contact opens and the grid voltage rises to the unregulated supply voltage of about -100V, so cutting off the valve.

The fitting of any substantial capacitor across the output is not required, and will upset the regulation; in severe cases, the circuit can oscillate due to such an output capacitor.

CONTROL GENERATOR

The Control Generator for a simple radar system needs to generate several signals that are all synchronised to a common clock.

Signals are required to switch the transmitter stages on and off and to supply the transmitter pulse-shaper. Also needed are the signals that activate the receiver stages when the transmitter is off and to trigger the CRO display for the range indicator.

In the circuit below, this is all performed with two low-cost CMOS ICs. No doubt a more elegant solution could be devised using a microprocessor, but the circuit shown suffices. All the integrated circuits are powered from an 8V three-terminal regulator such as a LM7808 rated at 1A. This regulator also powers the receiver circuits.

The main clock is generated with a free-running CD4093 CMOS square-wave generator formed around IC1A. The frequency is adjustable over a narrow range by the 10k pre-set. The duration of the clock pulse is approximately 125µs.

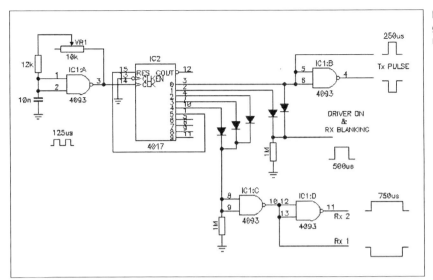

Fig 7.13: A control generator for a radar system

IC1A feeds the clock input of a CD4017 - a five-stage divide-by-10 Johnson counter. The CD4017 advances the count on rising edges of the clock. After one complete clock period, at the next rising edge, output 0 (pin 3) goes high for the duration of one clock period. This pulse duration is ~250µs and is the transmit pulse.

This pulse is inverted and goes to the circuitry that switches on the power amplifier screen supply. An non-inverted version is provided for the display triggering.

The transmit pulse and the following pulse from output 1 are combined, and feed a blanking circuit in the receiver IF and the switching circuits for the oscillator multiplier and driver valve screen supply.

This signal is a pulse of duration of 500µs, being the transmit pulse plus the next pulse combined. This is needed because the transmitter pulse is delayed in time by approximately 75µs while passing through the transmit pulse shaping circuitry.

If the blanking pulse was not used, the receiver would be switched on while the transmitter was still developing full power.

The crystal filter in the receiver also stretches the pulse and this causes the receiver to be desensitised for the start of the receiving period. This portion of circuitry is diode-summed to feed the blanking switch in the receiver front end and mixer module.

The outputs for the next three clock pulses (output 2, 3 & 4) each go high for one clock period and are summed with diodes and feed the receive control lines. This gives a receiver on-time of 3 x 250µs = 750µs, which equals a range-gate time of approximately 1ms.

When the count gets to the next one (output 5), pin 1 going high, the counter is reset back to zero by pulling the reset pin high. The counter then starts counting up from zero again and the sequence repeats indefinitely. The receive pulse is available as an inverted version or a non-inverted version. The need for both is because the control circuits in the author's receiver require the two different polarity signals.

CLOCK GENERATOR TIMING DIAGRAM

Fig 7.14: Clock generator timing diagram

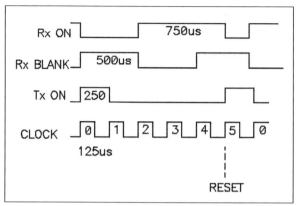

If a longer receiver on-time is required, the time can be extended in 250μs steps by adding more summing diodes to the next logical outputs and moving the reset pulse to the next logical output. With a multi-pole switch a variation in 250μs steps could be achieved to make a variable range gate. This will, however, alter the transmitter duty cycle.

With the circuit shown, the transmitter is on for one clock period and then off for the next four clock periods, hence the transmitter duty cycle is 20%. The indicated anode current and power output would therefore be 20% of the actual peak power, or 50W average in the case of the author's system.

The choice of transmitter pulse length and hence the receiver on-time is a bit of a compromise. The estimated round trip time for a meteor reflection is approximately 660μs for when the meteor enters the Earth's atmosphere at about 100km altitude. (The range is 150m per microsecond.) Hence it would be preferable to use a much shorter transmit pulse of, say, 100μs. This, it was felt, would cause more problems with spectral pollution as the occupied bandwidth would be a minimum of 20kHz and would be more difficult to keep the keying clicks down to an acceptable level. As long as the transmitter is turned off before the meteor echo is expected, with sufficient time for the receiver to recover to full sensitivity, reasonable results should be obtained. The long receive on-time is an attempt to hear echoes from meteors at the maximum range of about 150km as they start to enter the Earth's upper atmosphere and also to reduce the average power requirement of the power amplifier.

RECEIVER DESIGN

The receiver design was analysed with a software simulation package, and having looked through the junk box to see what was available, it was decided to use a single-conversion superhet with an IF of 10.7MHz.

A suitable 15kHz-wide crystal filter was rescued from an old commercial two way radio. The transmitter pulse being 250μs requires a receive bandwidth of approximately 4.5kHz minimum. The pulse stretching of the signal is a problem that could be avoided by using a wider IF filter bandwidth, but this would reduce the ultimate sensitivity and possibly cause interfering signals close to the working channel to appear as false signals.

A suitable local oscillator crystal was also found amongst the author's many surplus crystals gathered over the years; with some multiplication, this would get the local oscillator into the correct portion of the band.

It is necessary to trim the receiver LO a few kilohertz to ensure the receiver and transmitter frequencies are the same. A design was drawn up that used a varicap diode to pull the crystal several tens of kilohertz at the final frequency of 61.4MHz. The LO is a high-side injection type because of the crystal available, it would work equally well with a low side injection (~40.0MHz). If you have a suitable series-mode third-overtone crystal, you can dispense with the multiplier chain. Possible starting frequencies with different multipliers are:

High-side LO		Low-side LO	
7.675 MHz x 8 (x2 & x4)	= 61.4MHz	5.00 MHz x8 (x2 & x4)	= 40.0MHz
10.233 MHz x 6 (x2 & x3)	= 61.4MHz	6.666 MHz x 6 (x2 & x3)	= 40.0MHz
15.350 MHz x 4 (x2 & x2)	= 61.4MHz	10.00 MHz x 4 (x2 & x2)	= 40.0MHz
30.700 MHz x 2	= 61.4MHz	13.33 MHz x 3	= 40.0MHz, etc

Local Oscillator

The 5MHz crystal runs continuously, is then buffered by an amplifier and fed to the multiplier stages. The first multiplier raises the frequency to 20.46MHz and it is band-pass filtered to remove other 5MHz products (at ~15MHz and ~25MHz). The second multiplier multiplies the 20.46MHz signal and selects the third harmonic in another band-pass filter to give an output of 61.4MHz. These multiplier stages are gated on and off by the control generator. This effectively mutes the receiver during the transmit pulse. The crystal is moved in frequency by the application of a variable voltage on the VCXO tuning line that is applied to a varicap diode. The +8V supply is derived from the control generator module. (See end of chapter for schematic of the local oscillator).

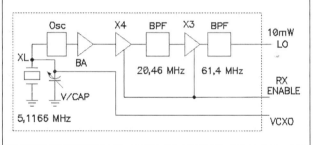

Fig 7.15: Local oscillator block diagram

Front-end and Mixer

The next portion designed was the receiver front-end amplifier and mixer stage. The low-noise amplifier will reside at the antenna and so the noise figure of the receiver does not have to be extremely low. Taking into account the necessary filtering to reject strong out-of-band signals, and the insertion loss in the filters with the available inductors, the tuned circuits were made fairly narrow, approximately 2MHz wide, and the insertion loss of the first tuned section was then approximately 2dB.

The first amplifier is a low cost 50Ω MMIC (INA-02186) with a noise figure of ~2dB and a gain of 30dB. The output of the amplifier passes through a second band-pass filter, identical to the first one, and then to the mixer. The first stage, therefore, has a noise figure of approximately 4dB and an overall gain of 26dB. As the LNA at the receive antenna will have a noise figure of approximately 1dB, the overall system noise figure will end up being approximately 1.2dB, which is quite adequate.

The amplified signal is applied to a dual-gate MOSFET mixer and the resulting 10.7MHz IF signal is passed via the crystal filter to a second MMIC IF amplifier with a gain of 30dB. The local oscillator gated signal from the LO module is firstly amplified in a dual-gate MOSFET and then applied to gate 2 of the mixer MOSFET. +8V is obtained from the control generator module. (See end of chapter for the circuit.)

Fig 7.16: Block diagram of receiver front end and mixer

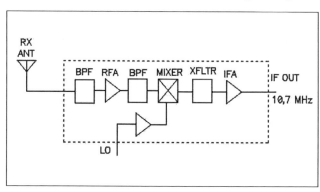

Intermediate Frequency Amplifier and Detector

The final portion of the receiver is the main IF amplifiers and detector. This could be a single high-gain IC with a linear detector and manual IF gain control. However, the author had a number of logarithmic amplifier ICs left over from another project (a noise-figure measuring system) and decided to use these. The advantage of a log-amp is that no AGC or manual gain control is required, because the IF strip has very fast attack and recovery time typically measured in microseconds. The ICs used were designed for use in low-cost radar IF strips.

The ICs used are the Plessey SL-1613C. Unfortunately, these are now obsolete. However, a log-amp IC from Analog Devices, the AD-606, is perfect and contains everything in one IC package.

The author's IF used five discrete ICs to achieve the required gain as the SL-1613C provides 12dB gain per stage. You may be lucky to find some on the surplus market.

The IF amplifier uses a process known as 'successive detection', and each IC provides a DC output current proportional to the RF level applied to it. As the input level applied to the IC rises, the gain progressively falls from the original 12dB to zero.

Hence, it is similar to a limiting amplifier in an FM receiver. The major difference is that the IC contains a very accurate amplitude detector with a well-defined RF-to-DC current at the detector port. The rise time of the detected output for a change in RF level is measured in nanoseconds and because the gain falls as the input level increases, the onset of saturation only occurs when the input signal is several volts.

The gain compression leaves the phase information unaltered, so it is possible to get good Doppler correlation from the signal. The ICs are connected in cascade and so the last IC has the noise of all the preceding ICs entering it. In practice, the last stage will be giving near to a full output on the receiver intrinsic front-end noise.

The 10.7MHz signal from the receiver mixer is carried by a 50Ω cable and enters via J1. The first stage has a filter at 10.7MHz to imped-ance-match the 50Ω

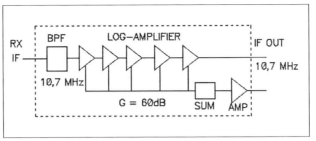

Fig 7.17: The loga-rithmic amplifier

from the front-end module to the high impedance of the IC and also to help reduce the broadband noise power entering the strip. The SL 1613C has a gain of 12dB up to at least 60MHz and, if the bandwidth was not constrained, the noise performance would be poor. For the same reason, it is imperative that the enclosure housing the log amplifier be as RF-tight as possible. Any signal leaking in will be amplified and detected, causing both a reduction in gain and a false-alarm signal. As the author lives only 4km from the local TV and FM broadcasting tower, the screening required was greater than normal.

The detected outputs from each log-amp IC are summed and the resultant cur-rents are converted to a DC voltage in a npn emitter follower. This is then buffered in an AC-coupled amplifier. The amplified 10.7MHz IF is available for further detection externally at J2. This might be applied to a product detector fed with a 10.7MHz carrier, so that audible detection could be made of the meteor pings, or fed into a wide-band oscilloscope to observe the shape of the received echo pulse.

The detected output is blanked during the transmit pulse to prevent false sig-nals being displayed. This is performed by a npn transistor that pulls the detect-ed output to ground during the blanking pulse.

Also included in the log IF module - but not shown on the block diagram - is a post-detection low-pass filter, built around a LM358 op-amp. The low-pass filtering increases the sensitivity by a great deal and eliminates most of the high-frequency 'grass' from the display. After the low-pass filter, the video

Fig 7.18: The SL-1613 logarithmic amplifier

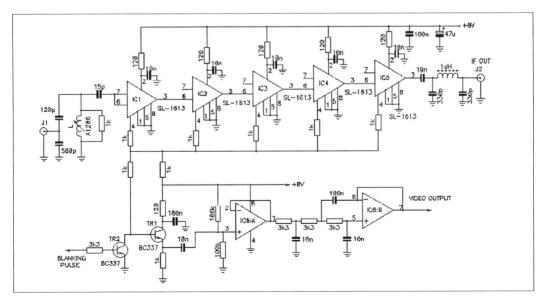

signal is fed to the CRO Channel 1 vertical amplifier. The CRO timebase is triggered from the transmit pulse. This can either be fed into the external trigger or to Channel 2. The timebase will need adjusting to accommodate the full sweep.

The log-amplifier module was built as a separate unit and not as part of the receiver because the intention is to expand the meteor radar system to the 70MHz and 144MHz bands at a later stage. Therefore, for the new bands, the only portion required will be a new receiver front end and transmitter oscillator and power amplifier. The control generator and display are already built and do not require any modifications.

One slight disadvantage of using the Plessey SL-1613C log-amp ICs was the fact that the DC echo pulse is inverted. With no received signal, the DC voltage from the detectors is close to the supply rail; when a signal is received, the open-collector detectors pull the voltage down towards ground.

Inter-stage Filtering

The Log Amplifier module is very wide-band, typical of most log-amp ICs. This means that any signal finding its way into the chain will be amplified and will appear as a valid output signal. One of the problems the author encountered was keeping the receiver LO out of the log-amp input. The crystal filter does a pretty good job of rejecting the 61.4MHz local oscillator signal but, even so, an extra stage of filtering is necessary. To understand this needs a little explanation.

The attenuation of the LO signal coming from the receiver at the IF port is about 70dB below the LO input level to the mixer, or about -60dBm. The noise floor of the log amplifier chain is about -90dBm. This means that the LO signal entering the log amplifier chain is well above the noise floor of the chain. If an external rejection filter is not fitted and the log amplifier sees the pulsing LO signal, it will show up as a false signal. To achieve this sort of attenuation requires not only a low-pass filter rolling off at about 12 MHz, but also a notch filter to eliminate the LO signal.

This is fitted in an external screened box and is inserted between the receiver module and the log amplifier module. The circuit of the filter used by the author is shown below.

The 1µH inductors are moulded chokes and the tunable inductor is the same type as used in the 50MHz filter stages in the receiver front-end. If you use a different LO frequency, the notch filter values will need changing to suit.

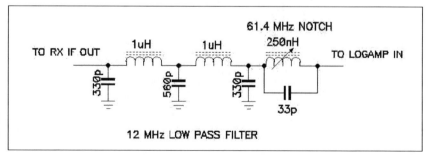

Fig 7.19: Additional IF low-pass filtering and notch filter

In the author's case, the 61.4MHz signal was not the only problem. Because the LO is derived from a 5MHz crystal, the first multiplier has some 10MHz product. This, if allowed to leak into the log amplifier, would show as a spurious response. The local oscillator chain was fitted in a very RF-tight enclosure to prevent direct radiation of this signal.

POST-DETECTION PROCESSING

In a conventional short-pulse radar with a wide IF bandwidth, the log-amplifier detected output would be DC amplified, filtered and then fed to the CRO vertical input.

In this design, because the transmitter pulse is, by necessity, much longer than the optimum, the technique is used with heavier filtering to get an adequate display signal.

The detector output is shown with a very small input signal. The top trace is the detected output at the emitter of the npn transistor; the bottom trace is the signal from the output of the log-amplifier chain. The signal was generated by a pulsed-noise generator connected to the log amplifier input. The signal is very small, and is only about 6dB above the receiver noise threshold. Because the SL-1613 IC uses open-collector detectors, it pulls the voltage down from near to the supply rail via a resistor. The detector output voltage is a negative-going voltage less than the supply rail. In the picture, the detector output is a signal of approximately 500mV peak.

The NPN transistor is an emitter-follower and this is fed to a non-inverting AC-coupled voltage-follower to provide the necessary low source impedance to drive the low-pass filter.

The input to the filter stage is biased to 0.5 of the supply rail, and hence the signal is maintained at about 4VDC level. The use of an AC-coupled signal means that the CRO can be set to AC-coupling and its sensitivity adjusted to obtain the required sensitivity for the small changes in output. The low-pass filter stage consists of the second half of the dual op-amp. This filter removes the high-frequency noise and leaves the signal to denote the leading edge of the echo pulse. This allows a better range display than a heavily-filtered pulse.

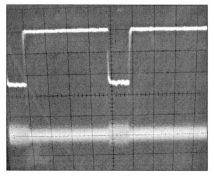

Fig 7.20: Log-amplifier detected output

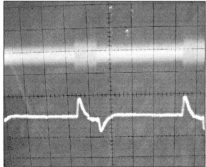

Fig 7.21: Final signal for the display Y-amplifier

Fig 7.22: Module interconnection diagram

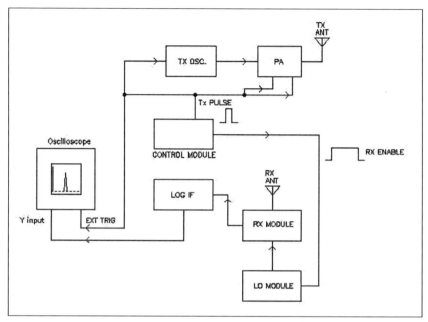

INTERCONNECTION

The system is connected together as shown in the diagram. All the modules are enclosed in RF-tight boxes with 50Ω coaxial connectors for the RF paths and feed-through capacitors for the supplies and other signals. The signals to the CRO should be run in screened cables to prevent RF from the transmitter getting into the CRO circuits.

SYSTEM IMPROVEMENTS

For increased receiver sensitivity, it is possible to use two receive antennas spaced some distance apart in an interferometer network. This was mentioned in previous chapters as a method to increase the gain or angular resolving power of an antenna. In this system, the requirement is for three similar Yagi antennas, one for the transmitter and the other two for the receiver. The receiver antennas would each feature a masthead LNA and the receiver coaxial cables would be brought together at a mid-point into a power combiner and then fed to the receiver. It is important to ensure that the two lengths of coaxial cable joining the antennas are of equal electrical length to provide phase coherence. If the two coaxial cables were not of equal electrical length, some signal cancellation would occur.

> **Note:** The use of equal electrical lengths does not mean that they have to be the same physical length. In practice, due to the varying velocity factor of commercial coaxial cable, it is often not the case. The important thing is to achieve equal phase and amplitude signals. It is possible for one cable to be longer than the other by half-wave increments to obtain equal phase. In the author's system, one cable is longer because of the physical problem of routing the cables back to the combiner.

A simplified block diagram of the bi-static system is shown in Fig 7.23. All three antennas need to be pointed to the same point in the sky for the best results.

In the author's original system, the antennas were based on the NBS design with a boom of 7.5m in length and have eight elements giving a gain of approximately 10dBd each.

An advantage of the bi-static anten-

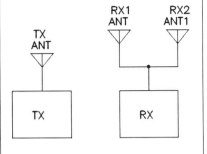

Fig 7.23: Bi-static antenna system

na is that no antenna changeover switch is required, with its attendant losses and the difficulty of achieving fast enough switching and isolation to the receiver.

ANTENNA COMBINER

As the requirement is for two antennas to be used on receive, the need arises for a simple 0° power combiner. As the power level is very low, it is not necessary to resort to the normal types used for transmitting, which are quite large. The need also is for the DC power for the LNAs to be carried by the feed-lines to each antenna. This can all be taken care with a simple matching network to convert the 25Ω of the two connected antennas to 50Ω. The series element, therefore, needs to be an inductor to carry the line-powering current. The problem was simulated using the ARRL RF Designer software, and a simple two-reactive-component network optimised. The capacitor value required is 62pF to resonate the 80nH inductor at 50MHz, therefore the 20pF trimmer will be at 3/4-mesh at resonance. The circuit detailed below will perform this function.

The inductor is wound with an air core and adjusted by squeezing or spreading the turns to obtain the correct value. The number of turns required is dependent on the internal diameter. With a 6mm former, the number of turns required will be approximately four. The RF choke need only be a small low-power type; the exact value is not too critical. The input of the receiver needs to have a blocking capacitor, to prevent the DC being shorted to ground. The RF choke could be built into the receiver module, as was the case in the author's version.

To set up, connect a 50Ω dummy load to each antenna port and a VSWR meter to the 50Ω receiver port. Apply a little power at 50MHz and adjust the inductor and capacitor for minimum reflected power. It should be possible to obtain a perfect match.

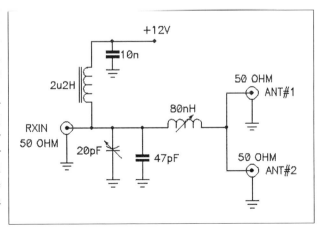

Fig 7.24: 50-ohm to 25-ohm antenna matching

LOW-NOISE MASTHEAD AMPLIFIER

The success of the system depends heavily on having a suitably low noise figure. Whereas there are many published designs for masthead preamps, the author has built many different types using a Hewlett-Packard noise figure measuring system to assess performance; very few are capable of the performance of the design about to be described. One of the best, and the lowest cost, is a simple design using a dual gate MOSFET. This design can give a >1dB noise figure on 6m or 2m; many of those built measured 0.85dB with about 25dB of gain. The design is straightforward and, with little effort, one can be built in an evening. It is not necessary to use a printed circuit board for a one off; in fact, printed circuit board versions always showed a slightly worse NF than ones built rats nest fashion. The design was first published in the Radio ZS magazine in July 1989.

The gain being high, it is essential to fit a metallic screen, with a notch cut out to pass over the MOSFET package, and soldered to the top ground plane so that the input and output inductors cannot see each other. If the screen is omitted, it will oscillate! The screen should be orientated to miss the package leads and at an angle of 45° across the MOSFET is the best option. The LNA must also be enclosed in a well-shielded box to keep interfering signals out. The 6m and 2m versions use different inductors and a few other component values. These are listed in a table below and in the notes. The preamps are designed for line-powering from a nominal 12V supply. If 24V is required, the 180Ω resistor should be changed to 1.8kΩ.

Note: There is no resistor fitted between gate 1 and ground as may be found in similar designs. Such a resistor will severely degrade the noise figure due to thermal noise generated in it and the reduction in circuit Q. It is imperative to strive for the highest possible Q in the input network to minimise the noise figure. The 1N4148 diodes across the input are to clamp the RF during the transmitting period.

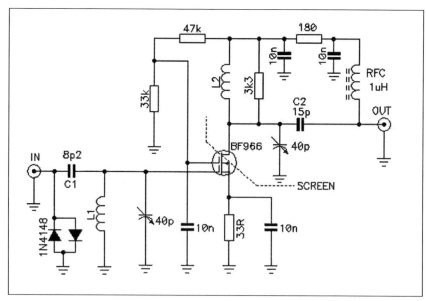

Fig 7.25: Dual-gate MOSFET preamp for 50MHz

The capacitors are Philips ceramic plate with a 63V working voltage. The leads should be trimmed as short as possible to reduce inductance; chip capacitors for the gate 2 and source would be preferable. The 3.3kΩ across the drain tuned circuit is to lower the gain slightly and preserve stability. This should have very short leads.

The input RF connector should be a low-loss, constant-impedance type. Please do not use SO 239/PL-259s - they are awful at 30MHz and above and are not waterproof. BNC or N-types are much better.

Component values for 50MHz and 144MHz

50MHz	144MHz
C1 = 8.2pf	C1 = 4.7pF
C2 = 15pF	C2 = 5.6pF
L1 = 10t	L1 = 5t
L2 = 10t	L2 = 4t

Notes:

L1 & L2 are close-wound with 22SWG enamelled wire on a 6mm-diameter mandrel former and have 3mm-long leads.

Trimmers are Philips plastic film 808 series (7mm diameter) or air-spaced trimmers. 6m version uses 40pF and 2m version uses 20pF.

Decoupling capacitors = 10n for 6m version and 1n for 2m version.

All resistors 0.25W carbon film (non-inductive).

Typical voltages with a 12V supply

Drain	$= \sim$10V
Gate 2	$= \sim$4.5V
Gate 1	$=$ 0V
Source	$= \sim$0.5V - (all voltages with respect to ground)

Typical gain & noise figure

Gain	$= \sim$25dB
NF	$= \sim$0.85 to 1.3dB

HARMONIC LOW-PASS FILTER

One of the problems when using high power at 50MHz is the possibility of causing interference to FM broadcast listeners due to second-harmonic radiation at about 100MHz. At the author's location, this is not a problem, as I live only 4km from the local broadcast transmitter and the signal is saturation level. However, for those who live far from a FM broadcast station it may be a problem. In the author's equipment, the second harmonic suppression of the valve push-pull PA is quite good, being over 30dB down. Even so, some additional filtering can be advantageous. Those using single-ended amplifiers will experience a higher second harmonic content than with a push-pull design. In the push pull design,

Fig 7.26: High-power harmonic filter for 50MHz

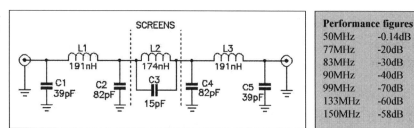

Performance figures	
50MHz	-0.14dB
77MHz	-20dB
83MHz	-30dB
90MHz	-40dB
99MHz	-70dB
133MHz	-60dB
150MHz	-58dB

the odd order harmonics are normally higher, being some 5dB worse than the even harmonics. Even so, the filter shown below is well able to clean up even a very bad power amplifier with minimal insertion loss.

The design shown is one I have used for many years, and provides about 70dB of attenuation at 100MHz and nearly 60dB at 150MHz. It is based on a Chebyshev Cauer seven-pole elliptic filter design and the component values are optimised for standard value components. The shunt capacitors need to be very low-loss types, or they will literally explode with high power RF. The best types are the clamped mica capacitors made by Semco or Unelco and rated at 500V. These can handle many amperes of RF current, which will be flowing in a filter of this type at 200W or so. The measured insertion loss at 50MHz is less than 0.2dB and the input and output impedance match is better than 1.1 VSWR. The coils are wound with 1.6mm enamelled copper wire on a 10mm diameter mandrel and then adjusted by spreading the turns. The Q of the inductors needs to be very high to reduce the insertion loss. The coils typically exhibit a Q of 250 or more.

The centre section features a second-harmonic trap network and the attenuation at 100MHz is nearly 70dB. The filter easily handles over 400W of RF at 50MHz. It must be constructed in a RF-tight enclosure, and care taken to keep all leads very short and thick. A partition plate should be fitted between each section to prevent coupling between adjacent coils. The lead-through in the partition plates can be a PTFE lead through insulator such as those made by Oxley. A better option is to use 82pF feedthrough capacitors, if these can be obtained.

The frequency plot looks like Fig 7.27 (simulation of response using the ARRL software):

Fig 7.27: The attenuation at approximately 100MHz dips to a minimum of about 70dB and then slowly re enters towards 200MHz. The rippled trace is the input impedance match. It stays better than 1.1:1 between 0MHz and 52MHz. The insertion loss in the pass-band between 0MHz and 55MHz is less than 0.2dB (~4%)

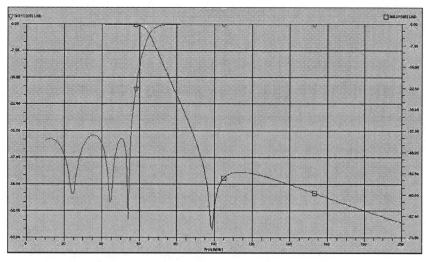

CIRCUITS

Receiver

The receiver circuits are split into several diagrams, as it is not possible to get them all on a single page. The first amplifier and filter stages use Toko 7mm coils (A1957 or A1439) with a nominal inductance of 250nH and a Q of 100.

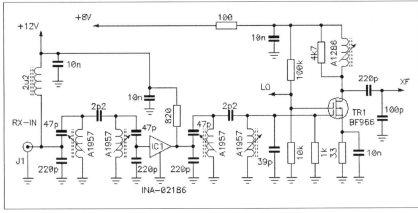

Fig 7.28: Receiver RF amplifier and mixer stages

The tuning range is approximately 20%. The 10.7MHz crystal filter matching uses another Toko 7mm-coil (A1286) with a nominal inductance of 1.25µH, a Q of 110 and a tuning range of 20%. All resistors are 0.25W metal or carbon film.

The first amplifier stage is fed with 12V, as is the RF choke that feeds the masthead LNAs. The remainder of the receiver is powered from 8V supplied by the Control Generator board. The crystal filter used is a Toyocom 10M3B6, a six-pole 15kHz-bandwidth filter for 10.7MHz. The input and output impedance is 3kΩ in parallel with 1pF. If you use a different crystal filter, the matching components will need recalculating. With the 250µs transmitter pulse width, a matched filter bandwidth of ~4.5kHz is the minimum that can be used. A 6kHz AM filter would therefore be suitable if you can obtain one.

As the crystal filter effectively stretches the pulse, this shows up as a signal occurring during the first portion of the receive period. The way this was eliminated was to clamp the IF output at 10.7MHz during the transmitter pulse and the following clock pulse. This is performed by a BFW92A npn transistor connected across the IF output and driven by the blanking signal derived from the Control Generator. The local oscillator amplifier stage uses a Dual-Gate MOSFET and a simple low-Q tuned filter to drive gate 2 of the mixer. Almost any MOSFET will work here. The drain tuned-circuit uses the same Toko 7mm-coil as the amplifier stage. The oscillator input level required is approximately 1mW that the oscillator and multiplier chain gives easily. The 68Ω resistor in parallel with the gate 1 capacitance of 4pF provides a load to the input signal of close to 50Ω.

Fig 7.29: Crystal filter and IF amplifier stages

Local Oscillator

The circuit for the local oscillator is shown here. The choice of starting frequency is largely a matter of what crystal frequency is available. The author's version uses a 5MHz crystal and multiplies the signal by 12. The varicap diode used

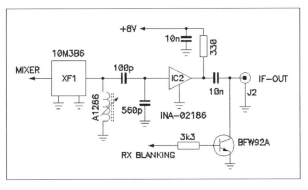

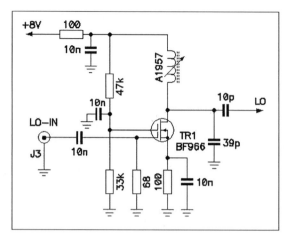

Fig 7.30: Local oscillator amplifier stage

for setting the oscillator frequency is a 30pF maximum type. The tuning voltage is derived from a potentiometer across the 8V supply rail. If a different fundamental crystal frequency is used, the 220pF capacitors in the Colpitts oscillator between base and emitter may need changing.

The choice of transistors is not very critical. The oscillator shown uses a BC337, which is an audio transistor. Whereas some purists would prefer a 'real RF transistor', at this low frequency it works fine. A 2N2222 would also function as both have a ft of approximately 100MHz. The multiplier stages need a fairly good device; here the BFW92A is used and it delivers approximately 4mW at the output connector at 61.4MHz. Alternatives would be BFR90, BFR92 etc. The spectral purity of 5MHz and 20MHz products are all more than 60dB down on the local oscillator carrier. The Control Generator module supplies the local oscillator enable signal. This signal should swing between zero and +8V to turn the two multiplier stages on when the receive time slot occurs. The CD4093B in the control generator module can drive this high impedance load without any difficulty.

Again, it needs to be borne in mind that any leakage from this module, if it can enter the log amplifier unit, will cause a false signal to be generated. As twice the crystal frequency is very close to the desired 10.7MHz IF, signal shielding and decoupling of the leads entering the oscillator module is critical.

Power Amplifier

Fig 7.31: Receiver local oscillator and multiplier

The amplifier follows fairly standard design practices with a few special tweaks to suit the application. The schematic shows the author's 6m power amplifier

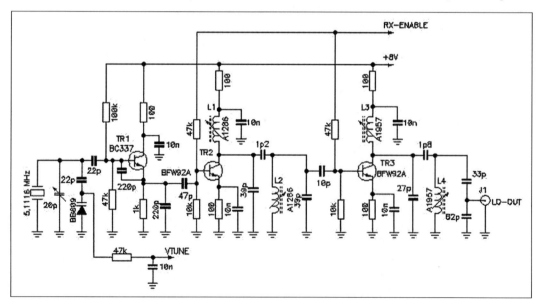

with suitable modifications for radar applications. Several design details need to be noted.

The resistors feeding the anode of the QQVO3-10 and the QQVO6-40 are 5W wire-wound types. These perform the function of radio-frequency chokes and help to maintain stability in this high gain line-up of approximately 30dB. A wire-wound resistor is also used for the screen grid of the QQVO6-40 for the same reason. Note the screen grid of the first valve is not decoupled; this is a form of negative feedback used to enhance the stability. The first stage provides a gain of approximately 14dB; the second stage a gain of over 16dB. All decoupling capacitors must be of a suitable voltage rating and rated for RF applications.

The anode tuning for the first stage uses a split-stator capacitor with the rotor connected to ground. This component was rescued from an old commercial transmitter (Pye Cambridge or Vanguard). The grid tuning capacitor for the final stage is a 20pF variable connected across the grid pins. A split-stator capacitor could also be used here, if available, but it complicates the physical layout.

The grid bias of the QQVO3-10 is provided by a 20V 1W Zener diode in the cathode. This should be well-decoupled with 1nF capacitors with short leads. With the value shown, the valve is biased towards Class-AB1. A screen is required between the grid and anode tuned circuits of the first valve to prevent instability. The screen used was rescued from a Pye Cambridge mobile transceiver.

The anode current metering of the output valve is performed by a 1Ω 5W wire-wound resistor in the cathode of the QQVO6-40. This resistor measures the total cathode current, including the screen grid current. This also needs good decoupling with 1nF capacitors with very short leads. By connecting a CRO across this resistor, the peak cathode current can be measured. In the author's amplifier a peak current of ~600mA is obtained (500W input) which corresponds to an output power of over 300W peak. As the duty cycle is low, the QQVO6-40 can cope with this level and remains cool. (In fact, the QQVO6-40 is capable of over 500W output in short pulse radar duty up to 450MHz. It was originally designed for this application near the end of the WWII, but arrived too late to be used in any substantial volume. The companion valve, QQVO3-20, is

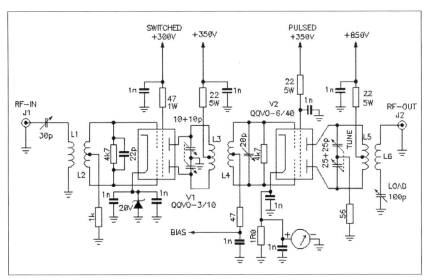

Fig 7.32: Two-stage RF power amplifier

also designed for radar duties up to 600MHz and was designed as a driver for larger radar valves.)

The anode tuning split-stator capacitor is a wide-spaced type because of the high RF voltages present and it has a 56Ω 2W carbon resistor connecting the rotor to ground. This provides a better balance between the two halves of the capacitor and acts as a parasitic stopper. Also note the very low value resistor used for the grid bias feeding the output stage. If this resistor is too high, the grid stabiliser will be negated and the valve will be driven harder into Class-C with a consequent loss of gain and pulse fidelity. If the drive from the first stage is too high, the damping resistor across L4 used to swamp the final stage grids, can be reduced in value. This resistor needs to be a low inductance type and rated at approximately 2W.

All inter-stage coupling is performed by mutual inductance between the push-pull-tuned circuits. This maintains the good balance essential in a push-pull amplifier and also helps to reject any out-of-band spurious signals. (The coupling between L3 and L4 in the author's amplifier uses a tertiary link to span the distance between the two tuned circuits. This is more from a point of convenience, as the link can be removed and the power from the first stage fed into a power meter to measure the gain. Similarly, the output stage can be driven by an external drive source to perform the same measurement. A possible source of a replacement transmitter is the high-power version of the Pye Vanguard mobile transceiver; these contain all the necessary hardware and can be obtained on the surplus market for a nominal sum. Most of these use the quick-heat filament version of the PA valve, QQZO6-40, and these can be replaced with little effort,)

The grid circuit for the first stage is damped for stability with a 4.7kΩ 0.5W resistor. As the gain required is not that high, a drive level of 250mW is more than adequate to drive the amplifier to full output. The grid inductor is tuned by a fixed capacitor and then the turns are spread or compressed to set the correct tuning. A variable capacitor could have been used, but it was not found necessary as the stage has ample gain.

A link-coupling coil provides the input drive matching with a 30pF variable to give a good match to 50Ω. The drive signal from the oscillator module is carried by a 50Ω cable. The output uses a similar link-coupling and the 100pF loading control allows matching to a 50Ω feeder or antenna.

ALTERNATIVE ANTENNA ARRAY

The author's system was originally designed to use three long Yagis with eight elements giving a gain over a dipole of about 10dB. Because these need to be elevated upward to about 60°, this can cause a problem with mounting. The plan was to use three short masts situated approximately 10m apart with the antennas mounted about 3m above the ground level. Running coaxial cables to three remotely-sited antenna posed some logistical problems, not the least being keeping a happy balance between the amateur shack and the domestic authority! An alternative design was drawn up to use a large corner or trough reflector antenna.

The details of these alternative antennas are contained in a later chapter dealing with meteor-scatter antennas.

8

Practical Low Noise Amplifiers

In this chapter:

- Which device to use?
- Low noise GaAsFET amplifier for 432MHz
- 1296MHz version
- Dual-gate GaAsFETs

- Shielding, filtering and switching techniques
- Commercially available LNA modules

T his chapter, by necessity, is not going to be just a few pages. The topic is extremely complex, despite the apparent simplicity of the device and its small physical size. The complexity arises because of so many conflicting parameters and the multiplicity of possible devices to achieve the same ends.

The successful reception of very weak signals requires a receiver with an extremely low noise figure front-end.

In radio astronomy, apart from the antenna, the most important portion of the receiving system is the first RF amplifier as this effectively determines the overall system sensitivity.

Many professional radio astronomy observatories use very sophisticated low-noise amplifiers. A large number use cryogenically-cooled amplifiers to obtain very low noise figures. This is, however, beyond the scope of most radio amateurs. We will, unfortunately, have to rely on lesser technology for our LNAs.

WHICH DEVICE TO USE?

Of the many possible available devices to choose from, it sometimes becomes difficult to select the optimum type for a particular application. However, with a little knowledge of the strengths and weaknesses of the different types, it becomes easier to see which device type is the best choice for an application.

The types can be broadly broken down into a few headings. We will only consider current types and not the older devices, such as valves, (these have already been covered in a separate chapter) as these are now superseded by lower-noise solid-state devices.

The available types, listed in historical order, are:

- Bipolar Junction Transistors (BJT)
- Junction Field Effect Transistors (JFET)
- Dual-Gate MOSFETs (DG MFET)
- Single-Gate GaAsFETs
- Dual-Gate GaAsFETs
- High Electron Mobility Transistors (HEMT)
- Pseudo-morphic High Electron Mobility Transistors (PHEMT)

Of these, the bipolar junction transistor, the junction FET and dual-gate MOS-FET are the oldest types. The single- and dual-gate GaAsFETs are the next generation and the HEMT and PHEMT are the latest developments. There are even more exciting devices, but these fall outside of the normal budget for most amateurs, so I won't deal with them here.

The characteristics of each type are listed below in historical order.

Bipolar Junction Transistor (BJT)

Originally, these were manufactured with germanium pnp-type junctions and later the npn became the more popular. Of the two, the pnp had the lower noise figure at first and later development saw the npn overtake it to become the class leader. Today, pnp low-noise RF transistors are almost non-existent. With developing technology, the changeover to silicon superseded the germanium types.

The silicon bipolar RF transistor has a useful operating range of about 1MHz to 10GHz; the majority of devices offer the best performance below 5GHz. The Fmax figure for modern devices is 40GHz (Fmax being the maximum frequency the device will function as an oscillator). Gains are reasonable; typically 10 to 16dB can be obtained in a single stage at 1GHz. As with all semiconductor devices, the gain at higher frequency tends to fall off at approximately 6dB per octave, so if the device gives 12dB at 432MHz we can expect only 6dB at 864MHz. Noise figures for typical bipolar devices vary between 1dB and 6dB, depending on frequency and type. Strong-signal performance is inherently poorer than the other types when biased to the low collector current required to achieve optimum noise performance, due to the base-emitter junction. Because of this, it can be overdriven, then behaving as a diode distorting the signal and generating harmonics. (It is an excellent frequency multiplier in local oscillator chains.) Operating voltage is medium- to low-voltage, many of the present day devices operating on as little as 2V collector-emitter voltage.

Collector current is also low, between 1mA and 20mA being the typical operating region, hence they are quite low-power devices and a popular low-cost solution. Circuit configuration can be common emitter, common collector (emitter follower) or common base (best for very high frequency), with common emitter probably being the most commonly-used. Input capacitance at the base varies between 2pF and 6pF. The input impedance is medium to low, depending on the frequency, and this makes it fairly easy to get a good match to 50Ω. In some cases, all it needs is a blocking capacitor from the base to the 50Ω source. A popular low-cost device is a BFW92A and a premium grade device is the Agilent Semiconductors AT-41435. The BFW92A costs about R5 the AT-41435 about R25. The AT-41435 is an excellent choice for a second stage device in a high gain LNA using a GaAsFET.

Below are the various circuit configurations in common use.

The limitation with the circuit shown in Fig 8.1 is the emitter decoupling capacitor. If the capacitor is not a low-enough impedance, the stability of the circuit becomes a problem. To alleviate this, it is preferable for the emitter to be directly grounded, as in the next circuit. The input impedance is greatly influenced by the base bias divider resistors; if these are a low value, the input impedance will also be low, and the available gain and noise figure suffers.

In Fig 8.2, the emitter is directly grounded and so stability into the UHF region is not a problem. However, as a BJT has a base-emitter voltage that is very sensitive to the junction temperature, the way the base biasing needs to be done is subtly different. In the first circuit, the base resistor RB1 is fed directly from the VCC point. With varying temperatures, the collector current will wander all over the place, changing the operating conditions. At very low temperatures, the device could be driven into cutoff and no current would flow. At high temperatures, the collector current could saturate and possibly damage the device. With the emitter resistor in circuit, this is offset to a large extent. Without the emitter resistor, the device becomes very sensitive to ambient temperature changes.

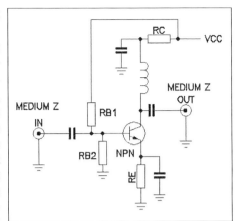

Fig 8.1: Aperiodic common emitter circuit (1)

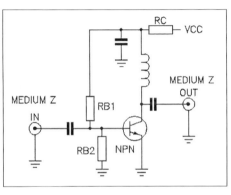

Fig 8.2: Aperiodic common emitter circuit (2)

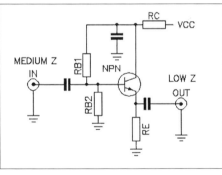

Fig 8.3: Aperiodic common collector (emitter follower)

By feeding the base divider resistors from the collector, the circuit is self-balancing and the collector current remains fairly constant over a wide temperature range.

The common collector (Fig 8.3) is more commonly known as the emitter follower. The voltage gain is slightly less than unity, but the power gain is high. It can drive low-impedance loads such as 50Ω cables. Again, note the improved biasing used to compensate for the temperature changes. It is not as serious here as the emitter resistor helps to maintain a more constant collector current.

Fig 8.4: Aperiodic common base

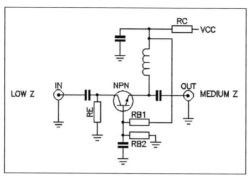

The common base (Fig 8.4) is the best choice for the highest frequencies, as the stability is much better. It can be driven directly by a 50Ω source. It offers good gain with the minimum of components. The decoupling capacitor on the base needs to be low impedance to ensure stability.

All the circuits so far have been untuned - aperiodic - with a simple choke in the collector to match a wide band of frequencies. Where the gain required is not that high this gives good stability, but the noise figure will be poor.

Junction Field Effect Transistor (JFET)

The junction FET, although having being proposed in 1937, long before the BJT was first made, had to wait for technology to catch up before the first versions were made. The JFET is a voltage-driven device and hence has an almost infinite gate resistance. It however has a similar input capacitance to the BJT and a drain structure almost identical to a BJT collector, so the upper frequency limits are similar for both devices. Gains are a little lower than similar BJT devices, but the noise figure is inherently slightly superior. Strong-signal handling is much better than BJT, due to the lack of a base-emitter junction diode. Operating voltages and currents are on a par with BJTs, with better strong-signal handling, as the drain-source current is increased at the expense of noise figure. Gain is fairly constant with drain current variations.

The average RF JFET is a depletion-mode device, meaning that the gate has to be connected to a voltage negative with respect to the source to control the drain current. If the gate were connected to the same potential as the source, the drain current would be maximum. Hence to bias the device into the optimum operating region requires the application of either a negative voltage to the gate (if the source is directly grounded), or to raise the source voltage positive with respect to ground and tie the gate terminal to ground. The raising of the source above ground with a resistor to set the required drain current is a popular method when the device is operated as common-drain and then it becomes more commonly known as a source follower. This features high input impedance and low output impedance - suitable to drive 50Ω loads. However, when operated in grounded source, the resistor needs to be bypassed with a low-impedance capacitor to hold the source at RF ground. If the source bypass capacitor does not have sufficiently low impedance, the circuit can oscillate. This is because the drain-to-gate capacitance is somewhat higher than that of a BJT, and stability becomes a problem at high frequencies in a common-source configuration.

For optimum high-frequency operation, the best choice of circuit configuration is the grounded gate. Also, the gate being almost infinite impedance makes it very difficult to match to from 50Ω and a common-gate circuit presents a match closer to 50Ω into the source. The wide variation in pinch-off voltage between devices makes the use of a source resistor essential and, in common-source, the difficulty of successfully-decoupling the source to RF means the grounded-gate circuit is an easier option. Noise figures can be quite low - at 144MHz, the typical noise figure in grounded-gate is ~1.3dB, but the gain is lower than a BJT, being of the order of 13dB.

At UHF, the JFET is somewhat better than a BJT, but the difference is marginal. The strong-signal performance is far better than the BJT and a JFET front-end can be expected to hold up better under crowded band contest conditions than a BJT. Operating voltages and currents are generally higher than similar BJTs, and this is partly the reason they have better IMD performance. Drain current averages 20mA for best noise and gain. Due to the wide variations in the pinch-off voltage, it is normally necessary to select the source resistor to get the correct biasing.

A popular device was the Siliconix U-310. The common-gate circuit is the basis used in the Chip Angle, N6CA, 'Angle Linear' range of 2m EME LNAs in the 1970s. This used selected U-310 devices and gave a guaranteed 1.2dB NF. The U-310 is now obsolete; it was a metal can device with the gate connected to the can. Hence, it was only necessary to solder the can into a hole in the pc board to get excellent low inductance grounding. The plastic version is the J-310 (TO-92 package) or the MMBF-310 in SMD version. Either will give performance similar to the original U-310.

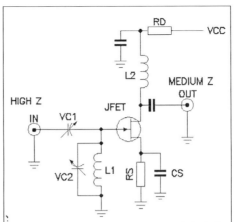

Fig 8.5: Tuned input - untuned output

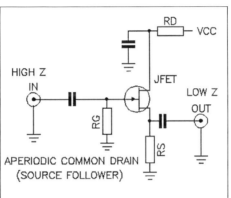

Fig 8.6: Aperiodic common-drain (source follower).

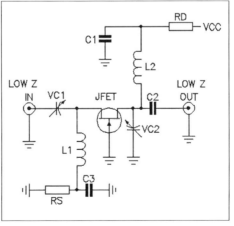

Fig 8.7: Tuned input and output. This circuit, with a suitable device, can achieve a low noise figure. The value of C2 needs to be fairly small to provide transformation to 50 ohms

Siliconix as a company no longer exists, it was swallowed up by the Vishay empire, but a great number of other semiconductor manufacturers make the modern versions.

The grounded-gate U-310 circuit today is a bit of a curiosity; in its day it was the benchmark for all others. Many 144 MHz EME stations got their first contacts using the U-310 so it couldn't have been that bad!

Dual-Gate MOSFET (DGMFET)

The dual-gate MOSFET is a development of the junction FET. It is actually two FETs stacked one on top of the other and the source of the top FET is connected to the drain of the bottom FET. The structure provides two control gates and RCA, who developed it, often referred to it as a 'solid-state tetrode'. The gate structure is made from Metal Oxide Silicon (MOS), a spin-off from the digital IC process made with the CMOS process (Complementary Metal Oxide Silicon).

The MOS gate has an input resistance much higher than the FET normal junction and is typically $10^{18}\Omega$. Because of this very high input resistance, the devices are prone to static damage, as are JFETs. Later versions incorporate gate protection Zener diodes to clamp any static charge to safe levels. These, however, slightly degrade the potential noise figure. Gate capacity of a typical DGMFET is about 2 to 4pF.

The DGMFET is the opposite of the JFET in the way the drain current works. It is an enhancement device and requires the gate 2 voltage to be positive with respect to the source. But the bottom half of the device behaves more like a depletion device. Hence, the source voltage has to be positive with respect the gate 1.

Again, the limitation is the goodness of the source decoupling capacitor to prevent oscillation. DGMFETs are operated almost exclusively in common-source with the amplified signal taken from the drain tuned circuit.

Operating frequency range is a little less than the other two types and around 2GHz is the accepted maximum. Many DGMFETs were developed for UHF TV tuner designs with low noise figures. These are low-cost and offer good gain at 800MHz, typically 20dB gain and 1.5dB NF. At lower frequencies, the gain rises, as it does in all semiconductor devices, and the noise figure bottoms out to around 0.7dB at 30MHz. The maximum available gain (MAG) at 30MHz can exceed 40dB.

Electrical AC Characteristics

V_{DS} = 15 V, I_D = 10 mA, V_{G2S} = 4 V. f = 1 MHz . T_{amb} = 25.C, unless otherwise specified

Parameter	Test Conditions	Symbol	Min	Typ	Max	Unit
Forward transadmittance		$|y_{21s}|$	15	18.5		mS
Gate 1 input capacitance		C_{iss1}		2.2	2.6	pF
Gate 2 input capacitance	V_{G1S} = 0, V_{G2S} = 4 V	C_{iss2}		1.1		pF
Feedback capacitance		C_{rss}		25	35	fF
Output capacitance		C_{oss}		0.8	1.2	pF
Power gain	G_S = 2 mS, G_L = 0.5 mS, f = 200 MHz	G_{ps}		25		dB
	G_S = 3,3 mS, G_L = 1 mS, f = 800 MHz	G_{ps}		18		dB
AGC range	V_{G2S} = 4 to –2 V, f = 800 MHz	ΔG_{ps}	40			dB
Noise figure	G_S = 2 mS, G_L = 0.5 mS, f = 200 MHz	F		1.0		dB
	G_S = 3,3 mS, G_L = 1 mS, f = 800 MHz	F		1.8		dB

(above) Fig 8.8: BF966S specification

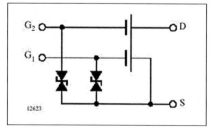

Fig 8.9: Dual-gate MOSFET with gate protection Zener diodes

Operating voltages and currents are similar to JFETs with the best noise figure being at the lower currents. Maximum gain occurs at the higher currents and hence the noise-figure-optimised current trades off some gain. The tetrode configuration means that there are now two control inputs. The RF input is normally gate 1, the lower device in the cascade pair, and the upper gate (gate 2) can be used to vary the drain-source current in the device.

Varying the gate 2 voltage allows AGC action to be applied and gain reductions of up to 50dB are possible. Hence, the DGMFET is a popular choice in RF front-ends and IFs where AGC is required. A mixer uses the LO applied to gate 2 and the input signal to gate 1. The conversion gain as a mixer is a little lower and about 10 to 15dB can be expected. The noise figure as a mixer is normally around 4 to 6dB.

Strong-signal handling is fair to good, depending on how much AGC is applied, it being better with some gain reduction. However, with a suitable narrow-band filter at gate 1, the noise figure and signal handling are considerably improved for out-of-band signals. For best noise figure, the input Q must be very high; damping resistors from gate 1 to ground will severely limit the noise figure although, for stability, it may be necessary to apply some damping. This also applies to the JFET and all the other solid-state devices with a similar structure, ie GaAsFET etc.

When gate 2 voltage is lowered by AGC, the noise figure degrades badly hence, for optimum noise figure, the DGMFET needs to run at maximum gain.

At low frequencies, eg below 100MHz, the gain can become excessive and the maximum available gain (MAG) the device can develop may be more than the maximum stable gain figure (MSG). If the MAG exceeds the MSG, the device is potentially unstable at some frequency and can oscillate. Normally lowering the MAG to the MSG figure ensures unconditional stability for any frequency or load mismatch. Drain damping with a shunt resistor is a popular way of reducing the gain without degrading the noise figure.

Introducing a small amount of inductance in the source grounding can make a further reduction in noise figure and an improvement in the input match. This does not need to be large - if it was, the circuit would turn into an oscillator. Normally, a very small amount, less than 20nH, will improve the MSG, input match, and noise figure, sometimes by a large amount. Overdo it and it will hoot!

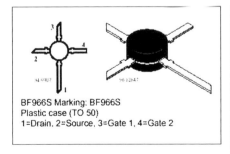

BF966S Marking: BF966S
Plastic case (TO 50)
1=Drain, 2=Source, 3=Gate 1, 4=Gate 2

Fig 8.10: Package details

(right) Fig 8.11: A typical VHF dual-gate MOS-FET low-noise amplifier with drain damping

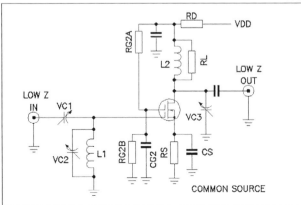

Often the inductance can be the source decoupling capacitor with leads left longer than normal, or a deliberate choice of a inductive-type capacitor. As the frequency rises, the amount of inductance required is less; this is because the maximum available gain is lower and the reactance of an inductor rises with frequency. By the time you get to about 300MHz, the gain has started to fall more steeply and any reduction in the source inductance will cause the gain to peak. The MAG is normally below the MSG figure at 300MHz and above, so the only way the device can oscillate is due to two other factors. The first is the internal feedback capacitance between drain and gate 1 and 2. This is a tiny amount, 25fF (25 femto-farads, femto = 10^{-15}), and is almost never the reason a circuit hoots. The biggest culprit is layout; if the grounding, shielding or decoupling aren't 100% then the chances of oscillation are good.

Using a software package such as the *ARRL Radio Designer* by Compact Software, the stability and match criteria can be analysed and the circuit values optimised to get good gain, noise figure, input and output match. It won't help with the layout; it assumes perfect shielding unless you introduce some feedback into the simulation circuit.

In common with all the other similar structure devices, the input needs to be very mismatched to achieve the optimum noise figure. Normally, the value of input inductor required is designed to resonate with the gate 1-to-source capacitance. At low frequencies, this presents a problem because the inductor value required becomes very large - gate 1 capacitance is only about 4pF maximum. So an additional shunt capacitance is required across the gate 1 terminal to make up the value. The noise figure is a direct function of the circuit Q. For the minimum noise figure the Q required becomes impossibly high with a lumped element tuned circuit; either the coil is the limiting factor or the Q of the capacitor. As the capacitor Q is normally much higher than that of the coil, the coil becomes the limiting factor. In some cases, because a lossy capacitor has been chosen, the capacitor is the dominant factor, so ensure the capacitor Q is adequate for your frequency of operation. In general, air-spaced trimmers are superior to plastic film trimmers at frequencies above about 400MHz.

If the input were conjugately matched, as would be the case for maximum gain or power transfer, the noise matching would be far from the required value. Hence, the input VSWR of a LNA using a DGMFET or a GaAsFET is usually very poor.

A popular device is the BF966S.

Single Gate GaAsFET (GFET)

As the technology of low-noise semiconductors evolved, it soon became apparent that silicon wasn't the lowest noise material for very high frequencies. With funding from various military projects, semiconductor scientists began to look at alternative materials to give better gain and noise figures into the high GHz regions.

One such material was Gallium Arsenide. This inherently has a much higher transition frequency than silicon. Soon experimental devices began to appear on the market. The low-noise performance was greatly enhanced, as was the gain. GaAsFETs have an extremely thin gate layer (~500μm) and so are even more sensitive to static discharges. Handling is critical before the device is safely in the circuit. Once the device is soldered into the circuit, it is normally quite robust. They are tiny. It has been estimated that more GaAsFETs have been 'lost' by dropping on the floor than have actually died whilst soldering into circuits.

However, armed with the necessary knowledge they are quite easy to work with, the soldering iron tip needs to be grounded to the work surface and any static discharged before picking them up with tweezers. With a little care, your success rate should be 100%. I have been playing with GaAsFETs for over 15 years and I have killed only one or two by static. The others that have died in service were due to lightning strikes nearby, an unfortunate legacy of living atop a mountain. A high volume LNA I designed some years ago had an unbelievably good record with a 3% variance of the noise figure over several hundred units. Of course you need access to a good noise figure measuring system to set them up correctly; however, many lower-grade systems designed by amateurs are more than good enough for our purposes. They might not have the absolute measuring accuracy, but they do at least tell when the lowest noise figure has been achieved. I will detail a few types in another chapter.

The gate of a single gate GaAsFET is much like a dual-gate MOSFET; it is almost a pure open circuit and hence very difficult to match at low frequencies. Another problem is the inherent gain and stability criteria. I have built LNAs with GaAsFETs for 144MHz, but I strongly advise against it unless you have an intimate knowledge of working with them. As for 50MHz, well I don't want to go there! I always perform a circuit simulation using a complex RF modelling package to see the stability criteria and matching problem. The gate capacitance of a typical GaAsFET is very low, only a picofarad or two.

The lower-cost devices, within our budget, are designed for frequencies of 4GHz and upward. The major users are satellite TV down-converters at C-band. At these high frequencies, the matching to a stripline design on a high-frequency substrate is relatively easy as the MAG is manageable, and the input capacitance brings the impedance into a workable region. However, at 100MHz and below, the devices are almost totally unstable with conventional circuit techniques. To get a typical GaAsFET stable at 100MHz means you have to damp the drain very heavily, and you end up with less gain than a DGMFET will provide at a fraction of the cost. You can forget about using normal air-wound coils on the input, even at 432MHz, as the Q you can achieve is far short of that required to achieve the device's potential noise figure. I will return to this topic a little later.

As with the DGMFET, the source inductance plays a large part in stabilising the device, improving the noise figure and the input match. At gigahertz frequencies, the source leads of the device are sufficient to invoke good stability, but at 1GHz and below you sometimes need to use an external inductor. The devices normally have two source leads.

Older devices when received from the manufacturer had full length source leads about 15mm long. Today it is very rare to get them this long - they

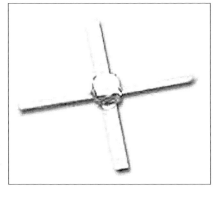

Fig 8.12: A typical GaAsFET package. The wide leads are the source leads

are nearly always cropped to fit on a board and are no longer than about 4mm. Most amateurs when working at VHF and UHF have had it drummed into them that all leads must be as short as possible, not so with LNAs. Source inductance is a powerful tool to stabilise a device and get more gain, lower noise figure and a better input match.

As well as my consulting work, I am an external moderator and assessor for a further education college. I oversee the course work and the practical construction projects of the microwave and communications syllabus. One of the projects all students have to do is to design, build and test a LNA for a certain frequency. Each student is given a different spot frequency and a GaAsFET, and they have to model the device, design the circuit and then build and test it. So far over 150 students have built LNAs with varying degrees of success. Some either don't work at all, or they oscillate at some supersonic frequency due to either poor layout or choice of components, or have poor gain or noise figure. I have seen every possibility of how not to do it! Mostly it is either lack of understanding or experience in working with tricky devices.

The same type of device given to the students I use regularly and have no difficulty achieving the required results, in a fraction of the time the student spends. This is because I have 'grown-up' with GaAsFETs and know them backwards. I know this sounds like bragging, but it is true. When I first started playing with them professionally I made a lot of mistakes. I was fairly late starting to use them professionally; this was for two reasons: firstly, this technology was denied to our country for political reasons; secondly, the early devices were simply too expensive for the class of products I was responsible for designing. As the costs came down, it became attractive to incorporate them into new designs. It was a steep learning curve and I read every available paper and application note to gain experience. As I grew accustomed to their little quirks I filed that bit of information away in the data bank for future use. My purpose for telling you all this is because I cannot expect someone else to build his very first GaAsFET LNA and achieve 100% success without some inside knowledge.

One of the final year degree students a few years ago chose to study the effect of source inductance and his thesis work was evaluating the required amount of inductance to obtain total stability with the chosen device. His thesis is now part of the textbook material for the course, it is such an outstanding piece of work.

Input Network

As has been mentioned, the input of the GaAsFET is a very small capacitance in parallel with, for all practical purposes, an open circuit. The drain-source is pretty much the same as a DGMFET or JFET, ie the drain at the optimum drain current is medium-to-low impedance. Hence the output network is not the problem.

To achieve the ultimate noise figure requires the 50Ω from the antenna to be transformed up to something approaching a few $10\text{k}\Omega$ in a low-loss manner. This is very difficult to do with conventional lumped networks. If you were to use an air-wound coil for the reactance, you would need a coil Q of several thousand to come close to that required.

Some years ago, I came across an article in the German *DUBUS* magazine by an amateur who worked with GaAsFETs in his day-to-day employment. This was a novel approach and one, which I built on. His idea was good, but stopped short of what was really needed. It used a piece of coaxial cable as a quarter-wave impedance transformer. We all know that an open-circuited λ/4 stub is an impedance-converter. If we 'look into' one end, the impedance will be low, but at a distance of λ/4 further along the line, the impedance is high. By shorting one end of the quarter-wave line, the other end appears as an infinite impedance at the design frequency, in theory. In practice it isn't quite so simple. The fact that the cable is made with dielectric filling lowers the actual impedance several orders of magnitude. It is still high but not as high as it could be.

If you connect a capacitor with a reactance of Xc = 100Ω across one end of a quarter-wave transmission line of 100 ohms impedance, such as a piece of coax, and then connect the other end across an impedance-measuring piece of test equipment, the reactance you will measure at the frequency will also be 100Ω, but it is now inductive, Xl = 100Ω.

This is a useful thing to understand as, in some cases, it is necessary to have an inductive reactance across a point, but it must not be a DC short. We could achieve this with an inductor and capacitor in series, but the series combination can then introduce an unwanted resonance. By using a λ/4 piece of coax with the correct value of capacitance and then connecting the other end across the required point, we achieve the correct conditions.

I did some modelling on the computer with different dielectric materials, and soon realised that none of them was good enough, not even PTFE, which is about the lowest loss available. I then modelled an air-filled line and voilà! I had the required Q. I made an experimental LNA using this idea and achieved a noise figure only 0.05dB higher than the theoretical minimum of the device I had selected. Prior to this, I could only get to within 0.2dB of the minimum.

This exercise taught me a great deal about low-loss matching. When dealing with high power, we can feel the effect in generated heat, with very small signal amplification it doesn't hit you in the face the same way.

I have built several LNAs using this technique, and every single one has got within a hair's breadth of the ultimate. One thing I also learnt was how awful some capacitors and connectors really are.

When striving for the ultimate Q, you need to look closely at all components in the input network. The tuning capacitors need to have very high Q; this means things like plastic film trimmers are not good enough. The only trimmers that come close are the microwave piston type made by companies such as Johanson; these have a Q of over 5000. These are expensive, but you only need one good one. The drain circuit can use almost any old thing!

Fig 8.13: Johanson microwave piston trimmers

Input Connector

Another factor is the RF connector that connects the antenna to the LNA input circuit.

I mentioned Chip Angle, N6CA, earlier and his low noise JFET design for 144MHz EME. I used to meet Chip at the Dayton Hamvention in the late 1970s when I had a company in the UK. My company was the UK agent for the Lunar Electronics range of linear power amplifiers. The company was owned by a ham who lived in San Diego, Louis Ancioux, WB6NMT, later KG6UH, who made the first EME contact on 220MHz. Chip made the Angle-Linear LNAs and supplied them through Lunar Electronics. One of Chip's other designs was a GaAsFET LNA for 432MHz. It was expensive and, because of this, we imported only a few. It came fitted with SMA connectors only. This caused a bit of a problem, as not many amateurs in the UK knew about SMA connectors or used them at the time. The SMA connector is rated up to 24GHz and is an excellent connector, having a very low VSWR up to 18GHz. When I asked Chip if the LNA for 432MHz could be supplied with BNC connectors, he nearly had a fit.

He told me in no uncertain terms that it was impossible to get the potential noise figure with such connectors. At the time, it did not mean much to me but, many years later, I saw with my own eyes what Chip meant. A 23cm LNA I built with the usual GaAsFET just wouldn't get down to the noise figure I expected. No matter what trick I pulled, it refused to go below 0.65dB. The device was good for 0.4dB so I was million miles away from my goal. After leaving it in frustration and going onto something else, it suddenly came back to me what Chip had told me all those years ago. The next day, I changed the input connector from the BNC to an SMA and hey presto, 0.45dB straight away!

Anyway, after that long diversion, I hope you now appreciate the pitfalls of building LNAs with the incorrect component types. As far as connectors go, forget about using rubbish like PL-259s - even on 6m they are terrible! Only use N-types or other microwave-rated connectors, even at 144MHz. The output connector is not nearly so sensitive and here we can use almost anything within reason.

> One of my favourite low-cost connectors for low power RF is the RCA 'phono' connector. Most people think this is only usable at audio frequencies - not so. If you look back at its history you will find it was originally developed as a low cost 50Ω UHF connector for wiring up the modules of 450MHz base-station equipment. It is, in fact, a very good 50Ω connector right up to several gigahertz. It unfortunately did not gain acceptance with the RF industry, and so RCA cut their losses and promoted it as an audio connector. However, companies such as Motorola used it extensively in its UHF equipment for power levels up to 50W without any trouble.

I have experimented with the $\lambda/4$ coaxial line design at all sorts of frequencies. One design used PTFE-filled semi-rigid coax, UT-141, for 144MHz. This $\lambda/4$ stub is quite long, but can be coiled up into a small space. After a struggle to stabilise the frisky GaAsFET, I achieved 0.6dB with 20dB of gain. The device I normally use, an Avantek ATF-10136 (now called Avago Semiconductors) is good for ~40dB MAG at 144MHz, but only an MSG figure of 24dB at 144MHz, so I had to throw away nearly 20dB of gain to get the device stable. The BF966S design for 144MHz regularly gets to 0.85dB with close to 30dB of gain. The difference in cost is over 5:1. So the GaAsFET isn't the cheapest solution at low frequencies.

Another surprising fact I discovered by accident, while modelling a new design on the computer is that, by paralleling two devices, the noise figure drops quite a bit. At first I thought that the RF simulation software was getting confused. I bounced the idea off the lecturer at the technical college and he promised to look into the oddity. He used a different simulation package, which cost about 100 times more than the ARRL package, and he reported the same results. Spurred on by this, I then took a standard production LNA and simply soldered another GaAsFET on top of the one in circuit and re-optimised the input matching and biasing. Sure enough I got an improvement of about 0.2dB. This has never been satisfactorily explained but it works!

LOW NOISE GaAsFET AMPLIFIER FOR 432MHz

The active device is the Agilent Technologies ATF-10136. The input tuned network is a 50Ω λ/4 shorted airline made from thin-wall copper or brass tubing. The inner line is a piece of 6.5mm OD (1/4in) tube of length 138.5mm. The outer tube is a piece of 15mm internal diameter. The inner line has a copper or brass disc soldered to the end and this is then soldered into the end of the 15mm diameter tube to provide a solid short circuit. The trimmer capacitor is a Johanson piston variable of approximately 5mm diameter with 5pF maximum. The exact value for resonance is calculated to be 1.7pF. If the exact diameters are not available, it is not too critical. The ratio of outer to inner for a Z_0 of 50Ω is 2.3:1. Slight errors in the line impedance are not too serious as the tuning capacitor has a wide tuning range.

The source inductance required is 3nH which is provided by leaving each source lead 6mm long. The source leads each attach to a 470pF chip-capacitor soldered to the ground. The 47Ω for biasing may need optimising for different devices. The important thing is get the drain voltage correct with respect to ground, a value between 2.75V and 3.5V is sufficient. The lead length of the drain load resistor is not too critical; the calculated self-inductance is 5nH. If it is a little higher, it will only change the gain and output match by a small fraction.

The input connector must be low-loss type such as an SMA. This is soldered on to the outer of the 15mm diameter copper tube with a 5mm hole to allow the centre pin to pass through and

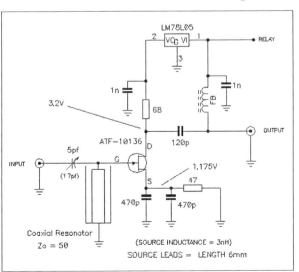

Fig 8.14: Low-noise GaAsFET amplifier for 432MHz

Fig 8.15: The physical construction looks like this

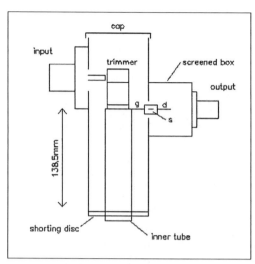

Fig 8.15: The physical construction looks like this

connect to the Johanson trimmer. The 15mm tube has a similar size hole drilled opposite the connector clearance hole, and a little lower down the 15mm tube, for the gate lead to pass through. This connects to the central line. The gate lead will need extending with a piece of copper foil. The remainder of the components can be built 'dead-bug' fashion into a small screening box made from tin-plated steel or brass which is soldered to the outside of the 15mm tube. The top of the 15mm tube is closed off with a plumbing cap with a small hole to allow the trimming tool to access the Johanson trimmer. The 5V regulator requires some extra decoupling capacitors to ensure stability, not shown in the diagram. Normally a 100nF capacitor from input and output to ground will suffice.

The drain does not have a resonant tuned circuit. This is because the stability criteria do not allow this at such low frequencies. The computed maximum stable gain (MSG) is 23.5dB. The drain load is a 68Ω metal film 0.25W resistor. This has a certain amount of inherent inductance and provides a good output match to 50Ω. The RF choke across the output allows the preamplifier to be line-powered up the receive coaxial cable.

The choke is 3 turns of 30SWG enamelled wire on a ferrite bead. If the LNA will be used with an antenna relay, the supply to this needs to pass out of the box via a feed-through capacitor of about 1000pF. A diode, such as a 1N4007, should be fitted across the relay coil to clamp damaging voltage spikes from destroying the GaAsFET. If a relay is not required, the feed-through can be omitted.

The drain is supplied with a 5V 100mA regulator operating from the main supply. The drain-source voltage for optimum noise figure is only ~2V. The resistor in the source sets the biasing to the correct negative gate voltage. The optimum drain current for best noise figure is approximately 25mA, which is quite a healthy current for a small signal device. The high drain current affords a good dynamic range and the preamp does not generate significant inter-modulation on a crowded band. Typical operating voltages are shown in the diagram, these are all with respect to ground.

Measured Results of the Prototype and the Computer Simulation

Parameter	Simulated	Measured
Centre frequency	432MHz	432MHz
Gain	18.26dB	17.5dB
Noise Figure	0.46dB	0.51dB
Ultimate NF	0.4dB	-

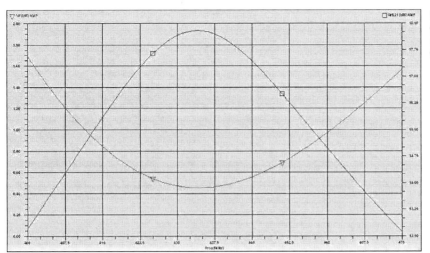

Fig 8.16: Plot of gain and noise figure for the 432MHz GaAsFET LNA

As you can see, the measured results compare very favourably with the computer simulation. The discrepancy in the noise figure is probably due to the loss in the input trimmer being higher than assumed. The automatic noise figure measuring system has an uncertainty of 0.1dB at these low frequencies. The Q of the $\lambda/4$ resonator was well over 2000 (the limit of the instrument) as measured on a Hewlett-Packard automatic impedance measuring system.

Tuning

Connect the LNA to a 70cm receiver and an antenna. Power up and check the voltage on the drain is within the tolerance of (3.2 ± 0.25)V. Adjust the source resistor value if necessary. Now tune in a very weak signal and adjust the Johanson trimmer, with a non-metallic tool, to peak the signal for maximum. When the signal has been peaked, set the trimmer approximately 0.25 turn more meshed to obtain the optimum noise figure setting. (The Johanson trimmer has approximately nine turns from one end to the other).

1296MHz VERSION

The same construction can be used for a 1296MHz version. The circuit follows the same construction details except the $\lambda/4$ line length required is 37.4mm. The trimmer needs to have a minimum value of 0.5pF. The source inductance only needs to be 0.5nH. Therefore, the source leads need to be 1mm in length. The calculated MSG is 19.3dB.

Simulated and Measured Results

Parameter	Simulated	Measured
Centre frequency	1296MHz	1297MHz
Gain	15.6dB	15.0dB
Noise Figure	0.46dB	0.48dB
Ultimate NF	0.4dB	-

As you can see by comparing the noise figure obtained with that of the 432MHz version, the GaAsFET is better at the higher frequency because of the easier input matching allowed.

249

Fig 8.17: Plot of noise figure for the 1296MHz LNA

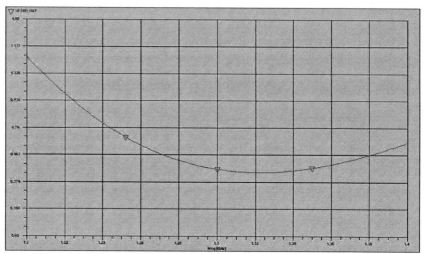

DUAL-GATE GaAsFETs

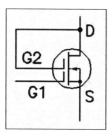

Fig 8.18: Dual-gate GaAsFET connection for maximum gain.

These are not as popular as the single-gate versions. The industry leader in this technology was Telefunken (now owned by Vishay) and several types were developed as low-cost devices for UHF TV tuners. In practice, they are very much like the dual gate MOSFET. The main difference is the obtainable noise figure and dynamic range, both of which are superior to the older devices. Like the single-gate variety, it does not have any gate protection Zener diodes like the dual-gate MOSFET.

The gate 2 terminal can be used for AGC in exactly the same way as for the DGM-FET. However, for maximum gain and lowest noise figure, gate 2 is connected directly to the drain.

Most of the circuits already described will work with the DG GaAsFET; they are almost a drop-in replacement for the older DGMFET devices and only the biasing needs to be altered. The safe drain-source voltage is a maximum of 5V, so the supply rail needs to be lowered to use them. The noise figure of a typical device at 1GHz is about 0.6dB, so they are slightly inferior to the single-gate types. Some type numbers are the CF-100 and CF-300, but they are obsolescent.

HIGH ELECTRON MOBILITY TRANSISTOR

Many of the traditional GaAsFET devices are now being phased out of production in favour of better types. One of the newer technologies is the HEMT and the PHEMT. These today have replaced many of the older GaAsFETs. There are many manufacturers of HEMT & PHEMT devices - NEC, Toshiba, Fujitsu and Agilent being but a few. In use, the HEMT and PHEMT are very similar and can be dropped into the earlier circuits with very little change required. They were originally very expensive, but with mass production they are now finding applications in all sorts of fields, the cellular telephone being the biggest user. They are available in plastic SMD packages and, whereas this gives an improvement in performance because of the very small packages used, it presents a bit of a problem for home constructors due to the very small size.

A typical low-cost device is the Agilent Technologies ATF-34143 or the slightly more expensive ATF-36077, which is a ceramic package. The noise figures obtainable are very low, the ATF-36077 being capable of 0.3dB at 4GHz and 0.5dB at 12GHz. The ATF-34143 offers a noise figure of 0.14dB at 1.5GHz and 0.23dB at 2.5GHz.

Things to be aware of are the two different types of PHEMT device available. The earlier devices, like the ATF-34143, are depletion-mode devices and hence require a negative gate bias. The later devices, such as the ATF-54143, are enhancement types and require a positive gate voltage. Of the two types, the depletion types offer a slightly lower noise figure.

Like the GaAsFET, the maximum safe drain-source voltage is quite low, typically 5V maximum. The main difference is the drain current. A GaAsFET device usually runs at between 15 to 25mA for optimum gain and noise figure. The HEMT and PHEMT require a larger current at a slightly higher drain-source voltage. The Agilent devices are normally specified at 60mA at 3V for maximum power output and about 20mA at 3V VDS for optimum noise figure. One of the benefits of this is the superior signal-handling capabilities. The ATF-36077 and the ATF-34143 can both develop +20dBm of output power (100mW). The output third-order intercept point is typically +36dBm (4W). Hence, they are very much better than anything else in coping with strong in-band or out-of-band signals.

ATF-34143 Electrical Specifications

$T_A = 25°C$, RF parameters measured in a test circuit for a typical device

Symbol	Parameters and Test Conditions		Units	Min.	Typ.[2]	Max.
I_{dss}[1]	Saturated Drain Current	$V_{DS} = 1.5$ V, $V_{GS} = 0$ V	mA	90	118	145
V_P[1]	Pinchoff Voltage	$V_{DS} = 1.5$ V, $I_{DS} = 10\%$ of I_{dss}	V	-0.65	-0.5	-0.35
I_d	Quiescent Bias Current	$V_{GS} = 0.34$ V, $V_{DS} = 4$ V	mA	—	60	—
g_m[1]	Transconductance	$V_{DS} = 1.5$ V, $g_m = I_{dss}/V_P$	mmho	180	230	—
I_{GDO}	Gate to Drain Leakage Current	$V_{GD} = 5$ V	µA			500
I_{gss}	Gate Leakage Current	$V_{GD} = V_{GS} = -4$ V	µA	—	30	300
NF	Noise Figure	f = 2 GHz $V_{DS} = 4$ V, $I_{DS} = 60$ mA	dB		0.5	0.8
		$V_{DS} = 4$ V, $I_{DS} = 30$ mA			0.5	
		f = 900 MHz $V_{DS} = 4$ V, $I_{DS} = 60$ mA	dB		0.4	
G_a	Associated Gain	f = 2 GHz $V_{DS} = 4$ V, $I_{DS} = 60$ mA	dB	16	17.5	19
		$V_{DS} = 4$ V, $I_{DS} = 30$ mA			17	
		f = 900 MHz $V_{DS} = 4$ V, $I_{DS} = 60$ mA	dB		21.5	
OIP3	Output 3rd Order Intercept Point[3] +5 dBm P_{out}/Tone	f = 2 GHz $V_{DS} = 4$ V, $I_{DS} = 60$ mA	dBm	29	31.5	
		$V_{DS} = 4$ V, $I_{DS} = 30$ mA			30	
	f = 900 MHz +5 dBm P_{out}/Tone	$V_{DS} = 4$ V, $I_{DS} = 60$ mA	dBm		31	
P_{1dB}	1 dB Compressed Intercept Point[3]	f = 2 GHz $V_{DS} = 4$ V, $I_{DS} = 60$ mA	dBm		20	
		$V_{DS} = 4$ V, $I_{DS} = 30$ mA			19	
		f = 900 MHz $V_{DS} = 4$ V, $I_{DS} = 60$ mA	dBm		18.5	

Fig 8.19: Typical performance characteristics of the ATF-34143

ATF-34143 Typical Noise Parameters

$V_{DS} = 3$ V, $I_{DS} = 20$ mA

Freq. GHz	F_{min} dB	Γ_{opt} Mag.	Ang. °	$R_{n/50}$	G_a dB
0.5	0.10	0.90	13	0.16	21.8
0.9	0.11	0.85	27	0.14	18.3
1.0	0.11	0.84	31	0.13	17.8
1.5	0.14	0.77	48	0.11	16.4
1.8	0.17	0.74	57	0.10	16.0
2.0	0.19	0.71	66	0.09	15.6
2.5	0.23	0.65	83	0.07	14.8
3.0	0.29	0.59	102	0.06	14.0
4.0	0.42	0.51	138	0.03	12.6
5.0	0.54	0.45	174	0.03	11.4
6.0	0.67	0.42	-151	0.05	10.3
7.0	0.79	0.42	-118	0.10	9.4
8.0	0.92	0.45	-88	0.18	8.6
9.0	1.04	0.51	-63	0.30	8.0
10.0	1.16	0.61	-43	0.46	7.5

Fig 8.20: ATF-34143 noise parameters as functions of frequency

Incidentally, it might be useful to explain the type-numbering system used by Agilent. The 'AT' prefix derives from the original manufacturer, Avantek, and stood for 'Avantek Transistor'. The 'F' suffix denotes it as being a FET. The first two digits are the generation of the technology, hence an ATF-10136 is an Avantek FET die process version 1-0. The third digit denotes the specification data, hence 101 is a version 1-0 specification grade 1. The last two digits denote the package type, a 36 package being a ceramic X package with cropped leads, an 86 package is a plastic version of the X package, and a type 43 package is the SOT-343 4-leaded version used for SMD.

The same generic device is offered in different part numbers - for example, ATF-10136, 10236, 10336 etc. These are graded parts, the premium device being the xx1 series; the xx2 series is a xx1 device process which does not make the tight specification, but is OK for a slightly less demanding application; the xx3 is an even less compliant specification, ie a dropout of the xx1 and xx2 series. Hence, the type xx1 device will be most expensive and have the best performance, the type xx2 should be slightly cheaper and offer a performance not quite as good as the type xx1 etc.

An AT-41435 is a bipolar transistor series 41 version 4 with type 35 package, which is the 36 package (ceramic X form) with the long leads.

During manufacture, all devices have long leads to attach them to the copper lead-frame that shorts all four leads together. After the device is processed, the final stage is to crop the device from the lead-frame and then the device is automatically tested and graded into gain and noise figure types in a test fixture. After testing, the leads are cropped to suit the customers' requirements. Hence, the long lead version is the after-test version and before further cropping and lead forming.

The same part-numbering logic is used for the Agilent MMICs. For example, an MSA-0886 is a 'Microwave Semiconductor Amplifier' type 08 and package 86. The Mini-Circuits Company also sells the MSA range, but these are even further dropouts. Avantek sold the out-of-spec devices to Mini-Circuits, which then re-graded them into the MAR series. Hence, a MAR-6 is a MSA 0685 or 0686 that failed to meet Avantek's tight criteria. The 85 package is identical to the 86, the 86 is the 85 with the leads cropped and bent for mounting on SMD boards; the 85 leads are full length. The difference in performance is very small and purely due to the extra length of the leads. Generally the '6' at the end of the part number tells you it is a short cropped lead version. The '5' is an uncropped type.

Avantek was bought by the Hewlett-Packard consortium and later the HP empire split up into different business units, the Hewlett-Packard name being retained for the computer division, the test equipment and semiconductor side becoming known as Agilent Technologies, so preserving the AT prefix. Note: very recently, the Agilent name has changed once again. Today it is known as Avago Semiconductors.

One thing to watch is the lead designations. In bipolar transistors, the lead with the chamfered end is normally the collector; in the GaAsFETs the chamfered lead is normally the gate and MMICs use the chamfer to designate the input terminal.

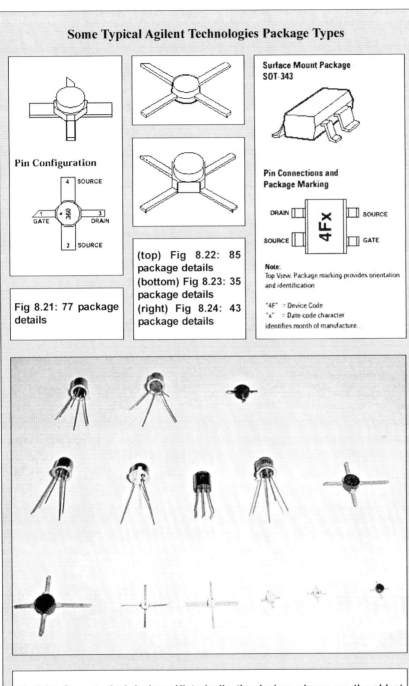

Some Typical Agilent Technologies Package Types

Pin Configuration

4 SOURCE

1 GATE · 360 · 3 DRAIN

2 SOURCE

Fig 8.21: 77 package details

(top) Fig 8.22: 85 package details
(bottom) Fig 8.23: 35 package details
(right) Fig 8.24: 43 package details

Surface Mount Package
SOT-343

Pin Connections and Package Marking

DRAIN — 4Fx — SOURCE

SOURCE — — GATE

Note:
Top View. Package marking provides orientation and identification

"4F" = Device Code
"x" = Date code character identifies month of manufacture..

Fig 8.25: Some typical devices. Historically, the devices shown are the oldest at the top and to the left, the later devices are towards the bottom and to the right. Top row: BJTs (left to right): MRF-903, BFX-115, BFW-92A. Middle row: JFET & MOSFETS: 2N-4416, U-310, J-310, 3N-201, BF-966S. Bottom row: GaAsFETs & HEMTs: CF-100, NE-72084, NE-71083, ATF-10736, ATF-10136, ATF-36086 (HEMT)

SHIELDING, FILTERING & SWITCHING TECHNIQUES

A LNA mounted at the antenna requires special attention to prevent unwanted signals from entering the enclosure. All LNAs will require two RF connectors and a means of supplying the low-voltage supply. The RF connectors need to be types suitable for the frequency range and of very low loss and VSWR. As well as this, they need to be weatherproof. Some types, such as the SO 239 / PL 259 families, are not low-loss, not low-VSWR or even weatherproof. If water can enter the LNA enclosure, degradation will result due to corrosion or other causes.

The DC supply to the LNA needs to pass through the enclosure with a decoupling capacitor to short unwanted RF interference signals to ground. The best way to achieve this is a feedthrough capacitor. However, the capacitor value chosen needs to act like a short circuit to all possible interfering signals. An LNA for, say, 1.3GHz could use a feedthrough capacitor of as little as 100pF to be effective but, at lower frequencies, the reactance to signals is too high to stop interfering signals effectively. For example, a 1000pF feedthrough would work effectively down to about 50MHz, but would be unsuitable for HF signals. Suppose the LNA is mounted close to a 40m dipole which has 400W applied. The radiated signal at 40m will enter the LNA via the DC supply lead and could be large enough to damage the sensitive device. Also, long DC supply leads act as good antennas to low-frequency signals, such as nearby lightning strikes, which can destroy a GaAsFET LNA.

The way the professionals get around these problems is to use 'belt-and-braces' when it comes to shielding and filtering. The best technique is the 'box within a box, within another box' approach. Each box is fitted with RF and feedthrough connectors so that the LNA is contained within several well-shielded metallic enclosures. Plastic containers are next to useless at RF unless they are coated with conducting metallic plating. Most types of plastic suffer from degradation from ultraviolet rays, which quickly attack the material.

The author favours a different means of supplying masthead LNAs, that reduces the amount of cabling required from the shack to the antenna. This is 'line-powering', where the DC supply is carried on the RF feeder between the receiver and the LNA output connector. This is inherently well-shielded and has the advantage that, when the station is switched off, the LNA is automatically powered down. The DC supply is fed via the receive feeder with a small accessory box that contains a bias-T. This is a small radio-frequency choke and a decoupling capacitor with a DC-blocking capacitor to convey the LNA signal to the main receiver.

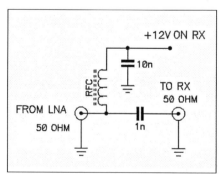

Fig 8.26: Bias-T schematic for controlling antenna-mounted LNA

A further advantage is that the antenna changeover relay can be controlled by the same DC supply that powers the LNA. In the simplest system, separate feeders convey the transmitter and receiver signals and only one high-power antenna relay is required at the antenna. The transmitter feeder can be low-loss cable, but the receive feeder can be something much higher in loss, such as RG-

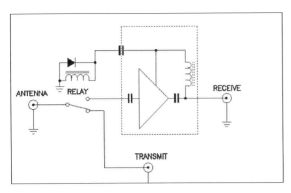

Fig 8.27: Line-powered LNA circuit. Relay shown in transmit mode

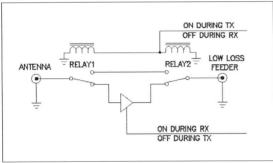

Fig 8.28: Antenna-mounted LNA with single feeder and two relays. Relays shown in receive mode

58/U, because the LNA effectively defines the system noise figure. Any loss after the LNA is not as significant as long as the LNA has adequate gain. The relay is energised during receive periods and the relay connects the antenna to the LNA input. During transmitting periods, the LNA is turned off, the relay drops out and connects the transmit feeder to the antenna. When the station is powered down, the relay drops out and connects the antenna to the transmit feeder.

This system is much less likely to cause damage to a sensitive LNA than the 'single feeder and two relay' setup. In this, the danger always exists that a large amount of transmit power can be fed into the backend of the LNA if relay 2 is slow to operate or fails. This will destroy the LNA in milliseconds! It also requires two high power relays and more control wires from the station to the antenna. High power relays with acceptable through loss are expensive! Even two very low-loss relays will supply less power into the antenna during transmit than one relay because the two relays are connected in series and hence the losses add. This may not be of much consequence on, say 50MHz or 144MHz, but at 432 MHz, 1.3GHz and above, the losses can be considerable.

COMMERCIALLY AVAILABLE LNA MODULES

Recently (2009) a new range of packaged low noise amplifiers has been introduced by Mini Circuits that offer good performance at an affordable price. The new receiver front end of the Durban Indlebe telescope uses these and the noise performance is lower than it was possible to achieve with discrete devices. The LNA shown is very compact and has a noise figure of »0.4dB at 1420MHz (measured in the lab over several samples). Another in the series is the ZX60-1615LN+ but this has a slightly higher noise figure of 0.5dB.

Ultra Low Noise
Amplifier

ZX60-1215LN+

50Ω   800 MHz to 1400 MHz

Features
- Ultra low noise figure 0.4 typ.
- 11V-13V operation
- Good IP3, 27 dBm typ.
- Reverse voltage connection protected
- Small size
- Low cost
- Protected by US patent 6,790,049

Applications
- Low noise amplifier RF front end
- Low noise pre-amp
- Buffer amplifier
- LNA for GPS application
- General purpose small signal
- Lab
- Instrumentation
- Test equipment

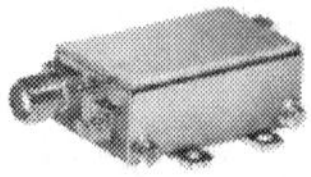

CASE STYLE: GA955

Connectors	Model	Price	Qty.
SMA	ZX60-1215LN-S+	$149.95 ea.	(1-9)

+ RoHS compliant in accordance with EU Directive (2002/95/EC)

The +suffix has been added in order to identify RoHS Compliance. See our web site for RoHS Compliance methodologies and qualifications.

Electrical Specifications at T$_{AMB}$ = 25°C

MODEL NO.	FREQ. (MHz)	GAIN (dB)				MAXIMUM POWER (dBm)	DYNAMIC RANGE		VSWR (:1) Typ.		ACTIVE DIRECTIVITY (dB) Isolation-Gain	DC VOLTAGE @ Pin V+ (V)	DC OPERATING CURRENT @ Pin V+ (mA)	
					Flatness	Output (1 dB Comp.)	NF (dB)	IP3 (dBm)						
	f$_L$- f$_U$	Typ.	Min.	Typ.	Max.	Typ.	Typ. Max	Typ.	In	Out	Typ.		Typ.	Max.
ZX60-1215LN+	800-1000	16.5	14.0	±0.7	±1.3	12.5	0.4 0.7	26.0	1.65	1.40	13	12	42	50
	1000-1400	14.5	11.0	±1.2	±2.5	12.5	0.4 0.7	27.5	1.70	1.40	13	12	42	50

Fig 8.29: Spec sheet and performance data for the Minicircuits ZX60-1215LN+ Low Noise Amplfier module (www.minicircuits.com)

Ultra Low Noise Amplifier

ZX60-1215LN+

Typical Performance Data

FREQUENCY (MHz)	GAIN (dB) 12V	DIRECTIVITY (dB) 12V	VSWR IN (:1) 12V	VSWR OUT (:1) 12V	NOISE FIGURE (dB) 12V	Pout at 1dB Comp. (dBm) 12V	Output IP3 (dBm) 12V
800.0	17.25	13.60	1.63	1.76	0.42	12.00	24.51
850.0	16.90	13.47	1.61	1.62	0.41	12.16	25.00
900.0	16.59	13.34	1.59	1.49	0.41	12.33	25.49
920.0	16.46	13.28	1.59	1.44	0.41	12.40	25.68
940.0	16.30	13.35	1.59	1.40	0.41	12.46	25.86
960.0	16.15	13.30	1.60	1.36	0.40	12.53	26.05
980.0	16.02	13.25	1.60	1.32	0.40	12.59	26.23
990.0	15.94	13.23	1.61	1.30	0.40	12.62	26.32
1000.0	15.90	13.30	1.61	1.29	0.40	12.64	26.41
1020.0	15.73	13.28	1.62	1.26	0.40	12.70	26.59
1050.0	15.53	13.34	1.63	1.23	0.40	12.77	26.83
1080.0	15.32	13.39	1.65	1.21	0.40	12.85	27.13
1100.0	15.15	13.39	1.67	1.21	0.40	12.89	27.32
1120.0	15.00	13.40	1.68	1.22	0.40	12.93	27.50
1150.0	14.79	13.43	1.69	1.25	0.40	12.96	27.73
1180.0	14.60	13.44	1.72	1.29	0.41	13.01	28.05
1200.0	14.45	13.51	1.74	1.31	0.41	13.03	28.23
1250.0	14.15	13.65	1.77	1.40	0.42	13.06	28.65
1300.0	13.73	13.78	1.81	1.51	0.43	13.05	29.11
1400.0	13.01	14.07	1.87	1.74	0.45	12.93	29.91

Although the cost at first might seem high, when the time and effort to construct one is taken into consideration it is good value for money. A direct comparison between the original receiver and the new receiver showed an increase of sensitivity of about 13dB.

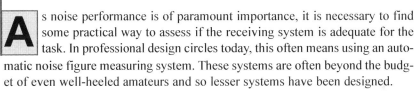

Assessing Receiver Noise Performance

In this chapter:

- ☐ Hot-cold noise source
- ☐ Broad-band noise source
- ☐ Professional noise figure measurement systems

- ☐ Myths about LNAs
- ☐ Noise figure test method

As noise performance is of paramount importance, it is necessary to find some practical way to assess if the receiving system is adequate for the task. In professional design circles today, this often means using an automatic noise figure measuring system. These systems are often beyond the budget of even well-heeled amateurs and so lesser systems have been designed.

The traditional method of assessing noise figure is to use a well-defined and stable noise source, which will give repeatable results with little error. One of the first types to gain wide use was the 'hot-cold' source.

HOT-COLD NOISE SOURCE

This consists of two low-inductance resistors with values equal to the system impedance, which means 50Ω today. One resistor is maintained at a very low temperature in liquid nitrogen or helium. The noise generated in the resistor is the result of kT times the bandwidth. Hence, as liquid nitrogen is close to absolute zero [77K], the noise generated will be very small. (At absolute zero the random electron oscillations stop and a resistor would become a noiseless source.) This resistor is the 'cold' source. The second resistor is maintained at room temperature, nominally 290K, and is known as the 'hot' source. Again, the noise power generated can be accurately calculated. In some systems the 'hot resistor' is maintained at the boiling point of water and this can be accurately measured.

The two resistors are connected to a low-loss changeover coaxial relay that allows either one or the other to be connected to the input of the LNA under evaluation. The output of the LNA is connected to a sensitive measuring receiver or spectrum analyser that can measure the absolute power.

In use, the LNA is connected firstly to the cold source and the measuring receiver sensitivity adjusted to give some convenient reading. This is the reference point. Next, the coaxial relay is changed to connect the hot source. With this connected, the noise measured by the receiver will increase. The ratio of the noise between the two sources gives the noise factor of the LNA, the noise figure being the logarithm of the noise factor. With care, this method can yield an uncertainty of about 0.1dB in the noise figure. This is, however, not a very practical way of making a noise figure measurement for most people, but is the de-facto standard against which more complex systems are calibrated. This measurement technique is known as the 'Y-factor' measurement. The ratio of the noise power measured when the source is the hot resistor against the cold resistor gives the Y-factor.

$$Y = \frac{N2}{N1},$$

where: N1 is the noise power with the cold source, and
          N2 is the noise power with the hot source.

The temperature of the two sources needs to be known accurately, T_H and T_C being the hot and cold sources in Kelvin. Knowing the two source temperatures and the Y-factor, the noise factor (F) can be calculated using the formulæ. Noise figure is the logarithm of the noise factor.

$$T_e = \frac{T_H - YT_C}{Y-1} \qquad F = \frac{T_e}{290} - 1.$$

> **Note:** In all the measurement techniques, it is essential to ensure that the only noise entering the LNA is the intended noise. It goes without saying that the LNA must be in a really RF-tight box. In receiver design laboratories, a screened room is used to exclude any interfering noise sources. In the author's professional work, the screened room had an attenuation of 100dB. When making measurements in the lab on the workbench, often an erroneous result would occur. This was often due to computer monitors, fluorescent lamps or coherent carriers getting into the sensitive LNA input. Usually, after work was the best time to make measurements, if the screened room was occupied for other tests. When all the other workers had gone home, computers and lights turned off, a drop in interfering noises of as much as 10dB was often noted.

BROAD-BAND NOISE SOURCE

A method used in early receiver design laboratories was a thermionic noise diode. This gives a well-defined noise power output over a wide frequency range. The noise diode output can be adjusted in level to give the required noise output. The variation of the output level is by adjusting the filament/heater current in the diode. The diode feeds an attenuator pad that sets the system impedance. Many professional laboratories used a Rohde & Schwarz SKTU noise source; this has a bandwidth of 1GHz. The noise diode has a limited life and, when the diode becomes old, the noise level drops off and inaccurate results occur. A replacement noise diode is very expensive and the cost of replacing one is often more than the equipment is worth.

In use, the LNA under test is connected to the measuring receiver or spectrum analyser and the noise power is measured with the noise source off. This measurement sets the zero noise level reference point. The noise source is then turned

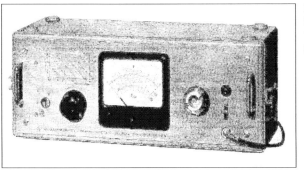

Fig 9.1: Rohde & Schwarz SKTU 1-1000MHz noise generator

on and the level adjusted to obtain an increase of measured noise power of 3dB, double the noise power. The SKTU meter is marked in dB of excess noise. The value of excess noise is read off as the LNA noise figure.

One problem with this technique is that the measuring receiver or spectrum analyser may be too insensitive to measure very small levels of noise power. In a case such as this, an additional low-noise gain stage needs to be inserted between the LNA under test and the measuring instrument. The noise figure of this additional amplifier needs to be accurately known, as well as the gain of the LNA. When this additional amplifier is used, the system measures the total noise figure of the two series connected stages. Hence, to calculate the first stage noise figure we need to use Friiss's equation to arrive at the correct measurement. (See Chapter 3 for details). When using the Hewlett-Packard HP8970, this can be calibrated out before the measurement is made. With a simple system it is not so easy to arrange.

Another measurement technique uses an accurate 3dB attenuator. This is connected after the LNA (between the LNA and the measuring receiver) and it is arranged so that it can be switched into and out of circuit with a coaxial relay. The noise source is firstly turned off and the 3dB attenuator switched out of circuit. The quiescent noise is measured as absolute power. Then the attenuator is switched into circuit, the noise source turned on, and the level adjusted to bring the measuring receiver meter back to the original point. The excess noise required to make the meter needle return to the original point is the LNA noise figure. This measurement method is known as the '3dB substitution method'. In reality, the two different methods are exactly the same, the difference being that it is not necessary to measure a 3dB increase on a measuring receiver. With the 3dB attenuator switched into circuit the only thing that needs to be done is to bring the meter needle back to the original point on the scale used as the reference noise level.

Today the majority of broad-band noise sources employ solid-state diodes. One advantage of these is that they hold their calibration for long periods and they can be gated on and off for automatic measurements.

Some early amateur noise sources employed Zener diodes. These are capable of generating a high level of noise power but a such a diode needs to be selected from a batch to find one with an acceptable noise output. The outputs are not particularly flat, and tend to vary with frequency. This is not too important

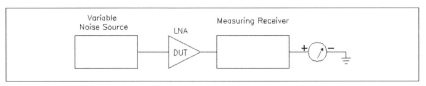

Fig 9.2: Noise figure measuring setup

Fig 9.3: 3dB substitution method

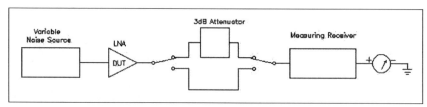

where only a spot frequency is needed but, if several amateur bands are to be covered, the accuracy suffers.

The noise diode generates an excess noise ratio, or ENR, and this characterises the device. Often an ENR of 15dB or more is possible with a broad-band noise source with a flatness of several gigahertz. The ENR is the measure of how much noise over and above the 50Ω room-temperature-generated noise is available. The HP8970 noise figure measuring system is equipped with a noise head that is calibrated from 10MHz to 20GHz.

Excess Noise Ratio is defined as:

$$ENR = 10\log_{10}\frac{T_H - 290}{290},$$

where: T_H is the effective noise temperature when the noise source is switched on.

A typical value for T_H is approximately 10,000K.

Various amateur designs have appeared over the years. Some are approaching professional systems in performance; others are simply useful as a tuning-up aid. One of the most popular was the G4COM design, originally published in the RSGB magazine *RadCom*, and can be found in the *RSGB VHF/UHF Manual* or the book by Ian White, GM3SEK, The VHF/UHF DX Book. This uses a noise diode selected from Zener diodes to give the highest noise output. The noise diode is gated on and off and the receiver audio from an AM receiver is fed into a quasi-logarithmic detector. The meter indicates the noise factor. When the LNA is optimised, the meter indicates the lowest reading. Hence, it is useful for tuning-up, but it cannot measure the absolute noise factor. An improved noise source is a reverse-biased emitter-base junction of an NPN transistor.

The circuit of this is shown in Fig 9.4. The attenuator pad is made from low-inductance resistors; chip resistors would be the best choice and these will yield the widest bandwidth. The 1nF output coupling capacitor should be a chip type for the best frequency response.

(left) Fig 9.4: Broadband noise head

(right) Fig 9.5: A home-constructed broad-band noise head. The head is built in a tin plate box. The BNC connector is for the pulsed DC input

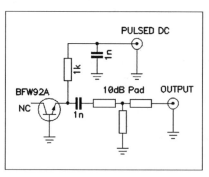

Some years ago, the author was in need of an accurate noise source for a military project. The cost of a packaged noise source was very high and it occupied too much volume. I experimented with the reverse-biased emitter-base idea and was pleasantly surprised at how consistent it was. Many different types of BJTs were tried, from humble audio transistors up to an exotic microwave transistor. The best performance was obtained with a 2N2222 with a flat noise power from about 10MHz to over 2.5GHz, the output level only varied by approximately 0.5dB over the range. In the production version, I used a surface-mount version of the BFW92A, as it fitted the layout better.

The circuit needs to be built into a well-screened box to prevent interfering signals entering. The noise output connector needs to be a low-loss constant-impedance type; an N-type or SMA is a good choice. The pulsed DC input can use a BNC connector. The excess noise ratio was measured to be 15.5dB after the 10dB attenuator, or 25.5dB at the transistor. This compares very favourably with noise heads costing many thousands of rands! The pulsed DC input needs to swing between zero volts and at least +8V for best performance.

The HP noise figure measuring system uses a 28V square-wave signal. The LNA under test is always terminated with a 50Ω load whether the noise source is on or off. The return loss through an unmatched 10dB attenuator is 20dB, which is equivalent to a VSWR of 1.22:1. In practice, the 10dB attenuator has some load on the input even when the noise source is off, so the VSWR will be a bit lower.

PROFESSIONAL NOISE MEASUREMENT SYSTEMS

One of the popular noise figure measurement systems was the Hewlett-Packard HP8970. This, in its basic form, could perform noise figure measurement and associated gain from 10MHz to 1500MHz.

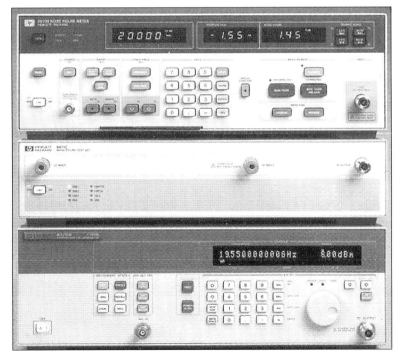

Fig 9.6: The HP-8970 (top box) can be used on its own or as an extended system with converter and signal generator for 20GHz range

With the addition of a wideband converter and a synthesised signal generator, the range could be extended up to 20GHz. Today, this system is no longer made by Agilent Technologies, who now manufacture the HP range of test equipment, but a more modern system has been introduced.

MYTHS ABOUT LNAS

Before I continue with details of a home-constructed noise figure measuring system, it is as well to highlight some of the misconceptions about testing LNAs.

When amateurs build an LNA, many believe that the extra receiver noise they hear when the LNA is connected is a measure of the extra sensitivity that the LNA provides. This is sometimes a false assumption. If the S-meter shows many S-points extra when the LNA is switched into circuit, there is generally something wrong. If the LNA had a 0dB noise figure, there should be an increase in ambient noise equal to the gain of the LNA. (If the LNA has a 3dB noise figure and a gain of 10dB then the increase in receiver output level will be of the order of 13dB).

If you connect a 50Ω termination to the input of the LNA and switch the LNA on and off, there should be very little increase in receiver noise with the LNA on. (The thermal noise generated in a 50Ω resistor at ambient temperature is low and so the input noise power to the LNA is also low). If there is a large increase in noise, the LNA has either a very poor noise figure or it is oscillating somewhere out of the frequency band for which t is designed. I refer to this type of LNA as an 'HNA' - high noise amplifier! If the S meter is sitting at S9 with no input signal it doesn't mean that signals heard are S9+. (S meters are normally calibrated in 6dB per S point, for an increase in noise level of from S1 to S9 this is an increase of 48dB).

To make an accurate measurement, you need to use a receiver with a fixed gain, if this is not possible, the next best option is to switch the mode to AM or SSB and turn the RF gain up to maximum. Set the AF gain to about half-way. Connect an analogue AC voltmeter across the loudspeaker or plug it into the headphone socket. Adjust the AF gain to obtain some convenient voltmeter reading towards 3/4 of full scale. Switch the LNA on and off and note the change in noise output power. A 3dB change in output is a 0.707 change in indicated voltage. The increase in noise power with the LNA switched on should be small if it has a low noise figure.

If the LNA passes this test, the next test is to connect an antenna to the LNA input and repeat the test. If possible, point the antenna vertically to a quiet portion of the sky. If the receiver noise is much louder with the LNA switched on, it is possibly due to the antenna being pointed at a noisy source, such as the Sun or a sodium or mercury-arc street lamp. If the noise drops when the antenna is rotated, the noise would have been due to one of these types of source. If the noise remains constant as the antenna is rotated, the LNA is almost certainly oscillating and producing a wide-band spectrum of noise. An oscillating LNA is usually a sign that the antenna matching is reactive and causing instability in the LNA. Most LNAs need retuning when attached to an antenna, as no antenna is a true 50Ω resistive load. A noise figure measuring system provides a very good 50Ω resistive load; in general antennas do not.

Another reason the receiver may show a high S-meter reading is due to reciprocal mixing from a strong signal that is out-of-band. The mixer in a superhet receiver is a very non-linear stage; it needs to be to perform the mixing adequately. If the presence of a strong out-of-band signal causes the mixer to be overdriven, noise sidebands of either the strong signal or the local oscillator can cause the receiver to show excess noise.

Generally, if the antenna is turned, the noise will diminish if this is the case. To prove if this is the cause, insert a step attenuator between the LNA and the receiver. If inserting a 3dB step drops the S-meter reading more than 3dB, the mixer was being overdriven. If the mixer is operating in a linear manner, the S-meter should drop dB for dB of attenuation inserted. Very often, the gain the LNA develops is too much for a sensitive receiver; a large increase in dynamic range can be achieved by reducing the LNA gain to the point where the gain just overcomes the feeder loss connecting it to the receiver. As the intermodulation process is a third-order law, inserting a 3dB attenuator after the LNA will increase the dynamic range by 9dB. Hence, a small amount of attenuation will bring about a large increase in dynamic range.

For good linearity, the noise power arriving at the receiver mixer should be not more than -10dB of the local oscillator power driving the mixer; it is better if the noise power is no more than -20dB of the LO power. If the noise power is comparable to the LO power, the noise is trying to take over the LO function. When you take into account the gain of the receiver front-end amplifier, which can be as high as 30dB, it can be seen that it does not take too much LNA gain to cause the mixer to be overdriven. If the interfering signal falls within the IF filter passband, the AGC will reduce the front end amplifier gain. But if the interfering signal is, say, 100kHz off the receiver frequency, the IF AGC detector will not see the signal. As most LNA devices give the optimum noise performance when operated at maximum gain, reducing the LNA gain will give an inferior noise figure. The only option in such a case to reduce the overall LNA gain is with an attenuator after the LNA. One of the best ways of adjusting an LNA connected to an antenna, is to tune in a very weak signal and select FM mode. Using a FM receiver, the change in receiver noise level as the IF quietens is a good way to see the effect of the LNA tuning. For very weak signals, the increase in sensitivity makes the receiver start to quieten. As the LNA is tuned, reduce the signal level by turning the antenna away to reduce the signal. Often, putting the beam antenna so that the first side null is pointing at the signal source will provide about 20dB of attenuation. Alternatively, use a step attenuator between the LNA and the receiver to keep the receiver just below the point of full quietening.

Another popular method of assessing the noise performance of a receiver is to use the Sun as a noise source. With the antenna pointed towards the Sun, you should experience a large change in receiver noise, the exact value is hard to give as the Sun could be experiencing a period of increased solar activity. However, a figure of at least 6dB increase is the average value that should be seen for a quiet Sun.

IMAGE NOISE CONTRIBUTION

This has already been covered in the section on receivers. If the device under test is a microwave converter with little selectivity, the image noise needs to be taken into consideration. To obtain a true measurement, the image noise needs to be suppressed by at least 6dB, and preferably higher, by either a narrow-band filter or an image-reject mixer.

For my EME system, I ran a twin-core lead from the shack to the top of the tower. This plugs into the headphone socket of the receiver. At the masthead is a headphone socket, into which I plug a pair of headphones. I placed a 'pip-squeak' transmitter about 1km away and adjusted the LNA at the masthead for best signal to noise by ear. With experience, it is quite easy to get within a few percent of the optimum.

**Fig 9.7: Noise fig-
ure test setup**

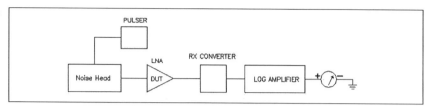

NOISE FIGURE TEST METHOD

The device under test (DUT) is connected between the noise head and a receive converter. The receiver converter feeds a logarithmic IF amplifier. The DC output of the logarithmic amplifier drives a meter. With the noise head switched off, the meter is adjusted to give a suitable reading. The noise head is now turned on and the change in meter reading noted. For a low noise figure, the meter deflection will be greater than for a LNA with a poor noise figure. The pulser circuit turns the noise head on and off rapidly, typically at a 50Hz rate, and the meter displays the difference between the noise source being off and it being on. With this type of automated system, the operator only has to adjust the LNA for the maximum meter deflection.

Limitations of Professional Noise Figure Systems

Many of the professional noise figure measuring systems, such as the Hewlett-Packard HP8970, have an IF bandwidth that is too wide for amateur applications. The HP8970 system features a 4MHz IF bandwidth and, whereas it is fine for LNAs of 432MHz and upwards, it is too wide for 2m and 6m LNAs where the typical bandwidth is only about 2MHz. This causes an error in the measurements. This error can be calculated but it is inconvenient. When the receiver converter has a narrow-band crystal filter following the receiver mixer, the error become high. An amateur system only requires a maximum bandwidth of about 2MHz and a practical system could use an IF bandwidth of as little as 100kHz.

Home-constructed Noise Figure System

The author built such a system, and it can cater for both 6m and 2m LNAs with a common local oscillator, mixer and a logarithmic IF amplifier. For other amateur bands, the LNA is followed by a receive converter to bring the first IF to either 6m or 2m. Thus, one simple set-up can cater for most amateur bands up into the gigahertz region. The logarithmic amplifier used the Plessey SL 1613 ICs and follows the design shown for the meteor receiver in Chapter 7. This only needs about a 20dB dynamic range, as the measurement takes place at very low signal levels. The local oscillator runs at 97MHz and the IF is at (47 ± 1)MHz.

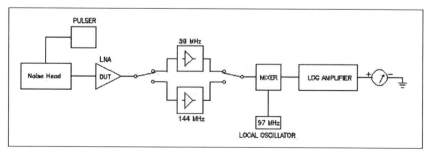

**Fig 9.8: The home-
built noise figure
measuring system**

The receiver features two RF amplifiers, which can feed a common mixer. In use, the 2m or 6m front end is switched into circuit as required.

The pulsating DC video output from the logarithmic amplifier is fed into a 'switching-summing' stage. This circuit comprises of two RC low-pass filters which store the signal voltages, and they are connected to the input of high impedance op-amp differential voltage measuring stage. This circuitry is driven by the same pulse signal that switches on the noise head. In use, the switching summer gives a direct reading of the ratio between the noise source being on and off.

Calibration of the system uses a low value 50Ω attenuator. These can be purchased quite cheaply or constructed to be very accurate using chip resistors. To calibrate the system, the DUT is removed and a 3dB, 6dB or 10dB attenuator is connected between the noise head and the front-end amplifier. The instrument is adjusted to give full scale on the meter.

The meter is scaled for 3dB, 6dB and 10dB, with increments in between the main marks. (To calibrate the 3dB range fully, for example, you will require accurate 1dB, 2dB and 3dB attenuators. These points are marked on the meter scale.) After calibration, the attenuator is removed, the DUT is connected and the noise figure is read directly from the meter. The noise head is the reverse-biased npn transistor shown earlier, and this gives a flat noise output up to at least 2GHz.

As the SL-1613 is now obsolete, an alternative devices is either the Analog Devices AD 606 log-amplifier IC or a Philips NE-604 FM IF with RSSI. The NE-604 has an operating frequency of only about 1MHz maximum, and so it needs to be preceded by a down-converter, such as the NE 602 mixer, or the composite versions containing the mixer and IF in one package, such as the NE-605/615. These operate very well at about 45MHz, so will fit the application nicely. Normally, the NE-604 IF will use a 455kHz ceramic filter to set the system bandwidth.

Fig 9.9: 47MHz logarithmic amplifier using Plessey SL-1613 IC

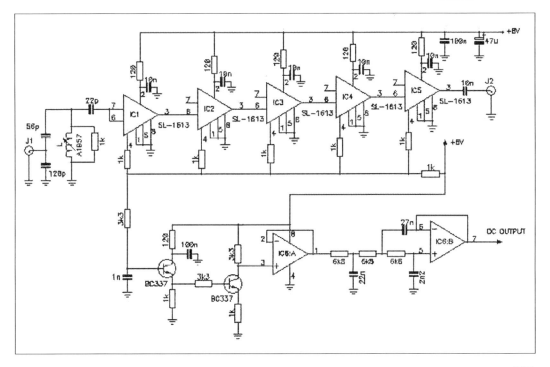

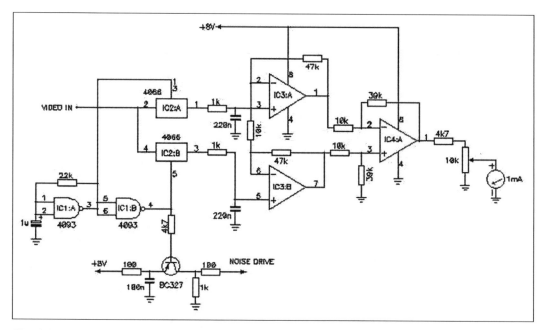

Fig 9.10: Control circuit

Control Circuit

This circuit generates the low-frequency square-wave signal to switch the noise head on and off, and performs the summing and meter-drive circuitry. The circuit is fed from a LM7808 voltage regulator.

The input signal from the log-amplifier is gated in two analogue switches by the drive signals. One drive signal is 180° out of phase with the other. IC1A is configured as a square-wave oscillator giving a pulse of approximately 20ms in duration. The signal is inverted in IC1B. When the output from IC1B goes low, the PNP transistor is turned on and the noise head receives a +8V supply. When IC1B output is high, the noise head is off. IC1A drives one of the analogue switch control lines that switch the video signal from the log-amplifier. While this switch is closed, the video voltage builds up across the 220n reservoir capacitor. This voltage is applied to the input of IC3A. This occurs when the noise head is on.

When IC1B output is high, the noise head is turned off and the first analogue switch is opened; the second analogue switch is now closed to pass the video voltage to the second half of the dual op amp, IC3B. The two outputs of IC3 are connected to IC4, and this is configured as a differential amplifier with feedback. The difference in the video voltage between the noise head being on and it being off generates a DC voltage proportional to the difference in the log-amplifier video output DC levels. This is used to drive the 1mA display meter. The full-scale deflection is adjusted by the 10kΩ calibration pot.

Station Accessories

In this chapter:

☐ Narrow band audio filter
☐ Low power 'pip-squeak'
    signal source
☐ Meteor 'ping' detector circuit

☐ Meteor radar product detector
☐ Linear IF and detector

H ere are a few bits of circuitry that I have gathered over the years. Most of these station accessories can be built in an evening and cost very little.

A NARROW BAND AUDIO FILTER

This audio filter is the one I use for my EME station and it makes a large improvement for weak signal reception. The filter has a bandwidth of 40Hz with a Q of 25 and is centred at about 800Hz. It is based on an application note by National Semiconductors. As with most very narrow-band filters, it is prone to ringing on strong signals. The circuit uses a dual op-amp such as a LM358N. The non-inverting inputs are biased to half the supply rail and decoupled with a 10µF electrolytic capacitor. The tuning capacitors are 10nF close-tolerance types such as a Wima polycarbonate; they all need to be the same value so, if

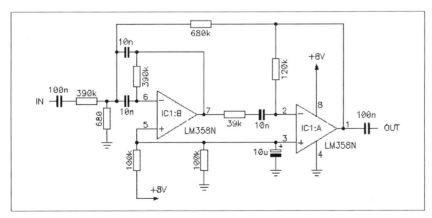

Fig 10.1: High-Q active audio filter

267

possible, use your DVM on the capacitance range to check that they are within a few percent of each other. The resistors are all 0.25W metal film types of 2% tolerance.

The filter is inserted into the audio stages of the receiver, between the volume control slider and the input to the power amplifier stages. A double-pole-double-throw switch (DPDT) can be used to switch it in and out of circuit. If you want to tune the exact centre frequency, the 680Ω input resistor can be made variable.

LOW POWER 'PIP-SQUEAK' SIGNAL SOURCE

When adjusting a sensitive front-end, it is often hard to find a stable weak signal when you need one, especially on the higher bands. This little circuit provides a reasonably stable carrier and it can be placed up to a few hundred metres away with a small antenna to radiate a tuning signal. The frequency of operation depends on the crystal used and the multiplication. This signal source was built to optimise a 1296MHz receiving system. The basic circuit can be used on any VHF or UHF band by changing the crystal and substituting a suitable output tuned circuit. For example, a 144MHz version could use a 24, 16, 12 or 8MHz crystal. This would provide signals for 144 and 432MHz. For this version a centre-tapped air-coil would be used instead of the line shown.

The crystal oscillator is a Colpitts circuit with a series mode crystal. (If a low frequency fundamental crystal such as 8 or 12MHz is used, the 560Ω resistor across the crystal should be removed.) The output of the oscillator drives a switching diode multiplier to the final frequency. A λ/2 tuned line selects the required crystal harmonic. The line is cut from a piece of brass shim-stock 6mm wide and 0.2mm thick, the ends bent through 90 degrees and soldered to a piece of single-sided copper-clad board. The bends should be so as to raise the line 6mm off the copper-clad board surface. The length of the line is 50mm. The trimmer capacitor is connected to the centre of the line and ground. The diode tap point and the antenna connector should be approximately 1/3 of the way up from the grounded ends. The rest of the components are built 'dead bug' fashion on the board.

A small whip antenna can be connected to radiate the desired level of signal, or the signal directly connected with a coaxial cable to the receiving converter

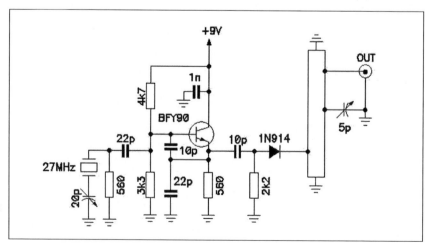

Fig 10.2: 1296MHz 'Pip-Squeak' signal source

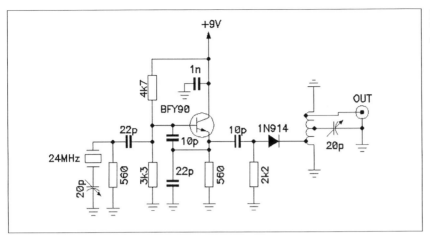

Fig 10.3: 144MHz 'Pip-Squeak' signal source

or LNA. The crystal used in this circuit is a 27MHz 3rd-overtone type. The diode multiplier generates harmonics and the half-wave tuned line picks off the 48th. A trimmer capacitor in series with the crystal allows the exact frequency to be set. The output at 1296MHz is approximately -90dBm, which is strong enough to find when a receive converter or LNA is first tuned up. With lower frequency versions, the output power would be greater. The oscillator is powered by a 9V transistor radio battery.

METEOR 'PING' DETECTOR CIRCUIT

When running a meteor radar system, it is useful to be able to hear when an echo occurs and to be able to record it on a cassette recorder. With the author's system, there is no audio output, only a varying DC output from the log-amplifier. The meteor radar design shown in Chapter 7 makes provision for an output from the last log-amp stage to drive a demodulator. This signal at 10.7MHz can be fed into a product detector and the audio then amplified to drive a small loudspeaker. However, it is rather tiring listening to the constant receiver noise while waiting for a random echo.

The circuit shown uses the log-amplifier DC output to trigger an external audio generator. The DC output from the log-amplifier is fed into a comparator (IC1A) with an adjustable threshold set by VR1. When the receiver output

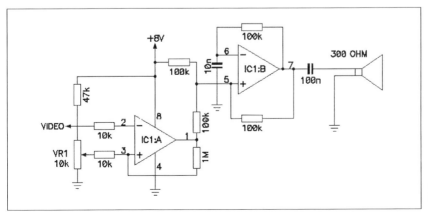

Fig 10.4: Meteor 'ping' detector

Fig 10.5: Product detector circuit

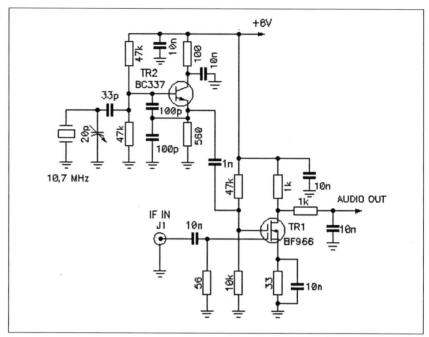

exceeds the threshold, a square wave audio oscillator (IC1B) is gated on for the duration of the echo pulse. The oscillator frequency is set by the 10nF capacitor on pin 6 of IC1B. With the values shown, it will be approximately 1kHz. The oscillator output drives a 300Ω earpiece. The op-amps can be either LM741 types or a dual type such as LM358N.

METEOR RADAR PRODUCT DETECTOR

For those who wish to build a product detector for hearing the receiver noises, the circuit below will provide demodulation of the 10.7MHz carrier. This detector provides an output of about 500mV of audio and this should be fed via an audio low-pass filter and then into a suitable audio power amplifier.

The CIO (carrier insertion oscillator) uses a 10.7MHz fundamental crystal configured as a Colpitts oscillator. A variable capacitor across the crystal serves to trim it onto frequency. The output of the CIO feeds gate 2 of a dual-gate MOSFET mixer. The gate 2 voltage should swing about 2Vp-p for best mixing. The 10.7MHz signal from the log-amplifier is applied to gate 1. The drain of the MOSFET has a 1kΩ resistor and a RC low-pass filter to stop the RF from entering the audio amplifier.

The circuit needs to be enclosed in a well-shielded box to prevent the 10.7MHz oscillator getting into the main IF amplifier chain.

LINEAR IF AND DETECTOR

This is a straightforward manual gain-controlled intermediate frequency amplifier and detector suitable for AM and similar modes. The amplifier consists of two high-gain MOSFETs with AGC applied to gate 2 of each device. The overall gain is approximately 70dB and the AGC range is of a similar level. The design frequency is 10.7MHz and the bandwidth is about 200kHz. For narrow-

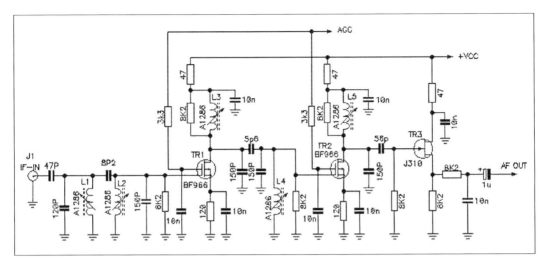

Fig 10.6: Dual-gate MOSFET IF amplifier and detector

er band applications, the use of a crystal filter before the amplifier will be needed. The input of the amplifier accepts a 50Ω signal.

The detector uses a junction FET configured as an infinite impedance detector. This is a very good AM demodulator with low distortion of signals up to 100% modulation. For general use, the audio can be filtered and fed into an audio amplifier. The signal appearing across the source resistor consists of a DC component, relative to the strength of the carrier, and the demodulated AM signal. The AGC voltage needs to be supplied externally and should swing from 0V for minimum gain to +6V for maximum gain. The supply voltage should be between 8V and 15V.

As the gain is high, the layout needs to be carefully done. A double-sided board with the top foil used as a ground plane would be the best approach. The inductors have a nominal value of 1.25µH.

Low Frequency Radio Astronomy

In this chapter:

- Jupiter signals
- Directional beams
- The Io effect
- Receiving the noise storms
- Lower frequency experiments

Whereas many amateurs are under the belief that the frequencies used for radio astronomy are in the VHF, UHF and microwave spectrum, this is not so. There are several lower-frequency bands where radio noise from planets and other objects emit strong radio signals.

We have already mentioned one meteor radar system operated by the University of Adelaide, Australia on 2MHz and further details will be given later.

For the amateur with a limited station, a topic that is of much interest is HF radio astronomy. The following is based upon an article written by Jim Kennedy, K6MIO / WB4OUC of the University of Florida, USA. It was first published in the August 1971 edition of *73 Magazine*.

JUPITER SIGNALS

The story of the puzzle begins in 1955 when two astronomers, K L Franklin and Bernard Burke, were testing a new 22MHz radio telescope. Quite unexpectedly, they discovered strong sporadic emissions from the vicinity of the planet Jupiter.

Jupiter is the largest of the planets in our solar system. This giant has a diameter that is more than 12 times that of Earth and it is so massive that it is believed it just missed becoming a star. Its surface is shrouded by layers of cloud beyond which lie 12 known moons. The four largest of these moons are bright enough to be seen with a pair of binoculars. In fact, Galileo discovered them the first time he turned his primitive telescope on this bright object.

In the years since the initial discovery of these radio signals, investigations have led to a number of interesting discoveries. Among these are that the emissions are essentially confined to a region below 30MHz, ie the region covered by normal communications receivers. The energy contained in these bursts of

Fig 11.1: Typical pen-recording of Jovian signals

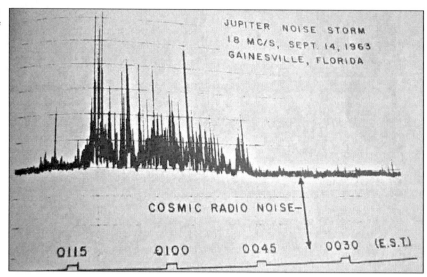

activity is so enormous that a simple three-element antenna and a communications receiver are all that is required to hear them.

The bandwidth of these signals is relatively narrow, sometimes no wider than 300kHz. Such an effect definitely points to a type of resonance effect taking place and being responsible for the generation of the signals. When observed, the signals may appear on one frequency and then gradually drift in frequency either up or down for several megahertz and then disappear.

It has been positively established that the lower the frequency, the greater the chance of occurrence. When heard with an AM receiver, the Jupiter (or Jovian) signals sound very similar to an unmodulated carrier being swished backwards and forwards across the frequency. Interspersed with the swishing are shorter pops.

The swishes, which last of the order of a second or two, are sometimes called L- (for long) bursts. The L-bursts are thought to be the result of scintillation (twinkling) of longer pulses of radio noise. The clouds of electrons that flow out from the Sun into the space between Earth and Jupiter cause this scintillation, through which the signal travels. The short pops are often called S- (for short) bursts. These appear to be caused by some mechanism at the source, and their explanation may well be an important clue to the cause of Jovian emissions.

DIRECTIONAL BEAMS

Another curious effect is that the signals seem to be directional in nature. That is, it appears as if the radiation is confined to beams about 70° wide and originate from specific confined areas of the planet. Observations indicate that the emissions observed are originating from no more than three or four locations that rotate with the giant planet. Radiation is detected only when those regions of the planet face Earth. Measurements made by two different techniques suggest that the source size has an upper limit of 400km, and may be as small as 3km.

Narrow beamwidth, directional beams, and fixed localised and limited sources quite naturally lead to speculation that the signals might the result of some 'intelligent' activity. However, partial explanations for these effects based on natural occurrences exist, and it seems probable that further investigations will, in time, complete the picture.

The explanation of the discrete sources may lie in the supposed existence of short variations or 'glitches' in the planet's magnetic field. Such anomalies are known to exist in the Earth's field and can be supposed to exist on Jupiter. Such glitches would be fixed in the planet's field and rotate with the planet. They could provide a collecting place for electrons at some level in the magnetosphere and perhaps provide a site at which some mechanism would excite these electrons into oscillation.

Another more recent explanation suggests that fast electrons following the magnetic field lines into the upper atmosphere near the north and south poles cause the radiation. These electrons would radiate in cone-shaped beams, due to the fact that the magnetic poles of Jupiter are inclined some 10° to its axis of rotation. This combination leads to the beams being aimed at the Earth during certain times of Jupiter's 10-hour day. This gives rise to the appearance of several sources, while there may as few as two. In a general way, this process bears some similarity to that which produces aurora here on earth. No matter which of the many explanations is correct, the combination of electrons and magnetic field would provide the necessary (gyro-magnetic or synchrotron) resonance effect for the narrow bandwidth emissions, but not necessarily the energy to produce the oscillation.

Just what source of driving energy does produce the oscillations? In the beginning, it was thought that the radiation might be caused by lightning strikes on the planet. However, measurements of the energy received here on earth indicate that the energy of the Jupiter 'noise storm' bursts is approximately 10^{11} times that of an earthly lightning bolt. Hence, this explanation is inadequate.

Fig 11.2: Showing the positions of Io which appear to trigger the various storms

THE IO EFFECT

Adding to the confusion about the source mechanism is the recently-discovered 'magnetosphere of Jupiter Io effect'. Io is the innermost of the four large satellites discovered by Galileo and is slightly smaller than our own moon. It has been found that a significant number of the noise storms occur when Io is in certain preferred positions with respect to the various source locations. Hence, storms may occur at any time one of the sources faces the Earth. Somehow, Io enhances the probability of a storm considerably.

The diagram illustrates this effect. When Io is at a position of 90° from directly behind Jupiter, one source, known as B, is most likely to produce storms. In fact, as high as 98% of all source B storms occur when Io is near this location. Likewise, when Io is at an angle of 240°, source C and

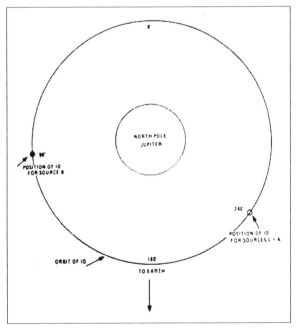

sometimes source A are likely to be active. Of course, not only must Io be in one of these special positions but, simultaneously, the appropriate source must be aimed at the earth.

One theory, called the 'dynamo hypothesis', holds that this moon, orbiting well within the strong magnetosphere at about 280,000 miles, conducts electricity well enough to interact with the rotating magnetic field of the planet to form a giant electrical generator. If this were so, in certain positions it could pump the large number of energetic electrons along the magnetic lines into the polar zones to cause the noise storms.

A full understanding of how this comes about will undoubtedly aid significantly in solving the basic problem of why the storms occur at all. In the meantime, the Io effect provides a convenient way of actually producing fairly accurate predictions of when noise storms will occur.

RECEIVING THE NOISE STORMS

Receiving signals from beyond our own ionosphere presents problems of its own. The same electrons that reflect 21MHz signals back to Earth and provide skip also reflect away incoming signals from outer space. Consequently, one must observe when the ionosphere is transparent. This means that observations must take place during the hours of darkness. This adds to the complexity of things, as it means that Jupiter must be visible at night. Therefore, it is only possible to listen for Jovian signals for a period of about 6 to 8 months in a year.

Receiving these storms is well within the capabilities of most amateurs who have at least a three element beam and an average communications receiver for 15m. This setup will produce excellent results. The only difficulty is that most tri-band beams do not point upwards, except maybe after a high wind! Depending on the time of night, Jupiter may be found as high as 40° in elevation above the horizon. Two possible solutions exist to cater for this. One approach would be to elevate the antenna to point at the source; this, with a small beam, is not too difficult to arrange. The normal antenna rotator can then be used to set the correct azimuth direction.

The second solution is to do nothing. All small beam antennas have a pronounced vertical lobe, which sends the signal skywards, either due to direct radiation, or due to reflection from the ground being very close to the antenna. Hence, if the antenna is pointed in azimuth to Jupiter there is a good chance of hearing the noise storms.

While Jupiter does not radiate at 21MHz continuously, the Io effect permits fairly good predictions to be made. Since some storms occur without correlation to the Io effect, it is possible to observe Jovian activity on other than the predicted nights.

One should be careful not to confuse lightning discharges with Jupiter signals. The raspy crash of lightning is quite different from the rounded swishing of Jovian signals. Those living in areas of high electrical storm activity will hear a good deal more lightning than Jupiter. Likewise, in the early evening or towards sunrise, those within skip distance of such an area may also experience activity of this sort. Occasionally, if sporadic-E is present, skipped lightning may occur at any time of night.

Despite the very great similarity between Jovian signals and that of a carrier being swished across the frequency (when you use an AM detector), this is only an illusion. If you use a product detector, do not expect to hear a carrier going back and forth with a resulting beat note. Both cases will yield only a strong rise in the noise that sounds like a carrier on an AM detector.

The interested reader who wishes to pursue the matter further will find in *Radio Exploration of the Planetary System* [1], an interesting and very readable account of the Jupiter story. At a somewhat higher level, the article 'The Magnetosphere of Jupiter' [2], contains more information.

LOWER FREQUENCY EXPERIMENTS

Several experimental stations exist for observation of meteor trails and other upper atmosphere reflection techniques. One of the leading stations is the Buckland Park system operated by the University of Adelaide, Australia.

This uses an array of dipoles operating at 1.98MHz. In total, 98 dipoles are available and, by utilising beam-steering, the signals can be bent down to an elevation of about 45°. Azimuth bearings can be steered to cover a wide range. The antennas occupy an area of approximately $1.2km^2$.

The transmitter is a short-pulse type with a typical pulse length of 30μs and a pulse repetition frequency of 16Hz. The peak transmitter power is 50kW (24W average). Using this setup, it is possible to observe objects out to a range in excess of 160km. However, because of the MF signals it can only be operated during periods when the ionospheric D- and E-layers are depleted. This means during the night and before sunrise. This limits the time when useful observations can be made.

The advantage of the MF system is that it can obtain reflections from meteors at a greater range than those for which the normal VHF techniques are used. Many meteoroids are not stony in composition and hence do not produce visible trails. These tar-like meteoroids may constitute the majority of those falling into the Earth's atmosphere, as recent observations tend to support.

In correspondence received from Dr W G Elford, he had this to say about the Buckland Park VHF and MF radar systems.

"The original 2MHz system predates what we now call the VHF systems, which are two narrow-beam radars transmitting on ~50MHz with arrays of dipoles 100m x 100m which can be phased to direct the two beams ±30° from the zenith in the EW or NS plane. They were designed and built in the 1980s to study the dynamics of the atmosphere between 60 and 100km, deduced from the motion of the of the weak ionisation in that region. However, with the beams set at 30° from the zenith East or West, and North or South, they make excellent meteor radars at a PRF of 2000Hz.

"The 2MHz system was designed by the late Dr B H Briggs and myself in the 1960s to study the motion of irregularities in the D- and E-regions by sampling the strength of radar echoes over an area of about 1 km2, using 98 pairs of crossed-dipoles. It is still the largest 2MHz array in the world. Each dipole is connected to an individual receiver with underground cables of about 70km length in total. It has gone through about four upgrades in its life, as technology has changed. Following the most recent change, it can now operate in a beam mode in transmission as well as reception, and a student has just been awarded his PhD for meteor studies using the system. The only parts of the original system still being used are the 10m wooden poles supporting the dipole wires and the cables!"

REFERENCES

[1]   *Radio Exploration of the Planetary System*, A G Smith & T D Carr, 1964, (D van Nostrand Company Inc, Princeton, NJ).

[2]   'The Magnetosphere of Jupiter', T D Carr & S Gulkis, 1969, *Ann Rev Astron & Astrophys*, 7.

12

The Science of Meteor Scatter

In this chapter:

- Some history
- Meter trail reflection
- Peak times
- Formation of an ionised trail
- Doppler effect
- Fresnel zone effect
- Meteor types
- Ionised trail formation

- Radar scattering equation
- Optimum antenna elevation angle
- Antenna azimuth pointing angle
- The head echo effect
- Daily meteor counts
- Special antenna systems
- Receiver parameters

This chapter is not about meteor scattering operating procedures, enough of those have been written over the years. It is rather the explanation of the mechanism of how meteor reflections are produced and the limitations of the mechanism. From some of the comments written in the past and published in amateur periodicals, there seems to be a misunderstanding of the way meteor scatter arises and the best antennas to use for the mode. Because of some of the misconceptions, many amateurs are not getting the optimum performance from this mode of communication.

Meteor scatter is a special mode of communication by scattering radio signals from a temporary reflecting layer in the Earth's upper atmosphere. In fact, meteor

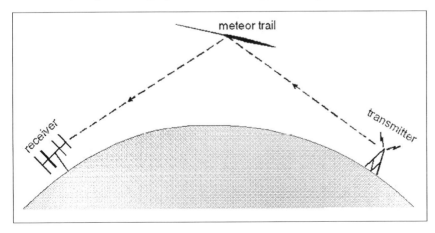

Fig 12.1 Simplified diagram of meteor-scatter propagation between two stations

scatter is a misnomer, as the correct designation of the small particles that cause an ionised trail is, in fact, a meteoroid. Meteors are defined by the International Astronomical Union as being objects greater than 100g in mass. Meteorites are larger particles than meteoroids that have sufficient energy to travel through the Earth's atmosphere, although suffering some loss of mass through friction, and eventually impact on the Earth's surface. The particles that generate meteor reflection trails are normally smaller than a grain of sand and have a mass of less than 200µg.

Nomenclature

To eliminate confusion as to the various names quoted about meteors in general, it is useful to note the International Astronomical Union's (IAU) recommendations for the names and their definitions.

Meteoroid: Dust particle moving in space or entering the Earth's atmosphere, where it is ablated.

Meteorite: Residual body that reaches the Earth's surface from space.

Meteor: The phenomenon of a meteoroid's interaction with the atmosphere, usually appearing as a transient trail of light ('shooting star'), and/or forming an ionised trail.

Meteor Trail: The linear nature of a meteor, implying luminosity or ionisation extending from the head. The term 'meteor' is frequently used in place of 'meteor trail'.

SOME HISTORY

Early observation of meteor-generated reflections occurred about 1925 when the HF ionospheric experiments first used vertically-directed beams to probe the upper atmosphere and detected the ionosphere D-, E- and F-layers. In 1932, an American group of scientists (Skellet, Schafer and Goodall), proved that the erratic echo signals returned to the low frequency MF and HF ionosphere sounding apparatus were caused by meteor-trail-generated ionised layers in the E-layer.

During WWII, British and American defence radar, operating in the low VHF bands, detected transient echoes that could not be explained. In late 1944, a civilian scientist working for the Army Operational Radar Group (AORG) of the British Army, James Stanley Hey, identified the source of the transient echoes as meteor-trail-generated reflections. This caused severe problems with the radar designed to detect the German A4 missile, known as V-2 to the Allies (Vergeltungswaffen zwei - vengeance weapon 2). The V-2 missile attained an altitude of 100km, the same as the E layer, and transient meteor echoes on the radar systems caused many false alarms. When the threat from the V-2 missiles abated in the spring of 1945, due to capture or bombing by the allied forces, and after the war finished, Hey and others at AORG HQ at Richmond Park continued studying the transient echoes in more detail. A modified V-2 detection radar, a GL2 (Gun-Laying Type 2) radar system fitted with four-element Yagi antennas was operated on about 5m by Hey at AORG HQ and Dr Bernard Lovell at Manchester University, Jodrell Bank Experimental Station, (using a similar radar supplied by Hey operating on 4m). In early 1946, they independently observed transient echoes from meteor trails. A surprising discovery, originally made by Hey and his team and later confirmed by Bernard Lovell at Jodrell Bank, was the existence of daytime meteor showers. Up until this discovery, it had been presumed that meteor showers only occurred during nighttime. From this point, the science of meteor radar has grown rapidly, and today there are many meteor radar systems throughout the world studying this field.

METEOR TRAIL REFLECTION

The generation of an ionised trail that can reflect radio signals depends on several factors. The velocity that the space débris enters the Earth's atmosphere and the electron density in the upper atmosphere at which it occurs are the two main parameters. Meteors and meteoroids are lumps of space débris or tiny specks of dust that travel in an elliptical orbit around the Sun and Earth. The period for one complete revolution around the Sun and Earth is one Earth year, or about 365 days.

Meteors and meteoroids are often associated with the tails of comets. Other types of annual major meteor showers occur at the same time every year. The Perseids shower, for example, is the result of débris from the Swift-Tuttle 1862 III comet. The Orionids shower has a measured age of 2.3×10^4 years. These major annual showers number about 20 but there are also many hundreds of minor showers occurring throughout the year, many of which have, as yet, no names. Some of the well-known showers are the Geminids, Leonids, Perseids etc. The names given to showers have nothing to do with their origin; the name is used because, when viewed visually, they appear to emanate from a particular constellation, for example, Leonids appear to have their radiant pointing towards the constellation of Leo. Although the origin of the débris is a comet, gravitational forces of the Sun and Earth pull the dust particles into orbit around these two large objects. Comets have orbital period of a few years or up to several hundred years; meteors have orbital periods of approximately 365 days. The tails of comets stretch out behind them for distances of up to a million kilometres. When the Earth's orbit sweeps through the cometary tail, meteors result.

Carl Sagan and Ann Druyan, in their book *Comet*, give a detailed account of how meteors are formed, and why major meteor showers occur at the same time every year. From year to year the magnitudes of the showers vary; some years are considerably better than others. This is because the comet has a very long orbital period, some as long as 100 years or more and some measured in thousands of years, and the amount of débris depends how close the comet approaches the Sun and how often. In years far removed from the last transit of the comet around the Sun and Earth the débris will be diminished. As has often been observed, some of the traditional meteor showers sometimes fail to live up to expectation. This is because the period since the last orbit of the Sun and Earth is too long and the amount of débris deposited from the comet's tail has been reduced. After the next transit of the Sun and Earth the shower activity will rise again to a new peak.

Some comets known in previous years no longer exist, as they have been entirely depleted by coming too close to the Sun. Comets sometimes appear from nowhere and several new comets have been found in recent years with

Fig 12.2: The orbit of the comet deposits a long string of débris as it orbits the Sun

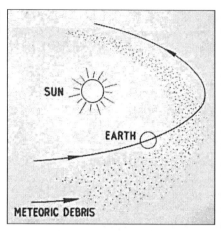

SUN

EARTH

METEORIC DEBRIS

orbital periods of only a few years; these are not likely to exist for very long, as they have orbital periods that will cause rapid depletion from the heat of the Sun.

The structure of a comet was first postulated by the American astronomer Fred Whipple, who described it is a 'dirty snowball'. The core of the comet is composed of frozen gas such as carbon dioxide, carbon monoxide, methane, ammonia, etc, or water. As the comet moves through the outer depths of the solar system, which is close to absolute zero in temperature, it picks up minute specks of interplanetary débris, which become stuck to the snowball core. This process can occupy millions of years.

For the comet's trajectory to be altered to swing around the Sun, it needs to be acted on by the gravitational pull of one of the larger outer planets, such as Venus. When the comet transits the Sun, some of the frozen gases are boiled off due to the intense heat and these release the dust particles to trail behind the comet. The altered orbital trajectory may now encompass the Earth, and the comet débris ejected from the tail will remain in orbit around the Sun and Earth, unless acted upon by another large planetary body. The familiar tail of a comet can stretch for 10^6km or more in the wake of the comet, and it is composed of dust and ice crystals from the comet core. The average dust particle is extremely small, often much smaller than a pinhead. High-flying aircraft have collected comet débris on sticky gel-coated panels and brought them back to Earth for study.

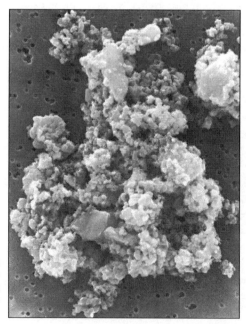

Fig 12.3: Electron microscope photograph of a comet dust particle, diameter 10µm

The escape velocity of a satellite orbiting the Earth and Sun is approximately 43kms[-1]. The Earth orbits the Sun at a speed of 29.8kms[-1], hence the velocity of meteors will lie in the region of the sum and difference of these two velocities, or approximately 12.5kms[-1] to 73kms[-1]. All the space débris and other particles that constitute comets, meteors and meteoroids are what are known as 'interstellar matter' and hence remain in orbit in our solar system. The origin of the débris responsible for meteors is usually cast off from a comet, which is a not in an annual orbit but some longer period, some of which are of up to 1000 years. The débris becomes trapped in an elliptical orbit around the Earth and the Sun and gradually gets drawn in by the gravitational pull of each object. To date, no meteors or meteoroids with a velocity in excess of 73kms-1 have been observed; if they had, it would mean that the object was not interstellar but 'extra-galactic', being from a solar system different from that of the Earth. When a meteor shower occurs, the material descending into the Earth's atmosphere is probably in excess of 10^6 years old.

The meteor rate per hour during a shower can be very high. In the Giacobinid-Zinner comet shower (the Draconids) that occurred in November 1946, Dr Bernard Lovell at Jodrell Bank established the count rate to be as high as 168 per minute at the peak. Hence, meteor scatter communication using one of these high-rate showers is almost continuous, allowing the use of SSB. Lesser showers have lower rates and the meteor-trail-generated reflections are shorter-lived and other modes such as high-speed CW or the newer digital modes are required to establish contact.

The common name used by amateurs for a short single event is a 'ping', being a transient echo lasting for about 0.1s to 0.5s on average. If enough individual pings occur in rapid succession, they are then termed 'bursts' and can last for up to 30s in favourable conditions.

Sporadic meteor trails occur throughout the year, on a day-to-day basis. Count rates can be as low as one trail every hour or two and up to 5 to 10 per minute, depending on the time of day. Until May 1945, daytime meteor showers were unknown, as the trail is not visible except during periods of darkness. Using the new radar technique, Hey established that sporadic daytime showers occur up to approximately 12 noon and then quickly taper off to a minimum during the afternoon.

PEAK TIMES

The period of the daily cycle where meteors are most common is normally after sunset, as the Earth is travelling parallel to the meteor's track. Activity gradually rises between the hours after sunset until about 2200 local time, and then rapidly reaches a peak at about 0500. From here, the activity declines from approximately 1000 to a minimum at about 1700. The diagram below shows the typical peak rate versus altitude and the minimum and maximum peak against the daily cycle. The Earth takes one sidereal day to complete one revolution on its axis, this being a time of 23h 56m 4s. (For convenience we round this time off to 24 hours and hence, every four years, we need to correct the time by inserting an extra day, this occurs on Leap Years.)

From the first graph, we can see that the predominant trails observable by VHF radar occur at an altitude of approximately 90km;

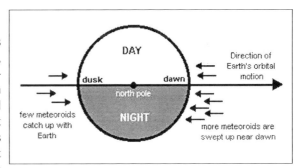

Fig 12.4: This is a diagram showing the direction of arrival of meteors. The earth rotates anticlockwise as viewed from the north pole. The Earth is also moving in an orbit around the Sun, from left to right in the diagram. For cometary trails approaching from the right, the velocity is maximum. For cometary trails trying to 'catch up' the Earth from the left, the incident velocity is much lower. Hence, the normal meteor trail is approaching the Earth head-on. At that point in local time and as the Earth rotates, the meteors will appear to rise from low on the horizon. As the Earth rotates further, such that it is at local midnight, the point on the Earth is now facing the meteor trails, it is at the zenith, and the highest peak is somewhere between this and the Earth approaching sunrise (dawn)

(left) Fig 12.5: Meteor echo altitude

(right) Fig 12.6: Hourly rate versus local time

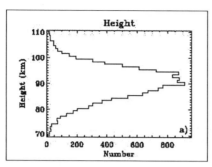

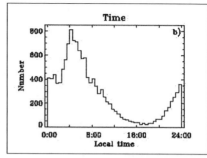

the maximum altitude is approximately 110km and the lower limit is approximately 70km. The second graph shows the 24-hour cycle of minimum and maximum; if the peak occurs at 0500, the corresponding minimum will occur 12 hours later at 1700.

The information shown is for the operating period of 24 / 25 July 2003, observing the Southern Delta Aquarids, using the Buckland Park radar at Adelaide, Australia. From this, it can seen that meteor scatter communication is very unlikely during the mid-afternoon but, for night owls, the dividends are enormous, as up to 800 pings per hour can occur in a good shower.

FORMATION OF AN IONISED TRAIL

When a particle of comet débris starts to enter the Earth's upper atmosphere, it experiences an increasing amount of friction as it collides with the rarefied atmosphere. The maximum altitude to generate friction is approximately 150km; above this altitude the atmosphere is too rarefied. The particle of dust, (meteoroid) travelling at a velocity of anything up to 72kms^{-1} relative to the Earth, plunges lower into the Earth's atmosphere where the friction generated causes it to heat up and eventually burn up, in astronomical jargon this is known as 'ablation'.

The ablation leaves a long relatively static thin trail of ionisation in its wake and these temporary ionised streaks in the ionosphere enable HF and VHF radio waves to be reflected while the ionisation is present.

The effect is very short - a typical streak decaying in about 0.1s to 0.5s. Dr Graham Elford of Buckland Park Meteor Radar facility, Adelaide, Australia, using a new technique, has managed to establish the diameter of the trail produced. This varies from approximately 0.4m to 2.5m, and the trail length can be as long as 25km under favourable conditions but is normally less than 10km.

The velocity at which the dust particle enters is dependent on the direction of approach to the Earth's atmosphere. The Earth has an orbital velocity around the Sun of approximately 42.8kms^{-1}. If the dust particle enters contra-rotating, the velocity is higher than if it enters in the same rotational direction as the Earth. Hence, the velocities typically measured are between 15kms^{-1} up to a maximum of about 70kms^{-1}. It is also useful to note that meteor trails do not normally occur at the Equator, they are confined to the two polar regions, the Arctic and Antarctic, and to places on the Earth's surface up to approximately 45° from each pole. For this reason, the best places to observe meteors are close to the poles.

DOPPLER EFFECT

One would assume that, as the meteoroid is travelling at very high speed, the Doppler shift present on a reflected signal would also be high. However, although the object that produces the ionised trail is moving very rapidly, the trail formed is almost static, being a locally-ionised streak in the upper atmosphere. This trail is moving only relatively slowly, measurements showing that this is only of the order of 2 to 10kms[-1] and is influenced by the upper atmospheric winds, the so called 'jet streams'. Hence, the Doppler Shift observed is quite low and not normally sufficient to cause the signal to move outside of the bandwidth of an SSB filter.

FRESNEL ZONE EFFECT

One of the early observations of meteor trail reflections using high power radar was the rapid variation in signal level whilst a meteor trail was present, about 15 times a second. This is caused by refraction in the trail-ionised medium, known as Fresnel Zones. Today, a lot of scientific effort is undertaken to use this variation in signal level and the phase variation of the returned signal to measure the trail drift accurately. Fresnel zone signal variation is similar to the 'flutter' observed when a VHF signal is reflected off an aircraft.

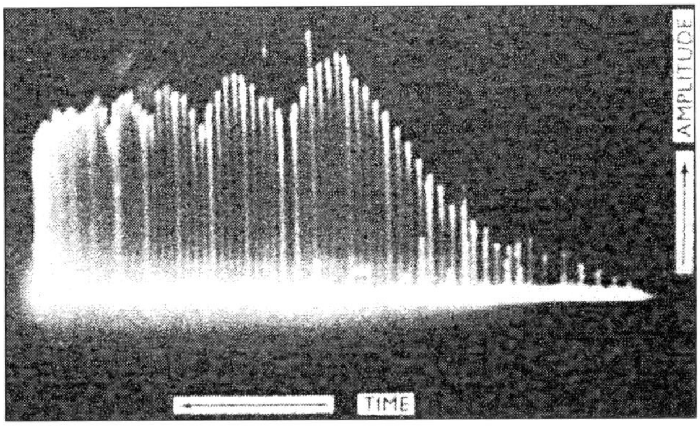

Fig 12.7: Fresnel zone signal variation

Ellyett and Davies identified the existence of Fresnel zone signal variation at Jodrell Bank in 1948. The previous picture is an expanded radar time base display showing the rapid variation in the echo signals from a transient meteor trail. Using the signal variation it was possible to measure the velocity of the meteor [1].

METEOR TYPES

There are two distinct types of meteoroid. The first is the one most people are familiar with causing a bright flashes of light, known as a 'shooting star'. The bright light is the result of the composition of the meteoroid and is caused by the metallic elements to be found in them. These types are known as 'stony meteors'.

The second type of meteoroid is known as a 'tarry meteor' and does not contain metallic elements to produce the bright shooting star trails. These types are composed of hydrocarbon. Hence, this second type of meteor is not normally visible. However, it does also produce an ionised trail, which reflects HF and

Fig 12.8: A stony meteorite recovered after impact with the Earth

VHF signals. The altitudes where each type produces ionised trails varies, the tarry meteors giving reflections at somewhat higher altitudes than the stony types. For most meteoroids, the altitude for the formation of an ionised trail is in the region of 140 to 70km, with a maximum occurring at about 85 to 105km. By the time the meteor dust particle has reached an altitude of 50km, it is completely burnt up, its velocity has fallen to almost zero and it exists as particles so small it is like smoke. These then slowly drift down towards the Earth's surface and eventually settle as fine dust. It is estimated that 100,000 such objects enter the Earth's atmosphere every day; of these, approximately 50% are moving fast enough and capable of forming ionised trails. Generally, if the velocity is below 40kms-1, the meteoroid is not capable of generating an ionised trail large enough for detection by low-power radar.

IONISED TRAIL FORMATION

The method by which the ionised trail is generated depends on several factors. The velocity of the meteoroid entering the Earth's atmosphere and the density of the atmosphere are the two main factors. A meteor travelling at a high velocity will generate more free electrons to form the trail than a slower one. The cut-off velocity is about $40kms^{-1}$. The amount of ionisation per unit length of trail depends on about the cube of the speed of the meteoroid. Also, as the density of the atmosphere is greater at low altitudes, the expectation is that upon first entering the rarefied upper atmosphere, the generation of the trail will initially be weak and it will increase as the meteoroid plunges lower into the denser atmosphere, with gradual deceleration occurring. When the friction generated becomes high enough to start vaporisation (ablation) the stony meteoroid, the 'shooting-star', will become visible to the human eye.

It is also important to note the importance of the approach angle of a meteoroid. If the meteoroid strikes the Earth's upper atmosphere at an angle shallower than 7°, it will bounce off and not enter the lower atmosphere. For larger bodies, on first entering the upper rarefied atmosphere, they will be slowed by the friction generated and the approach angle will become steeper due to the Earth's gravitational pull as the object is slowed down. In certain cases, the angle can attain 45° with the Earth's surface.

The writer has been in correspondence with one of the leading meteor scientists based in Adelaide, Australia. Dr Graham Elford has been studying the meteor ionisation effect since the early 1950s. Adelaide University operates two VHF meteor radar systems and also one operating on 1.98MHz from Buckland Park, near Adelaide. These radars are used to measure the upper wind drift on the ionised trails; from this information, the way the Earth's upper atmosphere moves can be inferred. The measurement of the trail drift is done by measuring the Doppler shift in the reflected echo and rate of change of phase of the echo signal.

Graham Elford describes the formation of meteor trails as follows.

"Assuming that the meteoroid has a stony composition (inferred from the spectra of bright meteor trails) collisions of the particle with atmospheric molecules cause the particle to heat and eventually reach ablation temperature. Just prior to ablation, a small particle will have melted right through, while larger one may have substantial radial thermal gradients. The transition size is about

200μm. Thermal gradients can cause fragmentation of the larger meteoroids, producing a bunch of particles all moving in essentially the same direction but becoming slightly spread along their path by differential deceleration depending on the size of the daughter particles. At the present time, there is no consensus as regards the prevalence of fragmentation, but my recent work in this area is partly directed to this question.

"Having reached ablation temperature (~2000K), atoms of the meteoroid commence evaporating into space while maintaining the speed of the parent body. Subsequent collisions of the individual meteoroid atoms with the (essentially stationary) atmospheric molecules cause excitation of the meteoroid atoms (typically Na, Mg, Ca, Si, Fe) which emit light as they decay to less-excited states. Molecules of atmospheric gases have higher excitation energies and thus there is only weak visible radiation associated with oxygen and nitrogen. Occasionally, a collision process is favourable to ionisation of the meteor atom and a free electron is formed. The associated ions are rapidly 'thermalised' by further collisions with the atmospheric molecules (~10 collisions, in about 1ms), and they and the free electrons form an ionised column (meteor trial) behind the ablating meteoroid.

"Ablation commences at a height of about 120km for meteoroids with speeds of 60 - 70kms^{-1} and at about 85km for those with speeds of 10 - 15kms^{-1}. The ionised trail diffuses radially at a rate controlled by the positive ions; a process called ambipolar diffusion. The physics of this process is well known from laboratory studies, and the ionisation distribution across the trail rapidly becomes Gaussian. As is shown in McKinley's book [2], diffusion causes the reflection coefficient of the trail for radar waves directed orthogonal to the trail (sometimes called transverse scattering) to fall off exponentially with time if the trail is under-dense (line density $<$~2×10^{14} electrons/m). The significance here is that this effect sets a height ceiling for scatter of VHF radar signals that is about 105km for underdense trails. For most meteor radars, the bulk of the echoes come from underdense trails. Thus, most VHF meteor radars detect almost all trails produced by meteoroids with speeds $<$40 kms^{-1} (assuming the trail line density is sufficient to give a detectable echo), but trails from meteoroids with speeds in excess of about 50 kms^{-1} form at heights above the 'diffusion ceiling' and are thus undetectable (unless they are members of the small population of overdense trails).

"There is evidence from the Giotto spacecraft observations of the dust around Halley's comet that there is a significant fraction of 'tar-like' dust, rich in hydrocarbons. Such material entering the Earth's atmosphere will ablate much more readily than stony material, and thus will form trails at greater heights, possibly as high as 150 - 160km. Such trails will not produce visible light, as the particles are deficient in metals. However, the trails will be ionised and should be detectable by suitable radar. Such a radar exists at Adelaide. Using an array of dipoles on 2MHz covering an area of about 1km2, we produce a relatively narrow beam that can be directed down to 45° elevation. With this system, we have detected echoes up to a height of 140km (roughly the 'ceiling' of the 2MHz system), thus confirming the existence of meteor trails at this height and, by implication, the presence of low ablation temperature material. The experiment is difficult, as one has to wait until the E-region has decayed sufficiently, which means observations are only possible for a few hours just before sunrise.

"At the present time, we have no idea of the fraction of 'tar-like' dust entering the atmosphere. I have conjectured that it might be the dominant form of meteoroid dust. Maybe the Stardust space probe will tell us. For the radio amateur, it is worthwhile keeping in mind that MF radio signals may be forward-scattered by trails at 150km when the underlying ionisation is weak."

The most important thing to note from this correspondence is that not all meteoroids produce a visible trail; in fact, the scientific community is tending towards the idea that as little as 50% of meteoroids entering the Earth's atmosphere will be stony and produce visible trails. Hence, although no visible trails are seen, the chance of a meteor trail occurring is quite high at any time of the day or time of year.

RADAR SCATTERING EQUATION

The equation for the radio frequency power scattered back to the radar receiver is:

$$\varepsilon = 3.3 \times 10^{-28} \frac{\alpha^2 \lambda^3}{R^3} P_0 G^2,$$

where: ε = Received signal power (W),
α = Number of electrons produced per cm path by the meteor,
λ = Wavelength (cm),
P_0 = peak transmitter power (W),
G = antenna gain (power ratio), and
R = range to the echo (cm).

Note: The antenna gain constant (G^2), being squared, assumes that the same antenna is used for transmit and receive. If two different gains are used for transmit and receive, this term is replaced by $G_t \times G_r$, where these are the individual power gains expressed as ratios.

The dependence of α on size and velocity is given in the theory of meteor ionisation developed by Herlofson [3], whose calculations indicate that a meteor of velocity of 40kms[-1] (a meteor near the limit of visibility), will produce α = 1 x 10[10] electronscm[-1].

Of significance is the effect the factor λ has on the echo signal amplitude. For low frequencies, the echo amplitude will be greater than for a higher frequency. As the factor is a cubed law, doubling the frequency will produce an echo signal that is one-eighth (~-9dB) of that at the lower frequency, for the same conditions. Hence, 50MHz will give correspondingly larger echoes than a 144MHz signal, by a factor of about 24 (~14dB) for the same system parameters.

Inspection of the equation will point to the reason for the lack of success at 432MHz. The equation contains the wavelength in the numerator and as this is a cubed constant, the higher the frequency, the lower the signal level returned from a meteor trail. At 432MHz, the signal level falls to approximately 1/27 (~4%) of that of a 144MHz signal, for the same electron density and meteoroid velocity. If the difference between 6m and 70cm is considered, the difference in signal level to be expected is 1/645, which is a difference of about 28dB. To obtain similar results at 432MHz as those at 50MHz would required an additional 28dB of transmit power, or 14dB more antenna gain to be used. There is, however, a second reflection mechanism that favours higher frequencies that will be explained later.

The signal level from a good meteor trail at 6m or 4m is quite often high, >S9+ in some cases and, using a modest antenna such as a six-element Yagi and about 100W, will yield good results on the 6m and 4m bands. For 2m, the ERP needs to be higher, because of the lower reflection coefficient of the meteor trail and the greater path loss attenuation, and this is most easily obtained by using an antenna with more gain. Using a 12-element Yagi should give good results with a 150W transmitter and an average receiver.

Plugging in some typical numbers into the equation for a 50MHz system yields the following.

Transmitter power	P_o	= 100W,
Transmit antenna	G_t	= 10dB (10x),
Receive antenna	G_r	= 10dB (10x),
Electron density	α	= 5 x 10^{10}cm^{-1},
Wavelength	λ	= 6m,
Range to trail		= 100km.

This gives a reflected signal power of 1.8 x 10^{-15}W.

Assuming a standard S-meter calibrated to 50μV being S9 and the steps to be in 6dB increments, the signal is equal to about S3. The above example is for a meteor trail near the limit of visibility, ie comparatively weak. From analysis of VHF meteor radar signal returns, the variation in reflection coefficient can be as high as 1 x 10^4 (10,000 times). Studies using a known system and measuring the meteor velocity allow the calculation of the electron density to be made on an echo-by-echo case. Hence, some trails will be much stronger and the received signals are also stronger. It is not uncommon to get S9+40dB returns off good trails using fairly modest equipment on the 6m and 4m bands.

OPTIMUM ANTENNA ELEVATION ANGLE

Studying results from scientific meteor radar systems shows that the majority of echoes occur from a region of the sky that is approximately 70° to the Earth's surface. A typical plot of meteor echoes is shown overleaf provided by Buckland Park VHF radar. This covers a 24-hour period and clearly illustrates the effect. The antenna system used is five separate dipole arrays, one being the transmitter and the others the receiver, with elevation angles of 0, 20, 40, 60 and 80°. It can be seen that the number of echoes when the antenna is at 0 or 20° is close to zero.

Fig 12.9: Buckland Park VHF meteor radar sky plot

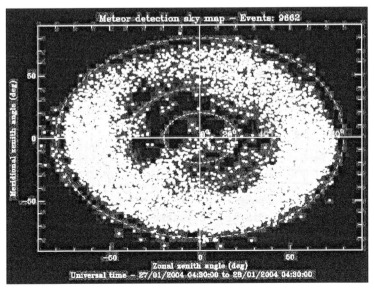

Fig 12.10: Buckland Park VHF meteor radar antenna system

Fig 12.10: Buckland Park VHF meteor radar antenna system

RANGE TO METEOR TRAIL

As the reflection occurs at an altitude of approximately 100km, the range to the reflection target will be of the same sort of order if the antenna is pointed vertically upwards. Meteor radars can measure the range to within ±0.5km and, knowing the antenna elevation angle, can compute the actual altitude using trigonometry. For antennas with a low angle of elevation, the slant angle range increases.

For example, if the antenna is only elevated to 30° the range to the meteor reflection point will be about 200km. This increases the signal attenuation, as the path loss is an inverse-square law. In the case of radar, and meteor scatter, the signal suffers two amounts of attenuation, one being the signal travelling towards the target and the second is the return path, hence the law becomes an inverse fourth-power law.

For a target at double the range the received signal power is 1/16 (-12dB) that of a signal at half the range. Also of importance is the noise generated in the lower atmosphere when an antenna is pointed close to the horizon. In such a case, the background man-made noise and sky noise will be at a maximum, and may mask the meteor echo signal.

For very low angles of elevation, the Earth's curvature also becomes a problem. The signal tends to be affected by the D- and E-layers, and hence follows the surface curvature and does not go in a straight line; hence the reflections off a meteor trail are much weaker, because little of the signal is directed to the reflecting zone. It is, therefore, highly beneficial to elevate the antenna as high as possible to obtain the best results. The distance that can be spanned by two stations using the same meteor trail is a function of the meteor trail altitude. For a single-hop mode, which is the most common in use, the distance that can be spanned with good signal levels is approximately 1000km to 2200km. This, however, assumes that there is a similar station within the distance 'window' to hear your echo!

ANTENNA AZIMUTH POINTING ANGLE

For optimum signal return from a meteor trail, the antenna needs to be orientated such that the meteor trail passes across the frontal lobe of the antenna beam, ie it needs to be orthogonal to the trail. If the antenna has a very narrow beamwidth, indicative of high forward gain, the success rate drops somewhat because only part of the trail is within the main lobe of the antenna. (This effect is not likely to affect amateurs too much, as the possibility of making an antenna with such a narrow beamwidth is extremely difficult).

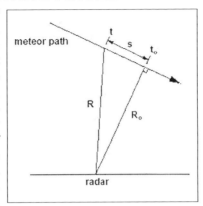

Fig 12.11: A meteor echo will only occur while the trail is within the antenna beamwidth. Hence, a wide horizontal beamwidth will yield better results than a narrow beamwidth

This reduces the total duration of the 'ping'. In practice, the arc subtended by the trail to an observer can be as much as 30°. Hence, for best results, it is better to use a wide azimuth beamwidth antenna. This factor can be illustrated in the following diagram.

In the author's case, the optimum position to point the antenna was determined by observing the visible trails from meteor showers over a long period. (The writer owns a large property, approximately 1.25 acres, on top of a mountain and far away from the city lights, so viewing of meteor trails is quite easy most evenings when the moon is not up.)

These vary somewhat depending on the shower but, as luck would have it, they coincided roughly with the placement of the house and parallel to the main building. This was very convenient, as plans to erect several low masts in the front garden could then be abandoned, much to the delight of my wife. Consequently, a change of plan ensued, whereby the antennas did not need to be long Yagis, and an alternative antenna system was designed using the house roof as the support structure. This was also convenient in that the feeder runs are kept very short and could directly enter the shack. More details follow later.

A secondary factor related to echo reception is that the antenna does not need to be mounted high above the ground. Many of the scientific meteor radar systems use vertically-pointed antennas, which are only a metre or so above the ground. With a horizontally-polarised Yagi, the antenna being very close to the ground (less than 1λ) aids the signal being sent skywards by reflection off the ground.

Ideally, for meteor scatter work, the antenna requires a positive horizon, something that most amateurs would consider a disadvantage for normal VHF DX communication, where a negative horizon would yield the best results. In the author's case, when first using a single six-element Yagi on 6m, a nearby hill is fortuitously in the correct direction and is used to launch the wave upward by using the grazing effect. An elevation angle of 45° or higher will yield far better results than an antenna pointed at the horizon.

Pointing the antenna to meet the meteor head-on will yield little or no echo for an MF, HF or VHF system; the beam, when orthogonal to the trail, will yield

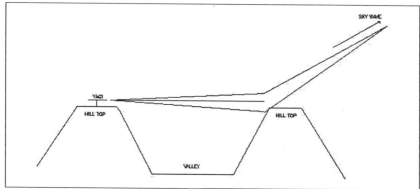

Fig 12.12: Using an adjacent hilltop to form a grazing elevated signal

the highest signals. There are, however, special cases where the echo does not arise from the trail but from the ionised 'head' of the meteoroid. This requires a very high frequency and extremely high power to get a usable reflection. This mode is not likely to be suitable for amateurs as the transmitter power required is very high, typically 50kW or more being required with a very high gain antenna. Transmitted ERP required is about 1MW for reliable results.

This effect is known as the 'head-echo' effect and the size of the target is very small. Unlike the normal meteor trail, which can extend for 30km or more behind the particle and hence has a large radar cross-sectional area (RCS), the head-echo diameter is very small. UHF and SHF radars have measured this and a typical cross-section is about 1 to 10m diameter.

THE HEAD ECHO EFFECT

A recent study undertaken in Scandinavia in 1997 and 1998 has identified a second mechanism for echo reflection. This is called the head echo effect. The size of a typical meteoroid is extremely small, being about the size of a grain of sand. This was not expected to cause a reflection, as it is so tiny. However, scientists have now demonstrated that an echo is possible, because the particle rushing into the Earth's atmosphere generates an electron cloud in front of it. This electron cloud is capable of reflecting a radar signal if the wavelength is short enough. The target size is small in comparison to the electron trail generated by the particle burning up, and hence a very high frequency needs to be used to detect the object.

The Scandinavian experiment used 930MHz radar with extremely high power (150kW) and three very large parabolic antennas (32m) connected as a tri-static antenna to form a 3D-search radar. The ERP was in excess of 1MW.

Out of approximately 200 meteors observed, using conventional VHF radar running in parallel, 10 meteors showed the head echo effect. As a high frequency gives little or no reflection from the ionised trail, the separation of this from the head echo effect was the clue to why echoes were observed only in some cases.

The system used is known as EISCAT, being the 'European Incoherent Scatter' radar. The transmitter is based in Norway and the two remote receiving sites in Sweden and Finland. Because of the very northern positions of these sites, much longer periods of meteor observation are possible than sites nearer to the Equator.

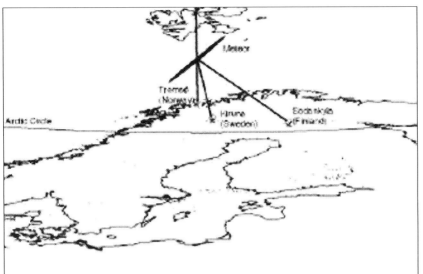

Fig 12.13: The IESCAT 930MHz tri-static radar system. This system consists of three 32m parabolic antennas. The transmitter receiver is located in Tromso, and the remote receivers in Kiruna and Sodankyla

In another recent study, undertaken by Australian and American scientists, several very high-power radars were used to observe the head echo effect. These used military radars situated at Roi Namur in the Kwajalein Atoll, Republic of Marshall Islands and are air defence radars operated by the Australian and American Air Forces. In addition to the main radar, known as ALTAIR, which transmits a 6MW peak power on 160MHz and 422MHz simultaneously, several other radars took part in the observation. These other radars were TRADEX, an L- and S-band radar, ALCOR, C-band, and MMW, a radar operating on Ka-band and W-band. Hence, the spectrum was covered from VHF to the upper microwave bands.

ALTAIR uses a 46m parabolic antenna and uses either right-hand or left-hand circular polarisation to determine the echo polarity and range. It was found that approximately 1.6 head echo returns per second occurred during the peak of the Leonid shower.

Relevance to Meteor Scatter Communications

In a very recent study performed at Arecibo Observatory in Puerto Rico with the 300m diameter fixed dish (operated by Cornell University) between 1998 and 2003, a definite factor emerged which is of great importance to amateurs involved in meteor scatter communication. It has been known for some time that the use of the UHF bands is not likely to be very productive because of the scattering equation, but the exact reason was not known. In this study, Mathews [4] used a dual-radar system operating at 40MHz and 430MHz to observe meteoroid reflections simultaneously. From this, it became apparent that the head echo effect is the predominant mode at UHF. As the echo decayed away after a very short 'ping', the VHF radar then showed a longer and more pronounced normal reflection from the ionised trail. The ionised trail which follows is a much larger target and extends for several tens of kilometres behind the meteoroid, and hence will act as a better reflector to VHF signals. The head echo effect occurs at altitudes higher than traditional trail reflections and these exist in the region of 120km down to about 90km.

Fig 12.14: Arecibo dual frequency radar display of a terminal meteor event. The initial
head-echo obtained by the
430MHz UHF radar is shown on
the top trace, and is caused by
the ionised cloud surrounding
the head, which quickly
decays to zero. At the time the
head-echo disappears, the
longer-wavelength 40MHz VHF
radar shows the longer normal
reflection from the ionised
trail. The VHF echo is smaller
in amplitude than normal
because the antenna is pointed 'up the trail' (to acquire the
head-echo signal), and not
orthogonally, as would normally be the case

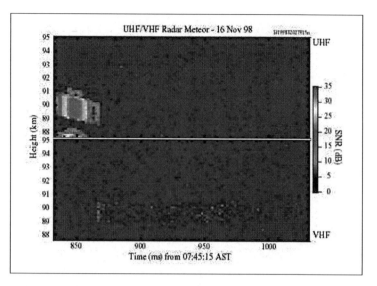

This picture is one taken from an earlier study using the Arecibo radar during
1998. In this is clearly seen the short UHF echo which abruptly disappears and
reappears at the lower VHF radar frequency. The VHF echo is weaker than normal because the dish is pointed head-on to the meteor (along the trail), and
hence the radar cross-sectional area is much smaller than if the dish was pointed orthogonal to the meteor trail.

The Arecibo radar uses a 6MW transmitter and the 1000ft dish located at
Peurto Rico and operated by Cornell University.

DAILY METEOR COUNTS

It has been estimated from collected data that as many as 100,000 meteoroids
may enter the Earth's atmosphere every day. Of these, about 50% are probably
large enough and travelling fast enough to give detectable ionised trails.

Sporadic meteoroids occur at any time of the year, whether day or night. The
highest incidence is normally after midnight and before sunrise. Quite how many
occur in an average day is an often-debated topic. Recent studies performed by
the Buckland Park station at Adelaide, Australia has, to some extent, answered
this question. This station uses 38.1MHz and 54.1MHz high-power radars with
a broad antenna beam to collect as many echoes as possible. This study occupied
five different operating periods between April 2001 and July 2003.

Discounting erroneous echoes, which were due to other signals such as interference, aircraft reflections etc, by rejecting echoes which apparently are due to
ranges outside those to be expected from normal meteoroid activity, the daily
count rate varies between 9000 and 14000. This is far higher than was originally
estimated.

The highest number of echoes or other signals received peaked at almost
38,000 in a day. Many of these were spurious and, after the computer algorithms
rejected the erroneous ones, this left the daily average of valid echoes that fitted
the criteria for an echo from an under-dense trail. The incidence of meteor
echoes does increase during traditional meteor showers (Leonids etc) but, even
so, the figure is still more than was expected.

This study used two separate radar systems, one operating with a PRF of 2kHz, and the second with a lower PRF of between 400 and 500Hz to resolve the range ambiguities. (The higher PRF radar had a range of 6 to 66km and the lower PRF had a range of 70 to 310km.) The antenna system consisted of crossed dipoles, one being the transmitting antenna and further dipole antennas being used for the receivers. The transmitter had a peak power of 7.5kW. The receiving antennas were arranged to give an omnidirectional azimuthal pattern and having elevation angles of 0°, 20°, 40°, 60° and 80°.

The plot shown previously clearly illustrates the greater incidence of meteors from high elevation angles. The number of echoes collected by the 0°, 20° and 40° dipole arrays are much lower than the 60° and 80° antennas. The bulk of the echoes occur at about 70° elevation. These echoes are actual real returns after computer analysis to remove bogus echoes and the total number is almost 10,000 in a 24-hour operating period.

SPECIAL ANTENNA SYSTEMS

Many of the large VHF scientific meteor radar system in use today use antenna systems that to amateurs seem strange. Often only simple dipoles are used and others use multiple low element-count Yagis. The scientists operating these systems are more concerned with collecting as many echoes as possible than a few from a discrete point in the sky.

> It should not be overlooked that if you point a highly directional antenna straight up at the zenith, the Earth as it rotates, will cause the beam to act like a transit telescope and be swept over a narrow strip of the sky. Hence, meteors entering the atmosphere close to the observer's horizon will not be detected unless they also transit across the antenna beam.

Another version commonly used from early on in the study of meteors, comprises two separate multi-Yagi arrays pointed in different directions - for example, due south and due west. These antennas are coupled to two separate receivers and the sky illuminated by a high-power transmitter, often using a wide beamwidth dipole array. As a meteor approaches, it will transit first one antenna and a little later the second antenna. By using trigonometry, it is possible to determine the altitude, velocity and the track of the meteor trail.

Because the Earth's surface is curved, pointing an antenna at the observer's horizon will only detect meteor trails at a very long range, and the sky noise will be at its highest level under this condition. With a high-gain antenna (which has a narrow vertical pattern) pointed at the horizon, and with no obstructions in front of the antenna, the maximum altitude observed would be only about 50km above the Earth's surface, which is too far below the lower limit of the meteor trail formation. This technique, therefore, limits the number of echoes that can be detected because, for maximum reflection using VHF, the trail needs to pass through the antenna beam at right angles at an observed altitude of about 100km. It is far more productive to elevate the antenna to a high angle, perhaps as high as 80° above the horizon.

A second factor, that is important for all forms of weak-signal reception, is the polarisation of the antenna. It is a well-recognised fact that, when an antenna is pointed at the horizon, the path loss attenuation suffered by a horizontally-polarised signal is somewhat less than with a vertically-polarised one. Also, the predominant polarisation of man-made electrical noise is vertical. A plane-polarised antenna, when illuminated with an orthogonal-polarity signal, eg a horizontally-polarised antenna attempting to receive a vertically polarised signal, the cross-polarisation loss is (theoretically) infinite. In practice, due to non-perfect antenna patterns, the loss will be less than infinite, but will still be of the order of 20dB. Hence, for optimum results when man-made interference is present, the best option is a horizontally-polarised antenna.

Antennas for Meteor Scatter

As has already been mentioned, ideally we need an antenna with a reasonable amount of gain but also reasonably wide vertical and horizontal beamwidths, to maximise the collecting area. These two factors are somewhat in contrast to each other. Normally, antennas with high gain will have narrow beamwidths, both in the azimuth and elevation planes. What we require is a horizontally-polarised antenna with a fairly narrow vertical pattern but a wide horizontal pattern. The way the scientists get around this problem is to use a large array of dipoles or very low element-count Yagi types. These have a large total collecting aperture and hence high gain over a simple dipole. These arrays occupy a lot of ground area, and are not very suitable for amateurs who have small properties in which to erect antennas.

One way to get a narrow vertical beamwidth but a wide horizontal beamwidth is to stack two or more conventional small Yagi type antennas above each other. When two or more horizontally-polarised antennas are stacked vertically, the horizontal beamwidth does not change - only the vertical pattern is reduced. For the lower-frequency bands, such as 6m and 4m (which offer the best meteor-scatter results), this is a cumbersome array.

To understand the limitations of Yagi antennas, it is useful to look at the published details in a book such as the *ARRL Antenna Handbook*, where several examples are given for the NBS design.

If we take a three-element NBS Yagi, the forward gain would be of the order of 7dBd; this is normally not sufficient if the transmitter power is limited. The boom length of a three-element NBS Yagi is approximately 0.4λ. The stacking distance of two three-element Yagis is about 0.25λ in practice, when the imperfect pattern over-lapping and extra feeder losses are taken into account, this will yield, at best, a total gain of about 9.5dBd. To get more gain requires more elements, hence a longer boom and a greater stacking distance. A single five-element NBS Yagi will yield a forward gain of approximately 9.2dBd. This antenna is approximately 0.8λ in boom length, or about 5m in total length in the case of the 6m band. The stacking distance required is approximately 0.6λ. When stacked, the expected gain is about 11.5dBd.

Continuing upwards in element number we see that a six-element version has a gain of 10.2dBd and a boom length of 1.2λ. This requires a stacking distance of 0.8λ. When stacked, this will yield about 12dBd. A 12-element NBS Yagi has a gain of 12.25dBd with a boom of 2.2λ. This is a large Yagi, and not many amateurs will be able to erect one this large. A pair of 12-element Yagis will require a stacking distance of about 2.5λ, approximately 15m for a 6m array. The expected gain when stacked is about 14dBd.

To continue adding extra elements quickly becomes counter-productive as the gain levels off at higher element counts. For example, a 17-element version has a gain of 13.4dBd, which is only 1.2dB more than the 12-element version but to achieve this little extra gain makes the boom 3.2λ. This boom is ~19m long for the 6m band. When the vertical stacking distances are calculated, ~6λ, the array soon becomes unmanageable.

However, there is a simpler solution to our problem. If one exam-

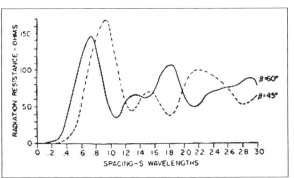

Fig 12.15: Radiation resistance of driven λ/2 dipole versus spacing for β = 45° and 60°

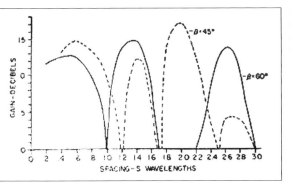

Fig 12.16: Gain versus spacing for β = 45° and 60°, direction f = 0° and 90°

ines the properties of the corner reflector antenna, we see that, although it also ends up being quite large physically, because it does not need to be rotatable, but simply needs to point upwards at a fixed elevation, it becomes a practical solution.

The structure can be made from wood and covered with a wire mesh. For 6m, the maximum mesh aperture should not exceed 200mm, hence 50mm or 100mm chicken wire would serve nicely.

Henry Jasik's Antenna Engineering Handbook, 1st edition, published by McGraw-Hill, contains the definitive description of the corner reflector. The curves shown below cover the 45° and 60° versions.

The corner reflector, when analysed from the field strength produced, is limited to certain angles. The basic formula is α = π/n, where α is the angle at the apex and n is an integer (α = π, π/2, π/3, π/4 etc). For these cases, only the following apex angles are practical α = 180 , (a flat reflector), 90°, 60°, 45°, 30° etc. Corner angles that are not π/n are not very good, and the polar pattern suffers from lobe splitting. Generally, for the cleanest polar pattern, the construction should be limited to integer angles.

Amateurs normally regard the corner reflector antenna as a type reserved for the UHF and low microwave bands. However, in the radio astronomy field, it is widely used in either in its original form or in the modified trough reflector version.

Blythe at the Cambridge Observatory in 1957, first used corner reflectors connected in an interferometer network to make a transit telescope at 7.9m (38MHz) with a beamwidth of 1°.

A corner reflector with a 60° apex angle and a side length of 2λ, will yield a forward gain of about 13dBd and has a narrow vertical pattern but a wide horizontal beamwidth, as it uses a simple half-wave dipole feed-point. By truncating the reflector into a trough reflector, the size diminishes somewhat.

A corner reflector or a trough reflector needs to have a minimum width of 0.6λ, but preferably 1λ or more, when fed with a half wave dipole. The length of the side (S) need to be in excess of twice the feed-point spacing when configured as a corner reflector. The typical value for the feed-point from the apex is approximately 0.3 to 0.5λ, hence the value for S can be as little as 1λ and still generate a useful amount of gain. The trough reflector reduces the total length and a 1λ size for S is capable of good gain and is manageable, as it can be laid flat on a sloping roof. The mounting arrangement should allow for setting the elevation angle to that required; fitting a hinge point at the apex allows the array to be tilted upwards. In the author's case, the rear roof of the house already pointed in the correct direction and was almost the optimum angle for a 60° corner reflector. Adjustable-length front legs set the required angle. In the author's case, the antenna is practically invisible from the front of the house.

As has already been mentioned, the choice of corner angle is somewhat limited, narrowing the angle towards zero increases the gain but lowers the feed impedance to very low values, although, as is to be expected, this gives a narrower vertical pattern. Probably the best option with a corner reflector is to choose a 60° angle and then the dipole is situated approximately 0.35λ from the apex, which gives feed impedance of close to 50Ω. The exact feed-point position does not greatly affect the gain - moving the dipole from 0.2λ to 0.5λ changes the gain by only about 1.5dB, but the feed impedance varies over a wide range. The dipole should be fixed to a boom that can slid in or out of the corner to set the feed-point impedance. A further gain increase can be made by fitting a reflector element in front of the dipole to make the feed into a two-element 'backfire' beam. This will increase the gain by about 3dB. In total, a gain of 13dB is easy to achieve. To get this gain with a conventional 6m Yagi would require a boom in excess of 20m.

More gain can be attained with a 45° angle, but the feed impedance falls to low values at small offsets of the dipole. A possible way around this is to design for a 12.5Ω feed-point impedance and then to use a 4:1 transmission line transformer or balun to transform back up to the 50Ω feed-line. These can be made simply and are low loss.

However, if the curves for a 45° corner reflector are examined, they show that, when the dipole is at a point of either 0.55λ or 1.2λ from the apex, the feed impedance is close to 50Ω. At 1.2λ, the gain falls almost to zero, so is not viable. Further examination of the gain and impedance curves show that the first maximum gain point on the curves rises to almost 15dB when the dipole is spaced 0.6λ from the apex. At this distance, the feed impedance is approximately 75Ω. and should match to standard 75Ω. coaxial cable with little difficulty. Increasing the spacing to approximately 2λ shows a gain of approximately 17.5dB, but the feed impedance is now 100Ω, making it difficult to match to a standard feed-line unless matching sections are used. One possibility is to combine two such antennas and convert the two 100Ω points to 50Ω by connecting them in parallel.

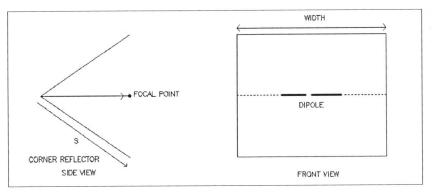

Fig 12.17: Basic diagram for a 60° corner reflector

The maximum theoretical spacing of the dipole feed from the apex is dependent on the polar pattern being free from break up of the main lobe and is given as:

~0.65λ for 90°
~0.95λ for 60°
~1.2λ for 45°
~2.5λ for 30°

The first peak in the forward gain, but not necessarily the ultimate maximum gain, occurs theoretically when the feed-point is spaced from the apex by the following values:

~0.5λ for 90°
~0.65λ for 60°
~0.85λ for 45°
~1.2λ for 30°

The Trough Reflector

By truncating the corner reflector into a trough reflector, we can obtain somewhat more gain in the same overall physical size. Gains of up to 17dBd are achievable at 50MHz from a single antenna occupying a space of 6m x 12m using an apex angle of 45°. To achieve this with a single Yagi would require a boom length of over 30m. The half-wave dipole should have telescopic elements to allow a finer setting of the resonant frequency and hence the feed-point impedance.

Either a simple half-wave dipole may be used, or a folded dipole offers better matching to a 50Ω feed-line in a narrow angle version. The use of a proper 'push-pull' feed balun is important to prevent beam-skewing, as with all antennas fed with a dipole. The W2DU ferrite sleeve choke balun is highly recommended as it has almost zero loss and gives perfect balance in amplitude and phase. The power handling is defined by the coaxial cable and, with a low-loss cable, it can handle kilowatts of power at VHF.

Fig 12.18: The trough reflector. This is a useful modification of the corner reflector The vertex has been cut off and replaced by a simple plane section

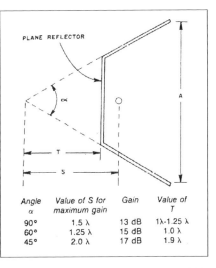

Angle α	Value of S for maximum gain	Gain	Value of T
90°	1.5 λ	13 dB	1λ-1.25 λ
60°	1.25 λ	15 dB	1.0 λ
45°	2.0 λ	17 dB	1.9 λ

Multi-band Antenna

A further advantage of the corner or trough reflector is that, because it belongs to the family of plane reflector types, it is inherently a wide-band design, like the parabola. Provided that the width of the opening is greater than 0.6λ at the lowest frequency, it will work well. Multiple feed dipoles can be arranged to allow operation on several different bands. The gain will be higher for the higher frequency bands provided that the wire-mesh aperture remains below ~0.1λ at the highest frequency. For the 6m version built by the author, readily-available galvanised wire fencing mesh 1.8m wide with a 90mm aperture was used, attached to a framework of 25mm square steel tubing.

The two sections of the author's corner reflector measure 6m x 6m, as a compromise had to be made due to available material length and the space available on the roof. The 1.8m wide mesh required four strips to be attached, overlapping each other to cover the 6m span. The stiffening struts that formed the two parts were arranged as fixing points for the mesh. The mesh was fastened with galvanised iron wire. A set of struts was fastened across the open mouth to prevent the structure collapsing and to support the far end of the feed boom. These were extended to form the legs to raise the mouth to the correct elevation.

The F/B of a corner reflector is very high - values of 25 to 30dB are typically realisable with a small enough mesh apertures. If the mesh were replaced with solid sheet, the ratio would approach infinity, but wind-loading could then become a problem. The side-lobe attenuation is also quite good, being of the order of 15 to 20dB, and if screening panels are fitted at the sides, this approaches the F/B.

F/B is important, especially on the lower bands such as 6m and 4m. Man-made noise on these bands can be high and, if the antenna has mediocre F/B attenuation, the noise picked up from the rear of the antenna can be enough to override the wanted echo signal. Long Yagis are not especially good in the F/B parameters. They are normally acceptable when the interfering signal is directly off the back of the beam. Figures of 15dB or more are common but, when the interfering signal occurs at an angle of 30° or more off the back, the rear lobes are often quite a bit higher.

Overleaf is the diagram for a proposed large multi-element trough reflector for a 6m meteor-scatter radar system. This features three sections, one for transmit and two for receive. The two receive antennas each have an LNA, and these are combined in a two-way power combiner to increase the gain, but maintaining

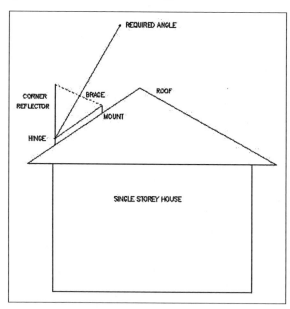

Fig 12.19: Typical roof-mounted corner reflector

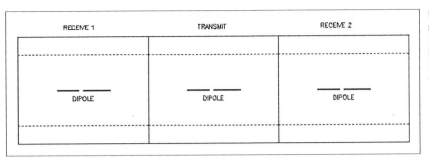

Fig 12.20: Three-section trough reflector for 50MHz meteor-scatter radar system under construction

the same horizontal beamwidth as a single antenna. As the radar features a very rapid transmit/receive period (~500 times per second), the use of an antenna changeover relay or PIN diode switch is not practical, and so two antennas were required to operate as a bi-static radar. The additional screening between the transmit and receive sections is required to prevent burnout of the receive LNAs, as it is not practical to switch these off during the transmit period. This radar system operates in the 6m band and features a 250μs transmit pulse period with 600W peak power, a receiver on-time of up to 2ms and a receiver noise figure of ~1dB. Echoes from meteor trails of up to 150km are possible. With the transmitter switched off, the system becomes a transit radio telescope with sufficient sensitivity to hear noises from the larger radio stars.

The width of each section is 1λ and the dipoles are half-wavelength. The individual sections have a wire mesh screen between them. If the need is for a single corner or trough reflector, the screening plates at the ends are not required.

Details of the corner and trough reflectors can also be found in RSGB and ARRL publications.

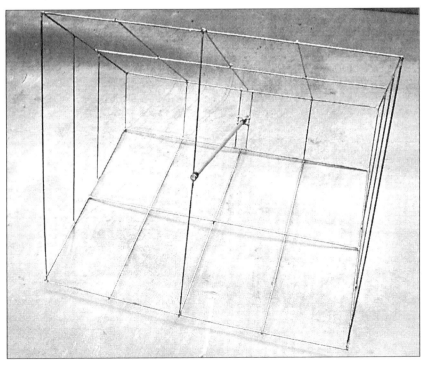

Fig 12.21: Twelfth-scale model of one section of the framework for the proposed trough reflector. This was built to assess the performance. Measurements were made at 600MHz. The picture shows the antenna before fitting the mesh. The framework is made from brazing rods soft-soldered together. The dipole element would be fastened to the aluminium pipe and the position adjusted by sliding it in or out. It is supported by short pieces of steam pipe

RECEIVER PARAMETERS

As the sky noise at 6m and 4m is still quite high, due to man-made, cosmic and atmospherically-generated noise, the use of a very low noise-figure receiver is of no real advantage. The lowest noise temperature that can be practically used at 50MHz is about 300K, this is a noise factor of 2 or about 3dB noise figure, and hence the receiver does not present a serious problem. With the antenna pointed at the horizon, the noise temperature is considerably higher due to the extra man-made noise that is picked up by the antenna. The greater length of noisy atmosphere the antenna sees raises the total noise temperature. On 6m this can be as high as 1000K, which equates to a noise factor of 4.5 or a noise figure of about 6.5dB. For 144MHz, the lowest noise figure required is about 1dB, which is simple to achieve with a low cost dual-gate MOSFET LNA.

To convert noise temperature (NT) to noise figure (NF), use the formula

$$NF = 10\log\left[1 + \frac{NT}{290}\right].$$

Hence,   300K noise temperature   3.08dB noise figure.
1000K noise temperature   6.48dB noise figure.

The receiver bandwidth required will depend on the modulation mode. For CW, the narrowest filter can be utilised, as the Doppler shift is quite low. For SSB and digital modes, the bandwidth will need to be greater, a maximum of 3kHz being about right. The use of NBFM is not very practical because of the loss of system sensitivity using a crystal filter of 8kHz or more bandwidth erodes the system sensitivity. However, with very strong showers this is still possible.

In the author's meteor radar system, the receiver IF consists of a very fast response logarithmic amplifier and a roofing filter using a 15kHz bandwidth crystal filter. A post-detection video low-pass filter of 4kHz sets the final system bandwidth. With this setup using a 1dB NF LNA, echoes as small as -139dBm are detectable. This sort of sensitivity is in the EME bracket. Sun noise measurements show that, when the Sun drifts through the antenna aperture, an increase of up to 16dB is observed.

REFERENCES

[1]   'Velocity of Meteors Measured by Diffraction of Radio Waves from Trails During Formation', C D Ellyett and J G Davies, 17 April 1948, *Nature*, 161, p596.

[2]   D W R McKinley, 1961, *Meteor Science and Engineering*, McGraw-Hill, New York.

[3]   N Herlofson, 1948, *Rep Progr Phys*, 11.

[4]   J D Mathews, 2004, *Journal of Atmospheric and Solar-Terrestrial Physics*, 66, pp285 - 99.

13

A Hydrogen Line Receiving System

In this chapter:

- The hydrogen line
- Equipment required
- Low-noise amplifier design
- Single stage design
- Additional receiver circuits
- 2nd IF & demodulator module

- First mixer module
- Local oscillator module
- Low noise oscillator supply
- Multiplier stages
- Choice of crystal type

In Chapter 6, we considered some of the possibilities, when choosing a system to receive radio astronomy signals. In this chapter, we now consider the requirements for a particular application, the equipment necessary to receive signals at the Hydrogen Line at 1420MHz.

The Search for Extra-Terrestrial Intelligence programme (SETI) normally focuses on the Hydrogen Line as being the most likely frequency that a form of intelligence would use to try to convey information to some distant galaxy. Before we examine the equipment requirements in detail, it is perhaps useful to see why the Hydrogen Line is the most likely frequency and some of the practical limitations.

THE HYDROGEN LINE

Hydrogen exists in copious quantities spread throughout space. Scientists today believe that 80% of all matter in space is comprised of hydrogen. The exact number of hydrogen atoms existing in deep space has been estimated as being one atom of hydrogen for each cubic centimetre of space. In other words, it is extremely thinly spread but, then again, there are an awful lot of cubic centimetres contained in space. The first clue that an emission may occur at 1420MHz was made by a Dutch astronomer H C van de Hulst in 1944, but it wasn't until 1951 that an emission was observed by Ewer and Purcell in the USA. The equipment the Americans used was quite crude, a 1m diameter parabolic antenna and a crystal detector; even so the signal was easily resolved.

In stars, hydrogen atoms are converted into helium, at the rate of four atoms of hydrogen to make one atom of helium. The word helium is derived from the Greek word Helios, meaning 'from the Sun'. The evolution of a star occurs when sufficient hydrogen has been attracted into a small volume by gravity from a massive body, where the density and pressure are very high and the reaction can start. As the hydrogen is converted an enormous amount of energy in the form of heat and light is generated, our Sun is currently burning hydrogen at the rate of about 4 million tons per second.

A component of the radio emission from the Milky Way comes from the spin flip transition of the hydrogen atoms in the interstellar medium. This spectral line arises from the fact that the electron and the proton in the hydrogen atom have a particular direction of spin. The energy of the configuration where the spins are aligned is different from that when the spins are in opposite directions. This difference in energy is emitted when the atom goes from one state to the other and has a wavelength of 21cm, a frequency of 1420MHz. Since the emission comes from the hydrogen atoms in the plane of the galaxy, the velocity of the line with respect to the solar neighborhood (or the local standard of rest) can be used to study the structure of the galaxy and its rotation.

The fact that we can receive signals from the hydrogen atoms present 'chirping' at 1420MHz allows us to search the sky for changes in the level received. Where the mass of hydrogen is greater, we expect to receive a stronger signal. This will occur in some parts of space where no known star or other object exists, but large hydrogen gas clouds are known to exist. In some areas of space, the hydrogen atoms are excited by the intense radiation from a nearby star.

Of interest, stars as well as emitting signals across a broad band of spectrum, as our Sun does, also emit signals at the hydrogen line frequency of 1420MHz. In optical astronomy, many hydrogen-line-emitting stars in the optical spectrum are not visible because of the dense clouds of dust between them and the observer on the Earth. Because radio waves have a much longer wavelength than light, they are able to penetrate the dust clouds and so signals can be received on Earth from these distant objects.

Doppler Shift

If we listen on the hydrogen line frequency of approximately 1420.4MHz and the signal is being radiated by a receding star, the frequency will be shifted in frequency due to the Doppler Effect. If the star is moving away from us at a great velocity, the signal is shifted lower in frequency. The average velocity of a star moving away from us is about 50kms-1. By knowing the exact signal centre frequency, we can calculate the effective velocity of recession. The exact centre frequency of the main hydrogen line is 1420.40575MHz without Doppler. With an object receding at 50kms-1, the signal will be shifted 237kHz lower in frequency. Hence, the local oscillator in the down-converter will need to be made adjustable to get the signal within the centre of the IF pass-band.

EQUIPMENT REQUIRED

If you follow the list of equipment shown in Chapter 6, the minimum equipment consists of an antenna, an LNA and a down-converter with a tunable IF. At the hydrogen line, we have a choice of antenna types to use. The best approach would be a parabolic antenna (dish), as it then could work on several bands by changing the feed mechanism. Another choice could be long Yagis or a large corner reflector. Making a dish for 1420MHz of about 3m to 5m is

Fig 13.1: G3JVL loop-quad antenna x 4, for 23cm. (Note the damage to the loops due to large perching birds!)

not that difficult, Although time-consuming, it would repay the effort spent as it could also be used for EME on 23 or 13cm. The long Yagi design offering the best gain would be an array of loop quads following the G3JVL design. These are easier to make and offer a far lower wind resistance than even a small dish. Four G3JVL loop quads will achieve about 26dBd of gain, which is equivalent to a 4m diameter dish. A single large corner reflector can achieve about 18 to 22dBd of gain.

The LNA needs to be carefully considered. For the ultimate sensitivity, we need a very low noise figure. At this portion of the spectrum, the sky noise temperature will be below 15K for an antenna pointed at the zenith, so a noise figure of 0.2dB or lower is practical. With the advent of very low-noise PHEMT devices, this becomes possible at a modest cost. The author is currently designing a SETI system with a 0.2dB noise figure using two inexpensive Agilent PHEMTs. Using the analysis software SysCalc, the sensitivity of the receiving system was determined when an LNA of 0.2dB noise figure was used with a receiver bandwidth of 2.5kHz (SSB filter). This receiver is designed as a Dicke receiver, with a changeover relay between the antenna and the LNA with an insertion loss of 0.1dB (see Chapter 3 for details). The system noise figure to a first order is therefore approximately 0.3dB and the MDS is -139.7dBm. This, with a modest antenna, will give reasonable results.

The down-converter can be a type as used on 23cm with retuning and a change of crystal frequency for the local oscillator. At 23cm, the image rejection requirement normally dictates the use of an IF at 50MHz or 144MHz, although there is an advantage in using a lower IF. Generally, it is a mistake to make the IF less than 10% of the signal frequency, because of the image filtering problems.

The choice of IF is determined by the potential interfering signals that may be present at the image frequency. In the author's design, the first IF was chosen to be 140.4MHz and a first LO of 1280.000MHz was used. This placed the image at 280.8MHz below the signal frequency, ie at about 1140MHz. A two-pole filter was made to eliminate the image response; this has an insertion loss of approximately 1dB. (The same filter was duplicated and tuned to serve as the band-pass filter following the final LO multiplier). Provided the gain of the LNA is much greater than the insertion loss of the filter and the coaxial cable between the antenna and the main receiver, the system noise figure will only be degraded by a fraction of a decibel.

If a second down-converter follows the first, and the second IF arranged to be somewhere in the HF spectrum, we could then use an HF receiver (with its wider tuning range) to search for signals several megahertz from the centre frequency. Depending on what receiving equipment you have will determine the best approach. Many modern HF transceivers offer general-coverage receivers with a wide choice of IF bandwidths. It would be advantageous to utilise a logarithmic amplifier to drive a meter or chart recorder to allow better detection. The AGC needs to be disabled and the gain adjusted manually for optimum results.

For best results, the final IF bandwidth needs to be narrow. Even 500Hz is not too narrow and the use of such a very narrow IF bandwidth will improve the system sensitivity considerably. The hydrogen line is more like a coherent signal than the normal broadband noise case, because the bandwidth is only a few hertz. However, this places an extra strain on the local oscillator stability and frequency-setting accuracy required to hold such a narrow-band signal within the IF pass-band. Also, the Doppler shift needs to be taken into account.

LOW-NOISE AMPLIFIER DESIGN

The basis of a low-noise amplifier design using Agilent PHEMTs is now described. The device chosen is the ATF-34143, which is an SMD device in the SOT-343 package. This device is readily available and offers a noise figure of approximately 0.14dB at 1.5GHz when correctly noise-matched to the antenna. The ATF-34143 is a depletion-mode PHEMT and hence requires a negative gate voltage with respect to the source to bias it correctly. Although a negative bias generator could be used, a simpler method is to use active source-biasing with a resistor to set the required gate voltage. (Using a switching converter to generate the gate voltage is often not the best option, as even a very small amount of ripple voltage at the switching frequency will amplitude-modulate the gate signal and cause noise sidebands to occur. If the switching ripple is as low as 0.01 of 1µV, this will still be detectable as noise sidebands.)

The biggest problem designing with PHEMTs and GaAsFETs at low frequencies is obtaining sufficient device stability. If the device is not stabilised across a wide range of frequency, the device can oscillate and will give a very poor noise figure. The second problem is attaining the required noise match to the 50Ω antenna. In normal low-noise amplifiers, the choice is often to resonate the gate capacity with a high-Q inductor or section of transmission line to achieve the mismatch required. For the traditional GaAsFETs used up until now, this is often the best option, PHEMTs are slightly different and require a different technique. The portion of spectrum from 70cm to 13cm is a transitional area between traditional inductors and strip-line designs.

When working in this grey area of spectrum, the use of a shunt inductor or transmission line brings about problems.

In order to get close to the potential noise figure of which the device is capable, the inductor Q needs to be very high, so high that it is impossible to achieve with normal air-wound inductors. For the earlier generation of GaAsFETs, where the noise figure is 0.4dB at best, this is not so important, but when the device can potentially attain almost 0.1dB noise figure, the inductor Q becomes critical.

An alternative method is to ulitise a series-tuned input inductor; this does not need such a high Q and can work satisfactorily at 1.4GHz. This is the method used by the author, and computer simulation shows that it is possible to get very close to the ultimate noise figure when an inductor Q of 200 is used. In a shunt inductor circuit, we would require an inductor at least 10 times this Q (~2000) to attain the same performance.

An air-wound inductor of ~8nH at 1.4GHz can attain a Q of between 150 to 250, depending on how the inductor is mounted. The inductor used here is a very low value, but possible to make with care. This will be approximately 1.5 turns of 26SWG wire wound on a 2.5mm former with leads 1mm long. This allows mounting on standard inductor pads used for 1008-style inductors.

The schematic of the LNA is shown below.

The components are all SMD and the printed circuit board material is Rogers R0-3203, 0.762mm thick with 1oz copper (35μm) double-sided. It is important not to change the material type or thickness because the 50Ω microstrip lines used for the input and output matching and the source inductors are designed assuming this material. The performance is greatly dependent on the high-frequency loss of the substrate material. RO-3203, although expensive compared to G-10 or FR-4 board, is an excellent choice and very little is required for this LNA design.

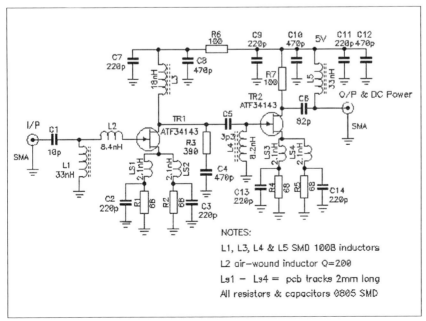

NOTES:

L1, L3, L4 & L5 SMD 1008 inductors

L2 air-wound inductor Q=200

Ls1 – Ls4 = pcb tracks 2mm long

All resistors & capacitors 0805 SMD

Fig 13.2: Two stage ATF-34143 LNA for 1.42GHz

Achieving Stability

The Rollet stability factor (k) is a measure of how stable a device is. If the value of k is greater than 1.00, the device is unconditionally stable, and will not oscillate no matter what the input and output terminations are. Most microwave transistors at frequencies below about 4GHz are potentially unstable even in a true 50Ω resistive network. If the ATF-34143 is analysed with software such as *ARRL Radio Designer* in a 2-port 50Ω network using the S-parameters supplied by the manufacturer, the Rollet stability is much less than 1, in fact it is closer to 0.4 and hence is potentially unstable at the frequency of operation. Not only this, but examination of frequencies much lower than the 1.4GHz centre frequency shows that the value of k drops to very low values below approximately 800MHz; in fact, at below 500MHz, the device is seen to be oscillating violently. This is because, at 500MHz and lower, the device is capable of 40dB of gain. So it is important, when designing with these very high-gain devices, to explore frequencies a long way from the operating frequency to see if the device is potentially unstable. Failure to correctly stabilise the device will result in an HNA (high noise amplifier).

In order to use the device successfully at its potential gain and noise figure requires us to stabilise the device. This is achieved in two ways. The addition of a small inductance, in series with the source ground leads, greatly increases the stability and also the input match and noise figure. In the schematic are two inductors per device (LS1 to LS4) these are nominally 2nH and are provided by short lengths of printed circuit board track with high impedance. (The reason two inductors are used in parallel is that the ATF-34143, like most microwave transistors, has two source leads.)

The second method of achieving stability is to use a resistor to load the drain of each device; this, however, can cause a large loss of gain. In the case of the first device (TR1) we also need an inductor (L3) as a matching element between the medium impedance of the drain of the first device and the high impedance of the gate of the second device. From the drain to ground of TR1 a 390Ω resistor is connected with a low reactance DC blocking capacitor to prevent the resistor upsetting the DC bias condition (R3 and C4). The second device also has a resistor loading the drain (R7) except, in this case, it also provides the match between the drain impedance and the 50Ω load and the DC biasing. (It would have been possible to use an LC output matching network, but this only increases the total gain by a fraction of a dB and the extra cost of the SMD inductor was not considered worthwhile.)

Both of these stabilising techniques result in a small loss of gain, but not enough to cause the noise figure to degrade severely. In the analysis software, the gain for the two stages fell about 3dB from the ultimate but the Rollet factor increased from 0.4 to over 1.00. The overall cascaded gain for the two stages is approximately 27dB at the lowest noise figure attained. The first stage is optimised for lowest noise figure (approximately 0.18dB) and a gain of 12dB. The second stage noise figure can be slightly higher without degrading the overall noise figure (see Friiss's equation in Chapter 3) and here a gain of about 15dB is attained with a noise figure of 0.22dB.

The DC biasing of each device is performed by the 100Ω series resistors (R6 and R7) to provide the required drain current of ~20mA at a drain-source voltage of 3V, this being the optimum setting for lowest noise figure consistent with acceptable gain. From the manufacturer's data, the gate-source voltage required for a drain current of 20mA is approximately 0.66V. In order to supply a voltage of 0.66V when 20mA is flowing, the source resistor required is 33Ω; this is provided by two 68Ω resistors in parallel. The supply voltage is designed for 5V, and hence the values of R6 and R7 are required to be 100Ω. (If a different supply voltage is used that is higher than 5V, a 5V regulator should be used to derive the correct voltage - an LM78L05 regulator would be appropriate.)

Note that the maximum safe drain-source voltage is only 5.5V and, therefore, the 5V supply should be considered the maximum upper limit.

Components

For optimum performance at 1.4GHz, the components used need to have low parasitic inductance and good Q. Also, because the cost needs to be considered and the handling of small components can be difficult, larger-than-optimum components have been selected. For the best high-frequency performance, we could select the smallest SMD devices currently available, the 0402 series (1mm x 0.5mm), but these are very difficult to work with for the average amateur constructor. Hence, all the components are readily-available SMD types with the exception of L2, which is wound with enameled- or silver-plated copper wire. The value of this component is critical to achieve the noise figure. By squeezing together or spreading apart the turns, the inductance can be varied over about 20%. Adjustments need to be made in a quiet RF environment with a good noise figure measuring system for optimum results. As the top cover needs to removed to do this, a screened room or shielding box needs to be used.

The rest of the inductors are SMD type with good Q, either Coilcraft HQ series or Pulse Engineering. These inductors are in the popular 1008 package size (4mm x 2mm). The Q-values for these need to be greater than 30 at the operating frequency. Note that L1 is essential to provide the DC return for the biasing. The design was slightly compromised by the available inductor values in the larger 1008 series, and these have been optimised to suit the manufacturer's standard stock items.

All resistors and capacitors are 0805 SMD (2mm x 1.2mm). The small-value capacitors are NPO material (up to 470pF) and the larger decoupling types are X7R. All the resistors are 2% 0805 metal film or carbon film; either type will work well.

The LNA is designed for line-powering from the main receiver, so saving an additional piece of two-core cable between the main receiver and the antenna. L5 provides the DC path for this as well as presenting a high impedance to the 50 receiver download. The DC supply for the LNA is designed to be 5V; if this is changed, the value of the drain current resistors will be incorrect. If line-powering is not required, omitting L5 will allow the DC supply to be fed in via an optional feedthrough capacitor.

Printed Board Layout

The board layout shown identifies the SMD components, which are all on the topside of the board. The bottom of the board is a continuous foil to serve as the ground plane. Numerous 'via holes' connect the top and bottom foils and these are 0.7mm in diameter and plated-through for low-inductance grounding. The

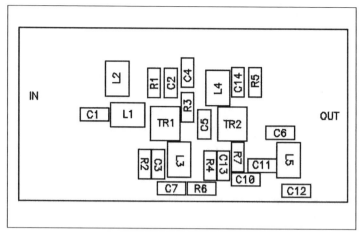

Fig 13.3: Two-stage LNA component layout (top side), not to scale

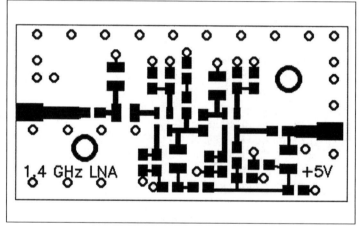

Fig 13.4: Two-stage LNA top tracks and pads, not to scale

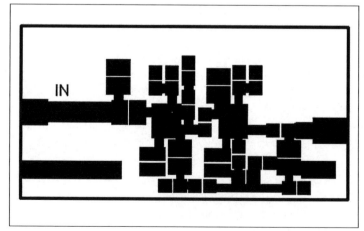

Fig 13.5: Two-stage LNA. Top copper negative relief plot

use of wires to stitch the top and bottom foils is unlikely to be good enough due to the stability criteria. This is also the reason why the 0.762mm board thickness is required; thicker board has too much inductance in the plated-through via holes and may cause instability and a loss of gain to occur. (In the computer simulation file, the extra grounding inductance caused by via holes has been included to get an accurate result).

The tracks and component pads are shown in black. The small circles are the 0.7mm via holes and the two large pads are mounting holes 2.7mm diameter to accept M2.5 screws.

In order to generate the top copper photo-master, the areas around components and tracks are relieved by a second layer. This provides the clearance between the component pads and tracks and the remaining top copper ground plane.

The top copper is removed where the black areas are shown; the white areas are solid top copper. To make a complete top copper photo-master, the top copper relief plot is photographed and a negative made. This will turn the white copper areas into black and the black areas into white. This is then combined with the top copper tracks and pads and a positive photo-master plot made.

The board measures 49.5mm x 25.4mm (1.95in x 1.00in). To reduce to correct scale, ensure the X and Y dimensions are correct. If sufficient interest is shown, the writer may be able to supply unpopulated boards or fully-assembled and tested boards.

Enclosure

Because of the extremely high sensitivity, it is imperative that the LNA be mounted in a very well-screened enclosure to prevent interfering signals causing spurious responses. The best option is a milled-out RF box with a tight-fitting lid. The board is designed to interface to SMA connectors with extended centre pins as coax-to-board interfaces. The bottom of the board is free from components and two fixing screws serve to clamp the board on to a flat surface made by milling a recess in a thick piece of aluminium plate.

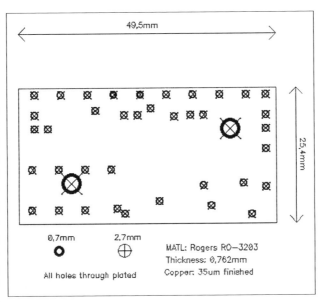

Fig 13.6: Two-stage LNA. Drilling drawing

The writer designed a box using 15mm thick aluminium plate 62mm x 41mm and milled a recess measuring 52mm x 31mm and 8.5mm deep in the top face. (The internal radius in the corners is 3mm; a 6mm-slot drill is the best tool for this machining operation.) The top cover is a piece of 3mm aluminium plate with 6 x M2.5 cheese-head screws tapped into the body to fix the lid in place. The basic dimensions of the enclosure are shown below. The depth of the recess is chosen to place the launching 50Ω strip-lines approximately 0.5mm below the SMA centre pin allowing easy soldering when the SMA connectors are mounted on the box.

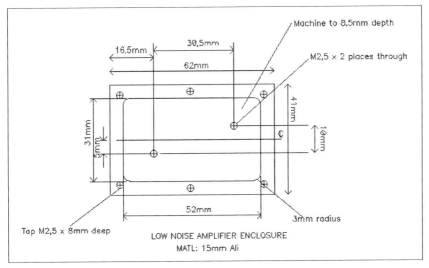

LOW NOISE AMPLIFIER ENCLOSURE
MATL: 15mm Ali

Fig 13.7: Two-stage LNA. Plan view of milled cavity

Fig 13.8: Two-stage LNA. Output end details

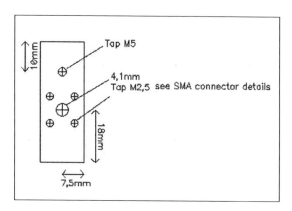

The diameter of the hole for the centre pin of the SMA connectors is critical; here a hole of 4.1mm has been specified which matches the diameter of the Teflon insulation on the SMA centre pin. This is to preserve the coaxiality of the 50Ω line impedance where it passes through the 5mm thick wall of the enclosure. The Teflon insulator should be a slight push fit in the hole. If the hole is too large, there will be a step VSWR generated that can increase the noise figure. If it is only the output connector, this is not so serious and only a very slight loss in gain may be noticed; the input connector is the critical one. Wrapping a thin piece of copper foil around the Teflon to make the connector fit tightly will reduce the effect of the VSWR step.

The output end of the enclosure has an SMA connector and a feedthrough capacitor should line-powering not be used. The feedthrough capacitor type is not critical, as long as the suppression of signals is adequate. A 1nF type with 50V or more rating should suffice, and a common type uses an M5-tapped hole for mounting.

The SMA connectors are flange-mounting and require two or four fixing holes. The four-hole version has been shown in the drawing. They may be either male or female, although females are normally used for this application. The type used is important to ensure a low VSWR transition between the coaxial cable and the board.

The picture below shows the preferred type, which has an extended centre pin and Teflon insulation. The centre pin and insulator are trimmed back so that the pin lies on the input and output 50Ω lines for about 3mm and the insulation is just touching the edge of the board.

With the milled recess shown, this will leave approximately 1.5mm between the ends of the board and the inner walls. Two solder tags on each connector are clamped by two of the fixing screws and bent to solder to the top copper either side of the 50Ω lines at each end. This ensures a low inductive grounding of the board to the enclosure.

Fig 13.9: Extended centre pin SMA connectors for stripline interface

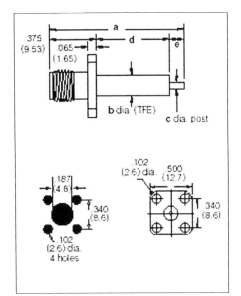

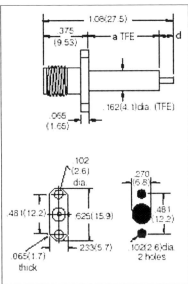

(Top left) Fig 13.10: Four-hole SMA connector details

(Top right) Fig 13.11: Two-hole SMA connector details

Bottom left) Fig 13.12: Two-stage LNA. Input connector end

Bottom left) Fig 13.13: Two-stage LNA. Top cover

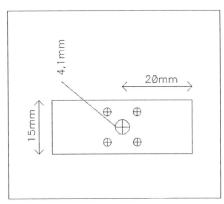

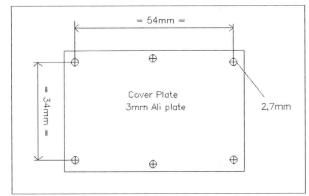

Assembly

You will require a soldering iron with a small tip, preferably a 25 or 50W temperature-controlled type. Ensure the soldering iron is connected to the mains earth and the tip is grounded. It is also helps to use a liquid flux (not plumbing flux which is corrosive!) to coat each pad before placing the component. Other items you will need are a pair of tweezers to hold the component while you solder it to the board and some fine solder, preferably not more than 1mm diameter.

Commence by fitting all the components but not the PHEMTs at this stage. Begin by picking up a component with the tweezers and placing it on the pads. Ensure the component is correctly orientated so it is square to the pads before tacking one end in place. When one end is tacked, solder the other end and then go back and solder the tacked end properly. Do not dwell too long on one end as the heat may cause the opposite end to unsolder. It should not take more than 1s to solder either end if the iron tip is at the correct temperature. The molten solder will try to align the component due to surface tension in the molten solder.

The ATF-34143 is very sensitive to static electricity and due care needs to be observed when the device is soldered into circuit. The soldering iron tip must be grounded and the tweezers used to pick up the device should be discharged by touching them to the ground before touching the device. A static wrist strap, which is bonded to earth, is also a good idea. A good idea is to spread a piece of aluminium cooking foil about 300mm square on the workbench and use a drawing pin with a piece of wire to ground the foil to the mains earth. Touch the iron tip onto this before soldering each lead of the PHEMTs into place.

When all the other components are soldered into circuit, finally fit the two PHEMTs. Carefully note the orientation of the device, the larger pad is one of the source terminals. When all the components are in place, the board will probably look a mess with the flux, and trying to inspect the solder joints visually is difficult. So it is best to clean the excess flux from the board. The writer uses a mixture of benzene and cellulose thinners mixed 50-50.

This, with a 0.5in paintbrush (12mm) with the bristles trimmed to about 6 to 8mm is an excellent way to clean the board. Immerse the board in a glass jar with the cleaning liquid for a few minutes and then fish it out and gently scrub all the components with the brush. If any joints look poor retouch them with the soldering iron before cleaning again. After the cleaning liquid has removed the flux, rinse the board in some warm water and dry, either in the sun or use a hair drier to blow warm air on the board.

Finally, install the board in the enclosure and fit the two SMA connectors and the feedthrough capacitor if required. Clean off any excess flux with the brush and cleaning liquid, and rinse under the warm tap and dry well.

Alignment

Before the LNA can be aligned for lowest noise figure, it is important to check that the biasing is correct. The source resistor for each device is made from two paralleled resistors of 68Ω. The calculated source resistor is 33Ω for the correct drain-source voltage and current. Hence, by fitting two resistors in parallel, we can remove one resistor and substitute a different value (without endangering the very static-sensitive device) should it be necessary.

Begin by connecting a good 50Ω termination to each SMA connector so the LNA is correctly terminated. Apply 5V DC, either via the receiver down-lead with a suitable bias-T, or via the feedthrough capacitor. The power supply used should be set to current-limit at approximately 50mA initially.

Switch on the power supply and measure the voltage across the source resistors, it should be approximately 0.7V with respect to ground. If this checks out, increase the power supply current-limiting to about 100mA and recheck that the results are still within tolerance. Now measure the voltages on the drains with respect to ground; they should be 3.7V. If the results obtained are very close to the optimum, the biasing is correct. In common with most transistors, there will usually be some variation; as long as the results are within 25%, this is acceptable.

For noise figure alignment, a good noise figure measuring system will be required. Even the best systems available on the market still have an uncertainty of about ±0.1dB when measuring these very low-noise figures. Because the adjustment of L2 needs to be made, the top cover needs to be removed.

Therefore it is important to contain the LNA within another screened box with a lid that can be removed to gain access to the device under test. The author uses a discarded biscuit tin with a tight fitting lid. Several RF connectors and feedthrough capacitors are fitted to the tin box so that different LNAs or other pieces of equipment under test can accommodated. The RF connectors are the types that have a connector on each end, known as 'bulkhead' connectors as they allow a coaxial cable and plug to be connected at either end. Using back-to-back adapters, the LNA is connected to the bulkhead adapter.

Predicted Results

The computer simulation predicts an overall noise figure of 0.2dB at 1.42GHz with an associated gain of 26.2dB and a Rollet stability factor of 2.02. A little more gain could be squeezed, but the noise figure would not significantly improve because the limiting factor is the Q of the input inductor, which was assumed to be 200 in the simulation.

Operating on Other Frequencies

The design is inherently broad-band, and the results to be expected at 1296MHz are very close to the 1.42GHz results. By a slight readjustment of the input inductor, the LNA can be brought on frequency. Without optimisation (ie tuned for 1.42GHz) the noise figure is predicted to be 0.23dB with an associated gain of 27.7dB when used at 23cm.

SINGLE STAGE DESIGN

The ATF-34143 is a very good device for a single-stage design where a slightly better noise figure is possible, but with less associated gain. Because the LNA will be remotely mounted at the antenna, the resulting cable loss between the LNA and the main receiver can impact on the system noise figure and this is why the two-stage design is preferred.

To give some indication of the capability of the ATF-34143, here are the predicted results for a single-stage LNA using the same circuit method. Here the Rollet stability factor is not as good but the ultimate noise figure is only 0.03dB short of the device capability.

By choosing a two-stage design, we have ended up with a greater stability factor because we are utilising the low Q of the SMD inductors in the second stage to improve the resistive loading. If these inductors were air-wound the k factor would be correspondingly lower.

One thing to note is how little the noise figure changes for large excursions from the design frequency; at

Fig 13.14: Predicted results for a single-stage LNA

Freq GHz	MS11 dB AMP	MS21 dB AMP	K AMP	NF kelvin AMP	NF dB AMP	MS22 dB AMP
1.000	-15.658	16.265	1.06	21.77	0.31	-9.95
1.020	-16.689	16.130	1.07	21.06	0.30	-10.13
1.040	-17.864	15.997	1.07	20.34	0.29	-10.33
1.060	-19.231	15.867	1.07	19.63	0.28	-10.56
1.080	-20.861	15.738	1.08	18.92	0.27	-10.82
1.100	-22.878	15.611	1.08	18.22	0.26	-11.11
1.120	-25.509	15.485	1.08	17.54	0.25	-11.42
1.140	-29.244	15.360	1.09	16.87	0.25	-11.77
1.160	-35.189	15.236	1.09	16.23	0.24	-12.15
1.180	-37.781	15.111	1.09	15.62	0.23	-12.57
1.200	-30.982	14.987	1.09	15.04	0.22	-13.03
1.220	-26.555	14.862	1.10	14.49	0.21	-13.54
1.240	-23.547	14.737	1.10	13.98	0.20	-14.09
1.260	-21.287	14.610	1.10	13.52	0.20	-14.70
1.280	-19.481	14.483	1.10	13.10	0.19	-15.38
1.300	-17.978	14.353	1.10	12.73	0.19	-16.12
1.320	-16.692	14.222	1.10	12.41	0.18	-16.94
1.340	-15.568	14.090	1.11	12.14	0.18	-17.84
1.360	-14.572	13.954	1.11	11.93	0.18	-18.84
1.380	-13.677	13.817	1.11	11.78	0.17	-19.93
1.400	-12.866	13.676	1.11	11.69	0.17	-21.09
1.420	**-12.125**	**13.533**	**1.11**	**11.67**	**0.17**	**-22.25**
1.440	-11.444	13.387	1.11	11.70	0.17	-23.27
1.460	-10.815	13.237	1.11	11.80	0.17	-23.89
1.480	-10.231	13.084	1.11	11.97	0.18	-23.87
1.500	-9.687	12.927	1.12	12.20	0.18	-23.20

Fig 13.15: Single-stage LNA using the ATF-34143

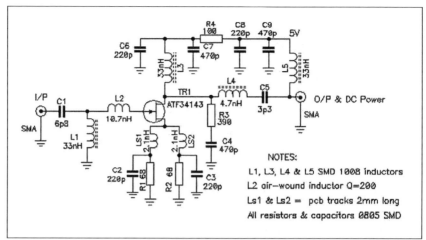

23cm, the noise figure has only increased by 0.02dB to 0.19dB, and at 1GHz the noise figure increases only to 0.31dB.

This is a marked difference from the normal shunt inductor approach, which has a very narrow bandwidth. Also, the input match is much better than the shunt inductor method, where a severe mismatch to 50Ω is generally the case.

The circuit of the single-stage design is shown here. Again, the choice of low-loss board material necessitates the more expensive RO-3203 material. This LNA can be fitted on a board of 25mm x 25mm using surface mount components.

The output matching in the single-stage design requires an inductor and capacitor to match between the medium impedance of the drain to the 50Ω load. This is performed by the components L4 and C5. The inductor used for L4 is a very low inductance SMD type made by Coilcraft or Pulse Engineering in the 1008 package style. The manufacturer's data gives a typical Q-value of 30 at 1.5GHz.

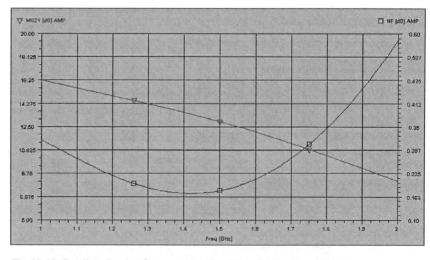

Fig 13.16: Predicted noise figure and gain of the single-stage LNA

ADDITIONAL RECEIVER CIRCUITS

The author designed a SETI receiving system for manufacture and distribution to schools and colleges. This system uses commonly-available SMD components and other semiconductor devices to keep the cost low.

The receiver was designed as modules for easy assembly and testing. The modules are:

- LNA module
- First mixer module
- First IF module
- Second mixer module
- Second IF and demodulator
- Local oscillator module

The first IF is at 140.4MHz and the second IF is at 21.4MHz. The final down-conversion is performed in an NE615 IC, which accepts the 21.4MHz signal and mixes it down to 455kHz. The circuit used is basically the Philips application circuit with one important difference.

SECOND IF & DEMODULATOR MODULE

In the Philips application circuit, the third IF filtering is performed by 455kHz ceramic filters to give an IF bandwidth of approximately 15kHz. This is too wide for the system sensitivity we require. Hence, the third IF filtering was supplemented with an additional filter to give a 1kHz bandwidth. This sort of bandwidth is not readily available from off-the-shelf ceramic filters and so a LC filter using pot-cores was designed.

The diagram of the basic Philips application circuit is shown below where two ceramic 455kHz filters are used.

The additional IF filter replaces the second ceramic filter (FLT2) and it is designed for the 1.5k impedance used by the NE615. This filter uses high-Q inductors wound on gapped RM-4 cores. The core material is M33 and the AL value is 63nH/t, hence the inductor

Fig 13.17: Philips application circuit for the NE615 IF amplifier

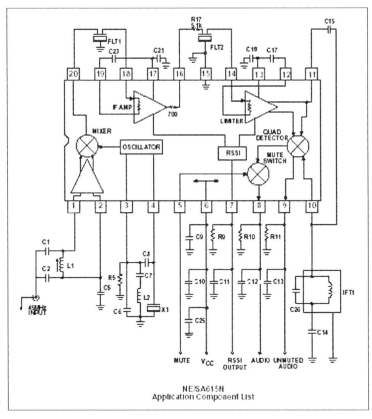

NE/SA615N
Application Component List

Fig 13.18: 455 kHz
band-pass filter

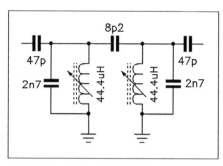

consists of 26.5 turns wound on the plastic bobbin. The cores are made by Siemens with the adjusting screw to set the exact inductance. The measured Q of these inductors is over 400.

The second IF can be either 21.4MHz or 10.7MHz by changing the third LO crystal. (For 21.4MHz, the crystal is 20.945MHz and, for 10.7MHz IF, the crystal is 10.245MHz.) The only output used from the NE615 is the RSSI signal at pin 7 that will drive a meter to indicate the strength of the received signal. This RSSI signal requires filtering and buffering with a voltage-follower constructed around a normal op-amp audio filter with a very low cut-off frequency, perhaps as low as 50Hz.

FIRST MIXER MODULE

The first mixer module consists of the second RF amplifier stage, which is preceded by a band-pass filter centred on 1420MHz between the download coax from the antenna-mounted LNA. This filter sets the image rejection performance and needs to be low-loss and matched to the system impedance of 50Ω. The first stage is another ATF-34143, based on the single-stage LNA design, and it exhibits a noise figure of approximately 0.4dB with 12dB of gain. Because the noise figure is not so important at this point in the receiver, the substrate used is normal G-10/FR-4 with a thickness of 0.76mm. The series input inductor used is a 1008 SMD with a Q of about 60, which is acceptable, as the noise figure is relatively unimportant.

The first LO is injected into the collector of the second-stage device, the AT41486 bipolar transistor, and the first IF matching network on the collector features a low-pass filter to prevent the high-level LO signal from being transferred to the rest of the receiver. All the inductors used are 1008 SMD types by either Coilcraft or Pulse Engineering, with the exception of the source inductors for the ATF-34143 (which are printed striplines approximately 2mm long), and resistors and capacitors are all 0805 SMD types. The first LO at 1420MHz is provided by the Local Oscillator module.

Fig 13.19: First
mixer module

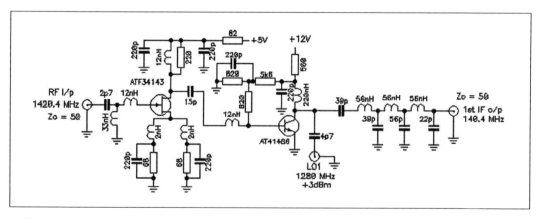

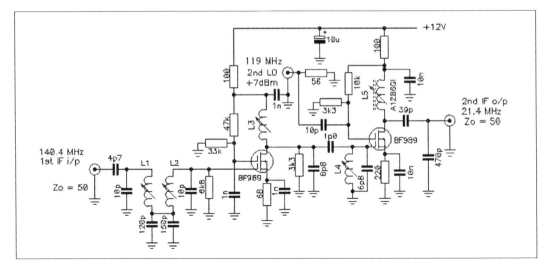

Fig 13.20: First IF and second mixer module

The first IF module uses Dual Gate MOSFETs as amplifiers and mixers; the popular BF989 was selected for this application. The second LO at 119MHz is provided by the Local Oscillator module.

The variable inductors L1 to L4 are made by Toko and are 10mm square by 15mm tall and have a nominal value of 100nH with Qs of approximately 120 at 100MHz. The RF amplifier and filter uses a modified Cohn filter for the first section with bottom coupling, and the second filter is a conventional top-coupled pair. The bandwidth of these combined is approximately 2MHz. The mixer uses the 119MHz from the Local Oscillator module injected onto gate 2. The resulting second IF at 21.4MHz is selected by the tuned circuit in the drain of the mixer MOSFET and uses a Toko 7mm square coil with a nominal inductance of 1.5μH and a Q of 100 at 21.4MHz. The second IF signal is routed via 50Ω coax cable to the final module, the second IF and demodulator module already described.

LOCAL OSCILLATOR MODULE

The local oscillator module provides the first and second LO signals to the modules. The choice of starting frequency is quite important, as we also need to avoid in-band 'sprogs' at the image of 1420MHz (~1140MHz), the first IF at 140MHz, and its image frequency of 97.6MHz, and at 21.4MHz. Hence, the filtering in the early multiplier stages is critical.

The choice was made to utilise two crystals of about 50MHz as the starting frequency. LO1 needs to arrive at 1280MHz with as clean a signal as possible. As we need to multiply by 24 times to arrive at 1280MHz, this means that we have a limited choice of the intermediate frequencies to be used. As the intention was to utilise commonly-available inductors and off-the-shelf helical band-pass filters, this somewhat limits the frequencies that can be used. It also means that the first multiplier from the 53.3333MHz crystal needs to be carefully done.

The first multiplier doubles the crystal oscillator to 106.666MHz and this will have spurious products of 106.666MHz, but also 53.333MHz, 160MHz and 213.33MHz. Hence, the filter needs to be able to reject all of these so that any spurious signals either side of the wanted frequency of 106.666MHz are more than 80dB down. If this is not achieved, spurious responses will occur during reception.

The second multiplier accepts the 106.666MHz signal and multiplies it up by four to 426.666MHz, where again it requires quite severe filtering to remove any products of 106.666MHz either side of the wanted signal. The most damaging signals are three times and five times 106.666MHz, and these will occur at 320MHz and 533.33MHz. This was achieved with a Toko or Temwell 7mm two pole helical band-pass filter with approximately 70dB of rejection to the spurious frequencies.

The final multiplier multiplies the 426.666MHz signal to the final LO at 1280.00MHz and is filtered by a two-pole filter similar to the RF amplifier band-pass filter. This signal is then applied to a MMIC amplifier with approximately 8dB of gain to give the required output level of +3dBm for the first mixer module. A helical band-pass filter could be utilised here, and Temwell lists a suitable 1270MHz two pole filter with acceptable insertion loss and selectivity.

It would have been possible to use a 106.666MHz crystal and so avoid the first multiplier stage, but the use of a 106.666MHz crystal requires a fifth overtone crystal with its limited 'pull-ability' to set the Doppler shifted LO requirements.

> The pull-ability of a crystal is a function of the inverse square of the overtone number; a third overtone crystal has only 1/9 the pull-ability of a fundamental crystal and a fifth overtone crystal only 1/25 that of a fundamental crystal. With the 53MHz starting frequency, the crystal is a third overtone with greater pulling achievable. To achieve the maximum Doppler offset of 237kHz means we only have to pull the crystal 237/24 = 9.875kHz, which is very easy to do.

The second LO uses a 59.5MHz crystal and a doubler to arrive at 119MHz for the second mixer module. The filtering here is not as critical and a spurious level of -60dB would be acceptable.

Oscillator Basics

The vast majority of amateur crystal oscillators are very far from perfect. This is due to a lack of understanding of the basics. Generally, the crystal can only be pulled lower in frequency than its nominal if a capacitor is added in parallel with the crystal. In a fundamental crystal oscillator, the crystal is operated as a very high impedance in its 'parallel resonant' mode. There is, however, a second resonant mode called 'series resonance' that is available to the crystal manufacturer. In this mode, the crystal acts like a very low impedance when connected as a series element in the oscillator. All crystals exhibit the two modes of oscillation and if we did not do anything to prevent the wrong mode operating, the crystal will be very skittish and may jump from one mode to the other.

In practice, the two modes are only separated by a very small frequency, typically about 1kHz. To prevent the third overtone crystal from acting as a fundamental oscillator at 1/3 of the marked frequency, it is important to shunt the crystal with a low value resistor. Typically, the value of this damping resistor needs to about 10 times the ESR of the crystal when operated in series mode.

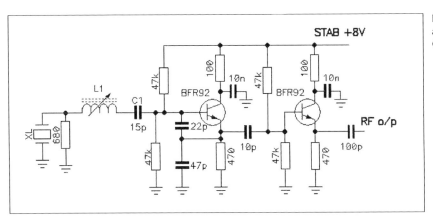

Fig 13.21: Basis of a series-mode Colpitts oscillator

Values of ESR for 50MHz to 100MHz crystals range between about 30Ω to 100Ω, hence a resistor of 680Ω is generally correct.

When operated in series mode, the addition of a capacitance in series with the crystal will raise its frequency by a very small amount (typically 0.001%) and the addition of an inductor in series will lower frequency by a similar amount. By using both of these additional components connected in series, the crystal can be pulled both lower and higher in frequency by a small amount before the oscillator experiences unwanted spurious modes.

The connection of the inductor and capacitor should result in a series resonant circuit at the crystal frequency with zero ESR. When setting up an oscillator of this type, the crystal is first removed and a resistor with the maximum ESR expected to be encountered is used. By adjusting the inductor or capacitor, the oscillator should be able to be brought to the correct frequency.

The basis of a series overtone oscillator is shown below. The inductor L1 and capacitor C1 are chosen so that the network resonates at the crystal frequency of XL. A potential divider made from the 22p and 47p capacitors between the base and emitter provides the feedback. Two high-value resistors of $47k\Omega$ provide the base bias. The collector must be securely grounded to RF, as this is a Colpitts oscillator. The output from the oscillator is connected to an emitter-follower stage to buffer the oscillator from any loading due to the multiplier stage that follows. The two transistors are fed from a stabilised 8V rail for maximum stability.

LOW NOISE OSCILLATOR SUPPLY

The stabilised supply feeding the oscillator and buffer stage needs special attention. This needs to be as stable and as low-noise as possible; do not even consider using Zener diodes for this application they are simply too poor. Zener diodes generate an incredible amount of wide-band noise which, if allowed to enter the oscillator, will cause very poor phase noise performance, because the noise riding on the DC supply amplitude modulates the carrier. Although the carrier is only amplitude-modulated when the signal then passes through a non-linear multiplier stage, the process of AM to PM conversion occurs, which causes the phase noise performance to degrade.

The best choice for a stable supply is a three-terminal regulator with adequate decoupling. Some modern three-terminal regulators offer noise performance

Fig 13.22: Additional
noise filtering for the
oscillator supply line

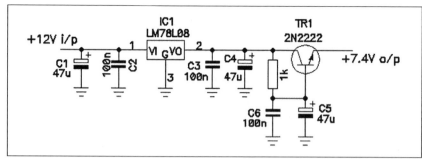

Fig 13.22: Additional noise filtering for the oscillator supply line

figures as little as 1µV over a broad bandwidth. In some cases, an additional noise filter is required to clean up the DC supply rail. The use of an emitter follower with a large value capacitor connected in shunt with the base to ground can reduce the noise voltage by 100 times or more.

With a 2N2222 transistor, which has a current gain of about 400 at small currents, the effective capacitance appearing across the emitter to ground is the product of the current gain multiplied by the capacitor value. In the following diagram, the effective shunt output capacitance is nearly 19,000µF. Of course, we lose approximately 0.6V across the pass transistor but this is not of too much concern as the pass transistor is only powering the crystal oscillator and first buffer amplifier, and the total current will only be about 20mA or so. (If you are concerned about this, simply add a silicon diode in series with the common lead of the LM78L08 regulator to raise the output by 0.6V or so.) The remaining stages are fed directly from the output of another 8V regulator, perhaps the 1A version such as the LM7808.

MULTIPLIER STAGES

The requirement to multiply from the crystal oscillator frequency to some higher frequency requires a stage known as a multiplier. A multiplier is an amplifier that is driven by a lower frequency and biased so that is a very non-linear. This then generates harmonics of the input frequency and the required harmonic is selected by a tuned circuit and then further filtered to remove the fundamental and other harmonic products.

The generation of harmonics can only occur at integer values, for example 2, 3, 4 etc and it is normally unwise to attempt too large a multiplication in one stage. Hence, we often limit the multiplication to about four although three is more common. In order to enhance the generation of the required harmonic, the conduction angle of the amplifier is deliberately limited; for high-order multiplication, the conduction angle will be low, and for lower-order harmonics, the conduction angle will be somewhat higher. In order to control the conduction angle, two things need to be done. The first is that there needs to be sufficient input drive power to force the active device into a non-linear region of its transfer characteristic, and the second is the device biasing needs to be such that the current flows in narrow pulses.

Generally, the optimum device for a multiplier is a BJT npn RF transistor biased towards Class-C and with an appropriately-decoupled emitter resistor. For high-order multiplication, the emitter resistor needs to be larger than that for lower-order multiplication. The output power of a high-order multiplier will be much less than that for a lower-order multiplier, hence the filtering that follows to select the required harmonic needs to be of a low insertion loss. It must not be forgotten that the fundamental signal at the collector will in most cases by a lot greater than the wanted harmonic. Not only this, but if the multiplier is a tripler, the doubler product will also be a greater signal power, somewhere between the fundamental and the wanted third harmonic in level. Hence, the band-pass filter needs to have exceptionally steep slopes to gain sufficient rejection of this and any other unwanted multiplier products.

Assume the fundamental power at the collector is 10dB greater than the wanted harmonic and that we require an output signal with no unwanted products greater than 60dB below the carrier. Therefore, the rejection to the fundamental signal needs to be at least 70dB. In the case of the tripler, the second harmonic power level will be approximately 6dB above the wanted third harmonic (four times bigger), and so the steepness of the filter slope out of the pass-band needs to be adequate to reject this. These values are for the signal power existing at the collector without any filtering components.

Often the bandwidth limitation of the filter we need to reject other harmonic products, means that the insertion loss is greater than desired and the available power to drive the next multiplier is then too small to guarantee adequate performance. In a case such as this, we need to employ an amplifier stage after the multiplier with sufficient gain to raise the signal level to that required for the next multiplier. This amplifier can also utilise band-pass filtering to improve the harmonic filtering. Generally, the closest multiplier stages to the oscillator need the tightest band-pass filters to reject the unwanted signals adequately.

As the frequency gets higher, the amount of drive power required for the next multiplier stage also goes up, because the gain of a semiconductor typically rolls off at 6dB/octave. If insufficient drive power is available, the higher frequency multipliers will become inefficient and the output power will be less than it could be, or may even stop working completely. Also the insertion loss of higher-frequency filters tends to go up due to the limited Q of the inductors at the UHF and microwave end of the spectrum. It is always possible to reduce the drive power should it be necessary, but not so easy to increase it.

When using BJT NPN transistors as multipliers, the choice of collector voltage is quite critical. From experience gained designing a great number of multiplier chains, the best supply voltage is about 8V; for lower supply voltages, the harmonic output power and efficiency fall. The same effect occurs for supply voltages much higher than 8V; at above about 10V, a similar loss of efficiency occurs. The 'sweet-spot' for most small-signal NPN RF transistors lies between 7V and 9V.

When designing a multiplier chain, the optimum drive level is often found empirically using a signal generator to vary the drive level into each stage. When the best multiplier efficiency has been achieved, the output power can be measured. Once this has been ascertained, the number of amplifier stages required becomes clearer and where they need to be placed in the line-up. As a rough guide, the input power level needs to be at least 3dB more than the maximum level that would be used when the device is operated as a linear stage. In other words, we need to drive the device well past the normal 1dB compression point to ensure non-linear operation. For an early multiplier stage, this may require as much as +10dBm from a 50Ω source when a device such as the

BFR92 or similar is used. (Generally, we are not using 50Ω as the impedance between stages and so the actual voltage swing on the base of the multiplier and the source impedance of the stage driving it is a more accurate way to determine the parameters.) However, too much drive will also cause the multiplier efficiency to fall with a result that too little harmonic power being generated. This can sometimes be corrected by varying the value of the emitter resistor of the multiplier or starving the driving stage of collector current to reduce its output power experimentally. It goes without saying that the power from the oscillator stage needs to be reasonably constant; if this varies over too wide a range, the whole multiplier chain can stop working correctly and the harmonic filtering may be less than optimum.

The optimum impedance at the collector of the amplifier can be found from the normal formula for amplifiers.

$$R_L = \frac{(V_{ce} - V_{ce-sat})^2}{2 \times P_0},$$

where: R_L is the load impedance (Ω),
         V_{ce} is the collector supply (V),
         V_{ce-sat} is the saturated voltage across the collector-emitter junction, and
         P_0 is the output power (W).

The typical saturated collector-emitter voltage for a small signal npn RF transistor is approximately 1V.

Hence, if we desired an output power of 10mW and the supply voltage is 8V, the collector impedance required for maximum power transfer is approximately 2450Ω. The collector tuned-circuit needs to present the correct impedance to match to the transistor correctly.

Another factor that is often overlooked is the choice of transistor. For efficient multiplication, the f_t of the transistor needs to be much greater than the output frequency desired. For operation up about 2GHz, types such as the BFW92 or SMD version BFR92, with an f_t of 6GHz are a good choice. To enhance the harmonic generation, we can use extra tuned circuits at the base or collector as idlers to increase the circulating current in the base-emitter or collector-emitter junctions. Often as much as 50% extra output power can be realised for the same drive level when suitable idler circuits are used.

In this circuit, an additional series-tuned idler circuit has been added to 'suck-out' the fundamental signal. This causes a high circulating current to flow in the collector-emitter junction and assists not only the harmonic generation but also reduces the level of fundamental signal prior to the normal band-pass filter.

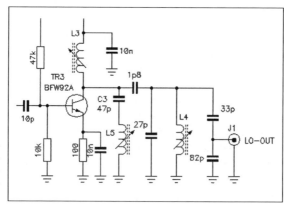

Fig 13.23: Idler circuit fitted at collector to enhance the harmonic generation

This technique can be expanded, and a variety of high-efficiency multipliers known as parametric multipliers are often used at microwave to generate large multiplier ratios. In a parametric multiplier, the active device is operated as a high-gain amplifier with a small amount of positive feedback. The feedback is not enough to cause it to oscillate, but when the drive signal is applied, the device becomes super-regenerative and delivers a high output power. The principle is in essence that of 'frequency locking'. The spectral purity is much better than a conventional multiplier, as the only significant products present at the output are harmonics of the output frequency plus a very small amount of fed-through fundamental signal. Hence, the filtering required is not very critical. One design the author was involved with generated a +10dBm power output at 1GHz when driven by a 100MHz oscillator - a multiplication value of 10 times.

Normal designs would utilise conventional multipliers employing two stages. One stage would need be a x2 and the second a x5 to get the required total multiplication of x10. The first stage would be the x2, so the output signal was at 200MHz. The second multiplier would be the x5, and the spurious products at 800MHz and 1200MHz would be the most difficult to eliminate. In total, at least four active stages would be required. Another possibility would be a varactor diode or step-recovery diode (SRD) to generate this sort of multiplication. The efficiency of a varactor or SRD multiplier is very low, perhaps at best 10% so, to obtain +10dBm output would require an input drive power of about 100mW. A varactor or SRD multiplier will generate copious harmonics of the fundamental as well as the required multiplier harmonic. This would necessitate more filtering to clean up the signal. Generally, harmonics of the final frequency are not of much concern, because the receive mixer will regenerate these when driven. Therefore, there is no need to reduce these; in fact in many cases, the higher the harmonic level of the LO the better the mixer seems to work.

CHOICE OF CRYSTAL TYPE

Another factor that needs to be considered is the frequency stability of the final output signal. This cannot be any better than the crystal oscillator stability. It is convenient to use the measurement of 'parts per million' (ppm) when dealing with frequency stability. If the oscillator has a stability of 1ppm per °C of ambient temperature change and the multiplication is 100 times, then the final frequency stability is still 1ppm per °C.

However, if the oscillator ran at 10MHz and the output was at 100MHz, the frequency drift with temperature would be 10Hz per °C. Typical low-cost crystals used by amateurs have temperature stability factors of between 50ppm and 200ppm. Hence, for a 200ppm crystal, the expected frequency drift over an ambient temperature range of 30°C (ie from +25°C to +55°C) could be as much as 200 x 30 = 6,000ppm. Generally, for normal AT-cut crystals, the frequency will drift lower in frequency for increasing ambient temperatures and higher in frequency for ambient temperatures below +25°C.

At very low ambient temperatures, another problem manifests itself. If any moisture is contained within the evacuated crystal envelope, this will form ice-crystals on the quartz wafer below 0°C and may cause the oscillator to stop working. Where very low ambient temperatures are expected, it is necessary to specify a nitrogen purged envelope when ordering the crystal.

If the crystal is a 200ppm type and operating at 100MHz, the frequency will drift 100 x 200 x 30 = 600kHz. Hence, as the frequency of the crystal increases, it is necessary to specify a lower ppm figure.

If we desired our 100MHz oscillator to remain within 10kHz of nominal over this temperature range, we would need to specify a temperature stability tolerance of (10,000 / 100,000,000)/30 = 33.3ppm per °C. This is readily obtainable from a relatively low-cost crystal. However, if we required a much tighter temperature tolerance specification, say, a maximum of 1kHz at 100MHz, we need a ppm specification of 3.33 which is very difficult to achieve.

It also ends up being a very expensive crystal. However, if the crystal temperature can be held within close limits, the frequency drift is much less. Consequently the usage of crystal ovens is the least expensive way to tackle this problem.

The crystal, when manufactured, is cut for a particular 'inversion' or 'inflection temperature'. The inversion temperature is the centre of a curve; often the temperature chosen is +25 C when normal ambient temperatures are encountered. As the ambient temperature deviates from the inversion temperature, the error in frequency gets progressively worse. At the two extreme ends of the temperature range, the frequency error will be greatest. Over the centre portion of the curve, the slope of the curve is quite flat and so very little error occurs. So if the inversion temperature was chosen as +70°C and the crystal is contained in a +70°C thermostatically-controlled oven, the frequency error falls to very low values. Typically figures of 0.1ppm maximum error are attainable with little difficulty over an ambient temperature range of -40°C to +65°C. For our 100MHz oscillator this is an error of 10Hz maximum because the oven controls the temperature to better than ±1°C.

An oven oscillator, when first turned on at normal room temperature, will be very high in frequency until the oven raises the crystal temperature to the operating temperature. Hence, it may take several minutes before the crystal oscillator is on frequency. This can be seen in the following diagram.

The next diagram shows how the frequency error varies above and below the nominal inflection temperature.

Fig 13.24: Typical warm-up characteristics of an oven oscillator

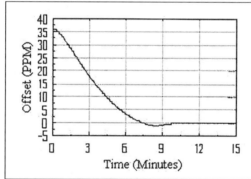

Fig 13.25: Temperature variation for various crystal cuts with +25°C inversion temperature

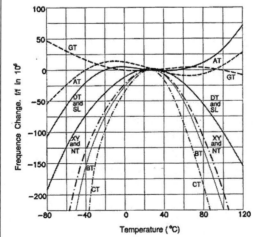

From this curve we can see that we could use a normal +25°C crystal in an oven oscillator at +70°C. This places the 'upper turn over point' at approximately +70°C. The output frequency will be approximately 20ppm lower than required but, provided we have enough pulling range in the oscillator tuning, we can then move the centre frequency up the required amount.

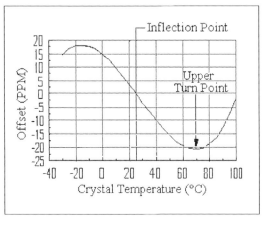

Fig 13.26: Effect of ambient tempera-ture on the crystal frequency

Crystal ovens have been used in a great many commercial two-way radio transceivers over the last 30 years. One of the most common to be found on the surplus market is the octal-based crystal holder used in some of the older Pye Telecommunication VHF and UHF mobile and base station transceivers. These were manufactured by Cathodeon (a Pye subsidiary) and accommodate two HC6/U crystals.

These octal-based ovens operate on either 6V or 12V and hold the crystal at 75°C with an error of less than 2°C. Several other manufacturers make similar types that can often be found on the surplus market or at amateur flea markets and mobile rallies for very little cost.

The copper cap normally fits on top of the crystal chamber and the outer sleeve fits over the top of the oven assembly. The heater element is wound on the outer of the crystal chamber and thermostatically controlled by components in the phenolic valve base.

Fig 13.27: Cathodeon crystal oven for HC6/U crystals

Modern crystal ovens are not only thermostatically-controlled heaters, but also can operate as refrigeration ovens. These use Peltier semiconductor devices which can both heat and cool. When the ambient temperature is below the oven design temperature the heater causes the crystal temperature to be above the ambient at, say +70°C. If the ambient reaches +70°C, the heater no longer needs to supply any heat and so switches off. If the ambient temperature continues to rise, the Peltier device is now reconfigured to extract heat from the oven. Using this type of oven, it is possible to hold a crystal oscillator to within 0.1ppm over an ambient temperature range of 50°C to more than +125°C.

Oven crystal oscillators are known as OCXOs but another technique is to use some form of temperature compensation to pull the crystal as the ambient temperature varies. These oscillators are knows as 'temperature compensated crystal oscillators' or TCXOs. Normally, a thermistor is used to measure the ambient temperature and then a tuning voltage is applied to a varicap diode connected to the crystal to alter the shunt capacity. With careful design and calibration it is possible to achieve temperature stability values of about 1.5ppm over the normal ambient range of -10°C to +60°C.

The writer uses such a TCXO in a home-built 1296MHz transverter and it exhibits almost zero drift from switch on when listening to a carrier on SSB. In fact, the 144MHz transceiver used with this transverter has almost twice the frequency drift from a cold switch on. Over the ambient temperature range of 0°C to +40°C, the maximum error is less than 100Hz at 1296MHz. This oscillator is made by NDK and is a type operating from 5V with a 12MHz output frequency. The output signal is a clipped sinewave of about 2Vp-p. This is firstly amplified and then multiplied x8 (x2 x2 x2) to 96MHz and fed into the normal multiplier chain to bring the frequency to 1152 MHz. As an added feature, the output of the second multiplier at 48MHz has a little bit of the signal tapped off and available to form a marker signal at 144MHz (third harmonic of 48MHz = 144MHz). By using this feature, the 144MHz or 432MHz transceiver can be accurately calibrated. Using a local oscillator line-up such as this, it is easy to set the receiver dial calibration to within 100Hz at 144MHz.

This makes searching for a very weak signal more productive, because the calibration is known to be accurate and you do not need to swing the tuning dial over much of the band to find the correct signal. Thi, of course, assumes that the transmitting station is on the correct frequency, which is often not the case; some are as much as ±25kHz from where they think they are!

14

Mechanical System Considerations

In this chapter:

- ☐ Mesh aperture considerations
- ☐ Legal requirements
- ☐ Antenna mount
- ☐ Positioning systems
- ☐ Torque
- ☐ Total computer control or not?
- ☐ Servo systems
- ☐ Modifying Bosch wiper motors

- ☐ D-A converter module
- ☐ Elevation axis detail
- ☐ Power supply details
- ☐ Servo boards
- ☐ Additional metering
- ☐ Feed horn supporting struts
- ☐ Adjusting the focal point
- ☐ Additional safety features

I n this chapter we will look in more detail at some of the mechanical problems and the options for positioning systems. Looking at the antenna requirements is probably the most difficult decision to make. Although we would all like to own a 20m diameter dish, (or even larger), in many cases it is simply not feasible for various reasons. One has to be realistic what one can construct and erect within your property. The larger the antenna the greater the wind loading will be and the more accurate the antenna positioning system needs to be to elevate and rotate the antenna structure. The mass of a large antenna is not a trivial matter, even using lightweight materials like aluminium, and this needs to be considered carefully and the stress calculations need to be performed by a competent person to ensure the structure is safe.

An example

Whilst designing the 7.5m diameter parabolic antenna for the Durban University of Technology new radio telescope known as *Indlebe Enkulu* (big ear in the Zulu language), the question of the weight of the reflecting mesh was

Although amateurs are very resourceful people the challenges can sometimes seem insurmountable. Probably the biggest challenges are the mechanical aspects. As radio amateurs we are taught to deal with electronics but little is taught on the mechanical challenges. I hope that some of the following will be useful information. During the design of the new 7.5m diameter dish antenna for the Durban University of Technology Indlebe 2 telescope I began to appreciate the enormous task that lay ahead. Having worked on the design of the 5m version and seen it up close one begins to realise how big such an antenna is!

a serious concern. (Due to the proposed site on top of a mountain, that experiences high wind at times, a solid dish was not possible). It will require approximately 40 square metres of galvanised wire mesh to cover the surface. Having sketched out the proposed rib design and had this analysed by the mechanical engineering faculty this highlighted the problem. The weight of the mesh alone was 70kg, not including the ribs and other parts of the antenna. The original choice of mesh was rejected after it was realised it would require 120kg to cover the antenna and a consequent extra load on the ribs, which would require thicker material to cope with this loading. All of this mass plus all the other parts has to be lifted by the elevation system, making it a concern from a mechanical point of view. In the final design a supplier of lower mass mesh was found that added only 40kg to the structure.

Although the elevation load can be somewhat alleviated by counterweights to balance the structure, this extra weight still needs to be catered for by the supporting structure. (The calculated mass of the 16 ribs of welded aluminium construction is 80kg and the other parts including the feed horn, supporting struts and focusing mechanism etc added another 20kg to the antenna). Having the feed horn placed a long way in front of the dish also causes stresses in the rib structure. In the case of the new Durban telescope the feed horn is placed about 4.5m in front of the vertex of the dish and comprises the focusing mechanism and the receiver front end up to the 1st IF stage. All of this mass on the end of the support struts needs to be carefully considered. These loads are taken by the feed supporting struts and fed into the dish rib structure.

MESH APERTURE CONSIDERATIONS

The aperture of the wire mesh used is required to be less than $\lambda/10$ for minimal loss of signal through the reflector. This also determines the ultimate front-to-back ratio, or how well the antenna is able to suppress interfering signals from behind the antenna, including the warm ground when the antenna is elevated. At 1.42GHz the average cold-sky temperature is about 5K, the ground is about 290K. At 1.42GHz the wavelength is approximately 21cm and hence the maximum dimension of the aperture of the wire mesh needs to be less than 21mm. Standard 'Weldmesh' fencing is available in 13mm x 13mm aperture and will be satisfactory. For 13mm aperture mesh the expected loss of gain and other parameters were calculated with a software program written by VK2ZRG called *Dishant.exe* [1]. Using 13mm mesh with 1mm wires the gain loss at 1.42GHz is 0.11dB, the feed through attenuation is 15.9dB and the contribution of ground noise due to signal leakage is 7.5K.

Richard Turrin, W2IMU, gives details in the Crawford Hills VHF Club technical note [2] (for a parabolic antenna for 23cm intended for amateur applications) on the effect of the mesh covering. Because the surface currents are low, as the antenna surface is a low Q structure, the effect of plating or corrosion has very little effect on the gain. Even a heavily corroded surface still acts as a good reflector. Similarly, the skin depth at 21cm is very small and the galvanised coating, although having some loss, has an insignificant effect on the gain (the mesh aperture has a greater effect). Electrical bonding of the layers of mesh where they overlap is not necessary as long as the overlap is greater than 0.25λ ($\geq$50mm). The portion of the surface closest to the centre has the highest surface current due to the tapering of the feed illumination towards the edges, this case being for a transmitting antenna. The edge of the parabola has substantially lower currents, typically –10dB for a transmitting antenna. For a radio astronomy receiving antenna the feed illumination tapering is often as much as –20dB to reduce the side lobes. For this reason it is beneficial to make the centre portion from a solid sheet and this fits in well as this also serves as the rib support hub.

In a report on the 64m-diameter Jet Propulsion Laboratory Deep Space Network antenna using a Cassegrain feed the focal point moved 120mm when the dish was declined from the zenith to 45° elevation caused by bending in the rib structure due to gravity distortions. To correct this an elaborate re-focusing mechanism was required to reposition the feed sub-reflector in three axes. This however added extra loads into the support struts due to the increased mass.

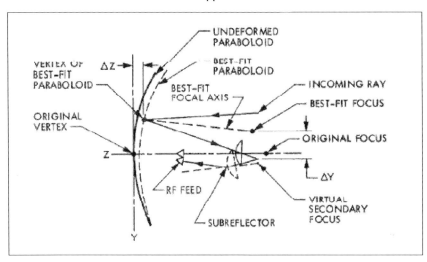

Fig 14.1: RF centre ray tracing and hyperboloid effects with gravity distortions

LEGAL REQUIREMENTS

Each local authority has slightly different rules and it is recommended that before you get too far into a project you have a talk with one of the authorities engineers or clerks to find out what you are required to submit and what other documentation is needed. Especially try to find out what restrictions may apply with your envisaged structure that may preclude the granting of planning permission. Rather find out earlier than later!

It is also worthwhile discussing any plans with your finance house if the property is mortgaged, they may have to sign an agreement with the planning authority stating they have no objections. Any insurance policy carried on the property would also need to be updated to cover potential damage to the property or neighbouring property should the structure collapse.

Many local authorities will require an engineer's report on a permanent structure signed by a chartered civil or mechanical engineer; at least we do in South Africa, showing the structure is basically a sound design within the laid down wind speeds in the legislation. Some authorities may also require a civil engineers report on the foundation structure proposed and soil samples to be taken and analysed to ensure the overturning load moments by the wind are able to be supported. Placing a large concrete foundation block close to a house or other building foundations may require the house foundations to be under-pinned to prevent damage. (In some cases it is not normally permissible to place such a concrete block within 500mm of an existing foundation).

The supporting tower or structure needs to be a certain minimum height to prevent the lower rim of the dish (or the back end of a Yagi array) from striking the ground or other objects. Consideration also needs to be taken of a person walking under the structure and adequate clearance needs to be provided for this if this is a possibility. If some cases if some elevation coverage can be sacrificed then the height of the support could be lower. In some cases elevation angles below about 10° may not be feasible from some sites due to obstructions in some directions such as nearby houses, trees etc. This will be dictated by the site logistics.

In the case of the new Durban telescope dish the supporting tower was to be placed at the rear of a single storey building and this meant the tower needed to be much higher to prevent the dish from fouling the roof.

The roof lies due South of the dish and as very little of interest occurs to the South at low elevation angles this was acceptable. Special planning permission was needed due to the tower foundation being close to the building foundations and also because the top of the dish exceeded the permissible 9m normally accepted as the maximum height of a double storey building. My brother, who is a civil engineer, on a recent visit inspected the proposed site and advised that in the UK underpinning would be required. Having discussed this with the local planning engineer it was accepted that as the portion of the building in question was the garage this would be waived as there was little risk to life or limb. In view of the special purpose the radio telescope was intended for this would be granted without too much difficulty. (The planning application will be made by the Durban University of Technology for a scientific research project partially funded by our National Research Foundation, the SA government grant giving organisation). Your conditions may be different.

RIGIDITY OF SUPPORT STRUCTURE

A common problem is to ensure that the support structure has adequate torsional and bending strength. It is pointless placing a narrow beamwidth array on a flimsy tower as the wind can cause the tower to bend or twist more than the antenna beamwidth. For HF and VHF Yagis where the beamwidth is normally tens of degrees a small amount of twisting is not too serious but for a microwave dish the twisting may be enough to take the object being observed completely out of the beam. Hence, the bracing of the tower needs to be much more complex to ensure this does not happen. It also usually means that the size of the tower has to be increased to stiffen the structure. For a large VHF EME array a tower of 300mm side may be adequate, for a microwave dish the tower needs to be more like 600mm side to prevent twisting.

Supporting Structure

Amateurs when considering a supporting structure often assume that a lattice tower with cross bracing is the only option. During the design of the new Durban radio telescope we ran across the cost of manufacturing the support tower for the bottom of the structure. Originally a 6m tall square tower of

600mm dimensions with 70mm x 8mm angle iron for the uprights and 30mm x 8mm flat bar for the bracing was the choice. This was analysed by the mechanical engineering faculty as a simple cantilever beam to assess the bending and torsional forces due to wind loading. However, having calculated the cost of the material and the predicted labour cost for the welding it was realised that a lower cost solution was possible. Rather than a welded lattice tower construction an alternative of using a round tube with flanges welded top and bottom turned out to be lower cost. For this method only two major welded joints are required. Metal is priced by weight (mass) and the mass of a steel tube of 16-inch (406mm) diameter with 6mm-wall thickness was about the same as the myriad pieces required for the lattice tower design.

Lattice Tower option	**Round Tube option**
Material cost R4660-00	Material cost R5041-00
Total mass = 351kg	Total mass = 377kg
112 welded joints	2 welded joints
56 parts	3 parts

Approximate conversion £1.00 = R12.00

Steel tube is available in standard lengths and the closest standard length is 6.2mm (20feet). Large diameter steel tubes are often rolled up in a helical fashion and continuously electric resistance welded (ERW) from flat sheet. A circular tube is inherently the strongest profile and it exceeds the torsion and bending strength of a lattice construction of the same size. A lattice tower to obtain adequate torsional and bending stiffness needs substantial bracing; a circular tube requires no additional bracing. The material cost of the steel tube and flanges was greater than the angle iron and flat bar by some 8% but the labour to fabricate was considerably less. As the labour cost to weld the myriad joints in a lattice tower is an important factor, also having to ensure the structure is true, the steel tube option was chosen. For a structure of this magnitude some legal requirements insist on a coded welder perform the welding.

A vertical round tube can be analysed as an infinite number of vertical lattice members with bracing between the individual members. A three-sided tower is the simplest form, a square tower has four vertical members, a hexagonal tower has six vertical members etc. When the number of vertical members exceeds about 24 the structure behaves like a round tube and the thickness of each vertical member and bracing can be reduced accordingly as the number increases.

The wind resistance of a circular tube is higher than an equivalent size lattice construction, but as the diameter can now be smaller (as well as a thinner wall) for the same load factor they are about the same for the same wind speed. Further advantages are that they have no climbing access so making it safer when children might be around. A retractable ladder can be fabricated or purchased that can be positioned when climbing is necessary, or climbing rungs attached above the height that a child could reach. They are also considerably easier to paint than a lattice tower.

Fig 14.2: 7.6 metre diameter antenna at Hart ROA with round tube for the support. (Note that the holding down bolts and levelling nuts leave a gap between the bottom flange and the concrete block to allow water to drain away)

The overall limitation is the foundation structure, if this is strong enough to withstand the over-turning moments due to the wind then it is adequate for the purpose. Engineering analysis of the round tube tower showed that it well exceeded the required safety factor with 160km/h (100mph) wind velocity.

Mass of Steel Sections

Looking at various steel stock lists gives us an idea of the weight (mass) of typical sections. Steel weighs 7.85-tonne per cubic metre. 50mm angle with 6mm thickness has a mass of 4.5kg per metre, 60mm x 6mm angle of thickness is 5.5kg/m and 70mm x 8mm angle is 8.4kg/m. Steel flat bar rectangular section of 30mm x 8mm is 1.9kg/m.

ANTENNA MOUNT

A consideration is what type of rotating and elevating method will be best suited to the antenna. There are several standard methods in use, the polar mount, meridian mount and the alt-azimuth mount. Alt-azimuth (altitude over azimuth) amateurs know better as the 'Az-El mount' (azimuth and elevation).

POSITIONING SYSTEMS

By this we mean the azimuth and elevation mechanics and the associated electronics. There are very few rotators or elevators made for the amateur market that are big enough or accurate enough to point a high gain narrow beamwidth antenna. Those that are available also rotate too fast to track an astronomical object. The fastest objects only move in azimuth by 0.25° per minute. In most cases the amateur radio astronomer often needs

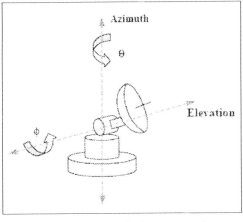

Fig 14.3: A dish needs to be rotated in both azimuth and elevation

to resort to custom made systems or modification of a standard rotator or elevator. Turning a large array requires a lot of torque, both to get it moving and then to stop

Fig 14.4: Azimuth drive worm gearbox for the new Durban radio telescope with final drive pinion and motor drive shaft. Universal couplings of 1/2-inch and 3/8-inch allow minor mis-alignment between the parts

335

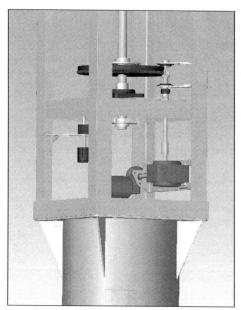

Fig 14.5: 3D CAD drawing of the azimuth drive system for the new Durban radio telescope

it when the target has been reached. Kinetic energy absorbed or given out by a heavy antenna array can also destroy some rotator and elevator gearing as well as any torque-tube connecting the azimuth drive and the antenna. Backlash in the axis rotator can be a problem as the antenna can 'windmill' in strong gusty winds, often rocking to and fro and placing a severe shock load on the final drive gears. For a heavy array a good choice is a worm gearbox with additional reduction gearing driven by a reversible motor. A worm gearbox is inherently self-braking when not being driven. It also has minimal backlash if correctly set up.

A choice also needs to be made which axis is moved first. As it is common practice to stow a large parabolic dish pointing towards the zenith in windy conditions, then the azimuth axis would be the first to be moved to the required position. Having set the azimuth position the elevation drive is then set to the required angle for the object under investigation.

The new Durban radio telescope has a substantial azimuth drive system. The worm gearbox is a 20:1 reduction ratio rated at 2.5kW and this drives a further 14.5:1 gear assembly. The final drive gear is an engine flywheel 310mm in diameter with the starter ring gear of 131 teeth engaging with a 9-teeth starter motor pinion. The meshing is adjustable to minimise the backlash.

Automated Tracking

For continuous automatic tracking of an object we need some sort of computer program that outputs the desired position of the azimuth and elevation drives and then a servo system to drive the antenna motors in the correct direction. We also need some sort of feedback system to tell the computer or servo system where the antenna currently is. There are many possibilities from simple potentiometers connected to the azimuth and elevation axis, or shaft encoders connected to the drive motor shaft. The choice normally boils down to what is available and the expertise of the constructor.

The shaft encoder method works by counting pulses as the motor shaft driving the reduction gearbox rotates. Most shaft encoders available have two outputs consisting of pulses in quadrature; hence a micro-controller monitoring the pulses can detect in which direction the shaft is being rotated and the speed. Knowing the exact reduction gear ratio between the motor shaft and the axis being moved allows the computer to run the motor in the correct direction for the required angular rotation by counting pulses to achieve the desired position.

However, this assumes that the gearing has zero backlash (lost motion), which many gearboxes do not comply with. There is always some backlash that causes a false reading. The closer the shaft encoder is to the final axis being rotated will give more accurate results. This however requires a much higher number of pulses for each 1° moved and often means the shaft encoder needs to be driven by step-up gearing between the driven shaft and the shaft encoder with zero backlash. A good choice for a low power zero-backlash drive is miniature toothed belts and pulleys (a smaller version of those used for engine camshaft drive) or sprockets and chain with an idler sprocket to take up any slack in the chain. Overshooting the required position and then reversing to correct the error can cause severe stress on the gearing. If the loop stability criteria of the servo system is not correct the antenna can remain oscillating forwards and backwards indefinitely. There needs to be a well controlled servo loop response (critical damping) and often a small amount of 'dead-band' (hysteresis) built in to prevent this problem.

Mechanical Resonance

Another consideration is the mechanical resonant frequency of the array. By this is meant the frequency it resonates at due to vibration caused by wind or movement. Large arrays have fairly low resonant frequencies, perhaps as low as 10Hz, and often a secondary resonance higher in frequency of about 100 to 200Hz. A fortunate factor of a heavy array is that the mass has inertia and this acts as a damper to sudden movement, the 'fly-wheel' effect. This needs to be taken into account in the damping factors of the servo control loop.

Unfortunately the resonant frequency is difficult to predict before the structure is built, but it becomes apparent when operational. For this reason some means needs to be provided to alter the damping factors and break points in the servo loop response. If the servo loop does not adequately damp oscillations they may build up to destructive levels placing undue stress on the drive mechanics.

Response of an Analogue Servo System

For an analogue servo system two DC voltages can represent the 'desired' and 'actual' positions. The desired position is a certain DC voltage and it should be a pure DC signal (no AC component, eg ripple or spurious noise spikes). Any AC component on the 'desired' signal is regarded as an uncertainty by the analogue servo system. The 'dither' around the wanted position on the 'actual position' feedback signal can be measured as an AC component superimposed on the DC value from the position sensing pot. To test for loop stability an AC signal can be coupled into the servo loop. Conversely, when ascertaining the natural resonance of the structure an oscilloscope can be connected to the feedback signal to measure the frequency of oscillation. Knowing this the damping components can be designed to suppress this frequency.

In Fig 14.6 the desired and actual position are represented by DC voltages. In this example the desired position is +45° where 0° is

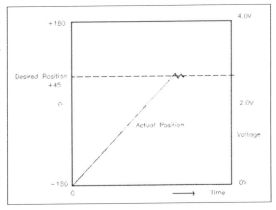

Fig 14.6: Positional dither appears as a damped oscillation

due North. The antenna starts at due South (-180°) and turns until it reaches the desired position, but it overshoots by a small amount and the servomotor is then reversed to correct this error. Because the damping is not optimal it again over-shoots, but by a smaller amount. After it has oscillated backwards and forwards for several cycles it settles to the desired position. This is a classic 'under-damped' response. The slope of the 'actual position' voltage versus time is a function of the speed at which the axis is rotating, for fast rotation the line is near-er the vertical and for slow rotation it is closer to the horizontal. As long as the AC component is much less than the varying voltage equivalent to the antenna beamwidth then no real degradation occurs.

Drive Motors

In the ideal positioning system the drive motors would have infinitely variable speed control with adequate torque to allow the motor to just run at the correct speed to hold the object within the antenna beamwidth.

Although some DC motors can be speed controlled with pulse width modula-tion schemes, some cannot. Pulse width modulated DC motors can also gener-ate a loud audible noise (known as 'cogging') and this can be a source of annoy-ance to people close to the system, particularly your family members and neigh-bours. A simple scheme to slow down the motor is to reduce the voltage fed to it. This works when the load on the motor is light but falls down if the torque generated is insufficient to cause the axis to be moved. Often a brief period of a higher voltage is required to generate enough torque to start the mass moving, after this the voltage can be reduced to just allow the antenna to move at the required rate.

> Generally, from a safety point of view, it is prudent to use low voltage DC motors rather than AC motors operating from the public mains supply. Voltages above 30V AC and 50V DC are considered to be lethal.

Another concern is being able to slew the antenna from some current position to a new position in a rapid manner. In professional radio telescopes the use is made of 'dual-motor epicyclic gearboxes'. In these two variable speed motors drive a common gearbox. These motors are normally large 3-phase types with electronic speed control. If both motors are running at exactly the same speed the output shaft is static. If one motor is slowed down by say, 10% and the other kept at the original speed the output shaft turns slowly in one direction. Speeding up the first motor by 10% causes the output shaft to rotate slowly in the opposite direction.

For rapid slewing one motor is stopped and the second run at maximum speed. Epicyclic gearboxes are expensive items and often custom made for a particular application.

TORQUE

Torque is what causes a shaft to rotate against a load. If a lever with an effec-tive length of 1m pivoted at one end has a force of 10kg applied to the other end then the static torque generated at the pivot is the product of the mass and the distance it is acting on. In this example the static torque generated is

10kgf-metre (10kg-m). In a reduction gearbox (speed reducer) the torque is multiplied by the step-down ratio, in a 'step-up' gearbox (speed-increased) the torque is reduced. If the 1m long lever with a mass of 10kg were now connected to the input shaft, and the gearbox has a 100:1 step-down ratio, then a torque of 10 x 100 = 1,000kgf-metre would be generated at the output shaft, neglecting any internal losses in the gearbox. What we have achieved is the same as using a lever 100m long with the same 10kg force applied to one end.

Gearboxes at low speeds are normally very close to 100% efficiency and the losses can normally be neglected. Torque is normally expressed in Newton-metres (Nm) where 1kg-m = 9.80625 Nm, normally rounded up to 9.81.

> The power transmitted (transferred) through a gearbox is a constant value, neglecting any internal frictional losses. If an input power of 1kW is applied to a step-down gearbox of 100:1 ratio then although the torque at the output shaft is 100-times that at the input shaft the power remains constant. Power is the product of revs per minute multiplied by the torque. The electrical analogy is a perfect transformer, the power is the product of volts x amps of the primary and secondary winding.

TOTAL COMPUTER CONTROL OR NOT?

During the design of the new radio telescope for the Durban University of Technology 'Indlebe Enkulu' system I had nightmares about using a computer to control the antenna positioning. Although modern computers are very reliable, I felt that if something should go wrong when I wasn't in attendance I could have the computer crashing the antenna into the end-stops causing damage to the gearing and motors. (The azimuth drive can generate more than 0.5 tonne of torque in overload mode; the elevation drive can generate nearly three tonnes of torque in overload mode). **It is imperative to have a backup safety mechanism, such as limit switches or an operator emergency stop button (E-stop), to abort movement should such an event arise.**

Fig 14.7: Typical antenna positioning block diagram

After laying the initial design down on paper I was intrigued to discover a paper by an engineer for the VLA in New Mexico for the 25m dishes. He had come to the same conclusion and had proposed the scrapping of full digital computer control and simply using it as a 'predictor' to where the antenna should be pointed. This report proposed the use of a system that took the desired positions and passed it onto analogue servo systems to control the motors. The computer simply 'spat-out' numbers that the analogue systems then acted on and reported the current position but needed no intervention from the computer.

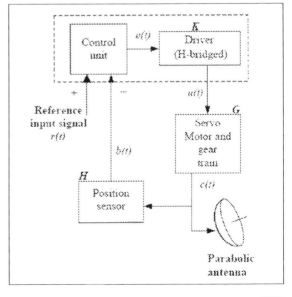

HOW ACCURATE THE POINTING NEEDS TO BE

There are several schools of thought on how accurate the antenna pointing needs to be, which although similar are subtly different. The common factor is how far off the target we can tolerate. For an antenna with a wide beamwidth obviously we can tolerate a lot more error than a very narrow beamwidth antenna. A good figure to aim for is about 10% of the total beamwidth. For an antenna with a 3° beamwidth at 3dB points this equates to approximately 0.3° total or ±0.15° either side of the target. In some cases we can tolerate a bit more, the determining factor is how strong the object is. For the Sun with a 3° beamwidth antenna an error of up to 1° either side of the correct position has very little effect on the receiver output because the signal is so strong. A very weak object has more degradation as the antenna off-pointing error rises.

It should now be obvious that this factor largely determines the accuracy the servo system needs to hold the antenna on target. It also determines the minimum number of 'bits' we need if we are considering D-A or A-D converters. If the azimuth axis is considered, and assuming we need to cover the whole 360° of possible rotation, then if the accuracy needs to be ±0.1° we need a minimum of 3600 steps. The nearest D-A or AD covers 4096 steps and is a 12-bit type (2^{12}). If we used the next lower converter it has 10-bits (D-A and A-D converters normally increment in 2-bit steps, although there are some exception to this) and this only gives 1024 steps, which is about ±0.4° accuracy and hence not accurate enough. If we choose a 14-bit converter (16384 steps) then each bit corresponds to 0.025°.

COMMISSIONING A NEW POSITIONING SYSTEM

It is recommended that on setting up a new system that the use of drift scans will point to any errors in the positioning system. In a drift scan the antenna azimuth and elevation are placed at the expected position for an object such as the Sun

Fig 14.8: The two plots are taken from the Durban University of Technology Indlebe 5m-diameter transit radio telescope operating on 21cm. These show the signal received from the Sun. The plot on the left is a linear scale with arbitrary measurements. The right hand plot has been converted into logarithmic values. In this second plot we can see the sidelobes of the antenna polar diagram more clearly. Also note that the increase in noise level from the cold sky value is about 40dB. This is a very strong signal

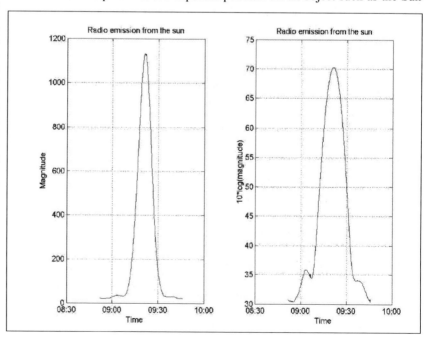

or other strong source that will pass through the beam at some later time. By observing the received signal, the output should rise to a peak and then fall away to the cold sky value again as the object passes through. By noting the exact time of the peak signal and comparing it to a software program, such as *Radio-Eyes*, any pointing errors can be identified. Knowing any errors allows us to tweak the pointing system to reduce these to very small errors. It should be fairly obvious that we need to know precisely where due North is at our location, magnetic North is of no use to us. Setting up the elevation axis is simple using a graduated protractor, but the azimuth axis requires us to know the position of North. An alternative method can use software to determine an object's position. Using a program such as *Radio-Eyes* the position of the Sun can be determined and the antenna positioned manually to give the strongest signal. This method takes into account any slight 'squint' the antenna may have. If the Sun is crossing the local meridian this corresponds to due North or due South (depending in which hemisphere you are located). This can then be marked as a 'timing-mark' onto a disc attached to the azimuth shaft with a suitable reference pointer.

AZIMUTH MID-SCALE CHOICE

Another factor that needs to be clearly defined is where the azimuth mid-range will be. In the Northern Hemisphere the best choice for mid-range is due South. In the Southern Hemisphere the point reverses to be due North. This is because the sky as seen from a location contains more or less objects of interest. A further choice is the elevation rotation angle to use. A common choice for amateur satellite elevators is 180°, in this scheme the antenna can follows an object when it passes through the zenith but complicates the computing and mechanical system. Most radio telescopes use the simpler 90° method as this simplifies the mechanics.

SERVO SYSTEMS

Although there are many different servo systems that can be used, such as proportional control (P) and proportional & integral (PI) up to full PID systems (proportional-integral-differential) these are complicated and time consuming to perfect. The proportional control system uses a variable speed motor whose speed is a function of how far from the desired position the antenna is. For large errors the motor runs fast and as the desired position is approached the motor speed reduces towards zero. This with a correct loop response gives zero overshoot but creeps up to the final position very slowly.

A modification of the pure proportional system is to use a 'dual-proportional' system. In this system it behaves the same as a true proportional system when the error is large but when the error has been reduced to, say 2%, then the motor speed is reduced in a step change to a slower rate, finally stopping as the beam is exactly on target.

In the new Durban telescope system a simple 'bang-bang' system was developed. This is basically a method where the motor is engaged when the antenna needs to be repositioned and then is turned off once the desired position is attained. Sometime later as the object moves in apparent position, due to rotation of the Earth, the off-pointing error exceeds the minimum required and the motor runs again to correct the error. (The gear reduction ratio chosen was such that the antenna azimuth drive would move at approximately 30° per minute when the motor was using the low speed winding). Hence, the azimuth motor runs in short bursts to correct the error. (For rapid slewing the high speed winding is used giving approximately 60° per minute).

Although this is not the optimum system there were valid reasons for choosing it. The telescope is being built on a limited budget and the servo boards were to hand from another industrial project that had performed well. The second reason is that the Durban University of Technology is an academic institution and is currently using the existing telescope as a teaching aid for electronic students. As time progresses a new student will be tasked with redesigning a particular portion as part of their degree project. At some later date a newer and more sophisticated servo system will probably be developed using the same motors and gearing but with a different control strategy. The important thing was to construct a working radio telescope although not the optimum solution. Further funding is expected later and then the design can be improved by replacing existing portions.

The motors used are 12V DC permanent magnet motors as used for automobile windscreen wipers. These are readily obtainable from scrap yards for a nominal sum and often feature a 2-speed motor with two sets of brush gear. The typical DC wiper motor has one set of brush gear (negative terminal) connected to the case so they can only be operated in one direction unless the body is electrically isolated from ground.

A simple modification lifts the grounded brush gear and allows two direction operation. Most wiper motors have an output shaft speed of 25rpm on the low speed brushes and about 50rpm on the highspeed brush gear. They can be safely over-driven with a higher supply voltage of up to twice the normal voltage for short periods.

The output shaft is a worm gear and can develop a surprising amount of torque when operated on 12V. (Earlier versions of these wiper motors used bronze or steel worm wheels; the later versions used nylon worm wheels. The nylon worm wheels are not as robust as the metal versions).

Fig 14.9: Unmodified Bosch wiper motor brush gear

MODIFYING THE BOSCH WIPER MOTORS

(left) Fig 14.10: Modified Bosch wiper motor brush gear

(right) Fig 14.11: Bosch 12V wiper motor modified to fit toothed belt pulley

After disassembling the motor to access the brush gear the grounded brush pigtail is cut off from the grounding post. This is shown in Fig 14.9. The slow speed brushes are the ones at 12-o'clock and 6-o'clock. The high-speed brush is at 2-o'clock and with the grounded brush gives the fastest speed. The modified connection details are shown in Fig 14.10.

The grounded brush has the pigtail lead tinned and soldered to the end plate. A wire is then soldered to the same point and routed via the hole in the body to the outside. The slow speed brush and the high-speed brush wire are replaced with wire of suitable colours.

After cleaning and lubricating the mechanical parts the motor is reassembled. The original wires are cut off and the contact fingers for self-parking are also removed, as they are no longer required. After reassembling, the hole for the wires and wiper fingers are closed with silicon sealant and the bolting holes also plugged to prevent moisture entering the motor, finally the motor is painted with Hammerite paint to stop corrosion.

A reversible DC motor servo system can use the H-Bridge scheme. In this a permanent magnet DC motor has a semiconductor bridge to drive the motor in two directions. The basic scheme is shown below. The DC motor has four switches to drive current through the motor in two directions. The switches are replaced with relays or semiconductors, either bipolar transistors or mosfets. In some cases the bottom switches can also be pulse width modulated (PWM) giving a variable speed system. The switch sequencing must prevent both sets of switches being on at the same time, if this

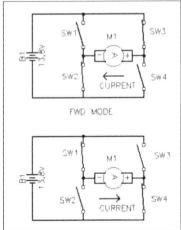

Fig 14.12: Basic H-Bridge circuit

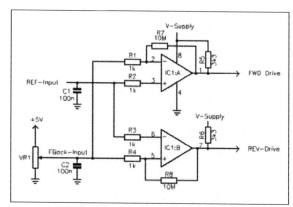

occurs a short circuit exists across the supply and a heavy current can flow. To derive the error signal a comparator scheme can be used. In this a DC voltage derived from a D-A converter gives the desired position fed to the REF-Input port and a feedback voltage from a potentiometer coupled to the axis feeds a signal to the comparator circuit.

Basic Dual Comparator System

The dual comparator scheme uses cross-coupled inputs such that only one comparator output can be high at any time. When the value of the REF-Input and Feedback-Input are the same value both comparators will be off. If the voltages are slightly different one comparator output will be on, so driving the DC motor in that direction.

Fig 14.13: Basic dual comparator

Feedback around each comparator by a high value resistor sets the hysteresis and hence the dead-band. The schematic for a dual comparator scheme is shown below. Note that the damping components are not shown, as they need to be determined when the system is commissioned.

The H-Bridge transistors consist of TR7 to TR10 and these are high current Darlington NPN transistors rated at 100V/10A. The outputs of the comparators drive the H-Bridge transistors via TR1 and TR2. These in turn provide the correct drive to the PNP transistors driving the top-switch transistors and the corresponding opposite bottom switches. When the antenna has been driven to the required position the DC motor is switched off and the two bottom-switch

Fig 14.14: Detailed comparator circuit

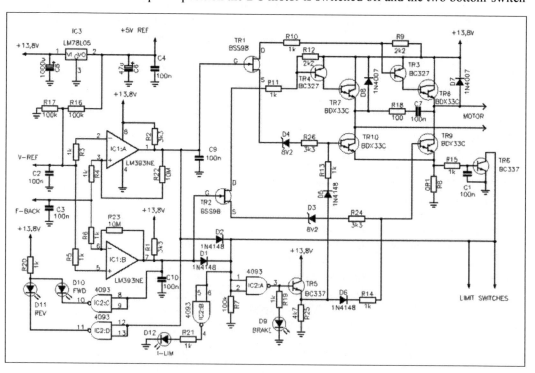

transistors turned fully on. This places a short circuit across the motor bringing it to a stop rapidly due to regenerative braking. This action also lights the Brake LED.

Current limiting is performed by TR6, which monitors the return current of the bottom switches in a low value resistor R8. This value determines the maximum motor current. When the voltage across R8 exceeds 0.6V TR6 turns on and aborts the drive. This same point allows the feeding in of limit switches that apply a short to ground if they are activated. Operator emergency abort is performed by a 30A relay that removes the 12V supply from the servo board when the relay is de-energised.

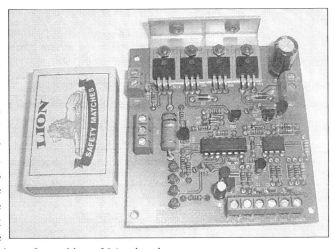

Fig 14.15: Analogue servo board

The V-REF input is derived from a D-A converter driven by the computer software to give the desired position. In addition to the D-A input two high value resistors R16 and 17 also apply a half-rail bias.

This will normally be overcome by the D-A output, which is low impedance. The reason the half-rail bias is used is to act as a fail-safe mechanism should the D-A voltage be lost due to some fault. In such a case the motor will drive the antenna to approximately mid travel and then stop.

Providing the Feedback and V-REF input

For the azimuth and elevation axis additional gearing with zero backlash connects to the feedback pots. The Indlebe-2 azimuth shaft has a toothed belt pulley system driving a 10-turn precision linear potentiometer with a 6:1 step-up. Hence, for one complete revolution of the azimuth shaft the pot slider moves over 60% of the range. In order to prevent the pot from being driven against an end-stop the pot is adjusted so that it is one full turn away from the lower end-stop. Because the pot is being fed from a 5V stabilised supply the slider will output 0.5V when the azimuth shaft is pointing the antenna due South. As the

Fig 14.16: D-A summing amplifier

azimuth shaft rotates the antenna through North and back to South at the end of its range the slider will now occupy the 7-turn position and the feedback voltage will vary between 0.5V to 3.5V, a span of 3V.

The D-A converter was set up to provide an output voltage between 0 to 4V for this range by using 4000 steps to cover 400°. The 0.5V offset can be eliminated by the use of a DC summing amplifier between the D-A converter and the servo board V-REF input. The output from the D-A providing 0 to 4V is attenuated to

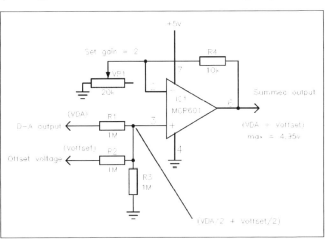

half this value by the series resistors on the input forming a potential divider with R3. The offset voltage is similarly attenuated. The composite DC voltage is applied to the non-inverting input of the precision operational amplifier IC1 and the gain is adjusted to precisely 2 by VR1. (IC1 has a "rail-to-rail" output stage and can swing up to within 50mV of the supply voltage).

D-A CONVERTER MODULE

Fig 14.17: Block diagram of the MCP4921/4922 from Microchip

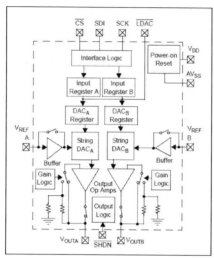

The D-A converter chosen was the Microchip MCP4921 being a serial loaded 12-bit type with rail-to-rail output. The D-A has an external reference input so the exact output voltage at full scale can be set. The output stage of the MCP4921 has a two-times DC gain so the reference voltage applied is half the required full-scale value. Other types have a fixed internal reference voltage and are not as easy to interface and calibrate. Each axis has its own D-A converter and the computer software writes to each converter by selecting the appropriate Chip Select pin. The serial data (SDI) and serial clock

(below) Fig 14.18: Schematic of the D-A module

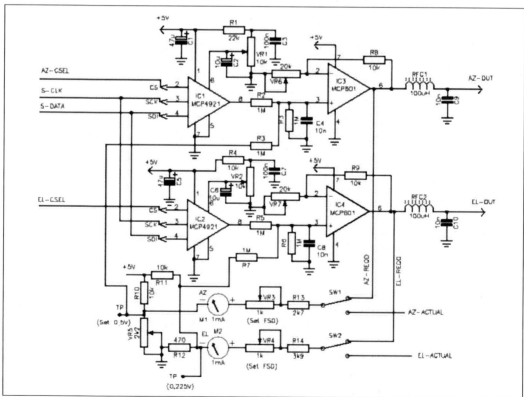

(SCK) pins of the two D-A converters are commoned together. Update rate can be selected from the software to be anything from 5 seconds between updates to several minutes. An initial update rate of 15s was selected.

The MCP4921 is a single D-A converter whereas the MCP4922 contains two D-A converters in a 14-pin DIL package each with external reference inputs. The dual version was not available from the local agents so two single 8-pin DIL D-As were used. The MCP4921 uses a 16-bit data stream to set the desired operating mode and output voltage. The first four bits configure the modes, select the reference voltage buffer amplifier (either buffered or un-buffered) and the output stage being a gain of 1 or 2. The remaining 12 bits set the output voltage required over 0 to 4095 steps in binary format. The 12-bit data is clocked in most significant bit first (MSB).

The processor module writes to the two 12-bit D-A converters one after the other. The serial data and clock lines are paralleled. The azimuth D-A is written to first followed by the elevation D-A. The chip select line is driven low when a write cycle begins and then high after the 16-bit word has been sent. The raising of the chip select line transfers the data to the output stage. VR1 and VR2 provide the reference voltages for the two D-As, which are multi-turn pre-set pots. The D-As each drives a summing amplifier (IC3 and IC4). A potential divider connected to the bottom of the indicator meters provides the offset voltages. VR5 sets the azimuth axis offset such that it is the same voltage as the azimuth shaft potentiometer was set to with the antenna pointing due South in the counter-clockwise position. VR3 and VR4 adjust the full-scale deflection of the two meters. The buffered feedback voltages from the azimuth and elevation pots are connected to the points AZ-ACTUAL and EL-ACTUAL. A pair of SPCO switches SW1 and SW2 allows the operator to switch between the desired and actual position. VR6 and VR7 set the gain of the summing amplifiers.

ELEVATION AXIS DETAIL

The elevation axis uses an identical set up of D-A and servo board, the only difference is that the elevation axis only rotates from 0° to 90° and so the feedback pot can be a single turn precision type. This is driven from the secondary elevation shaft driven by the 60:1 ratio worm gearbox that rotates through 342° and drives the final reduction 3.8:1 ratio gearing comprising a duplex chain and sprockets. The small duplex sprocket is a 10-tooth.

The elevation potentiometer is geared down 1.5:1 using miniature simplex chain and sprockets with an idler sprocket giving zero backlash and a travel of 228° out of a possible 270° pot shaft rotation. Again an offset is

Fig 14.19: Indlebe Enkulu elevation axis secondary shaft, worm gearbox and final drive sprocket. The small sprocket on the end of the shaft drives the feedback potentiometer via a chain

Fig 14.20: Elevation final drive shaft, flange bearing and 38-tooth sprocket. The sprocket is 240mm in diameter and the shaft is 30mm diameter

applied to keep the pot off its lower end-stop to prevent damage. The D-A reference voltage is adjusted to give the correct full-scale value. (The final reduction was originally designed as a 4:1 ratio to simplify the calculations. In the event only a 38-tooth sprocket was available).

The final reduction duplex chain and sprockets used are an overkill being a 20mm pitch (3/4") with a safe tension load of 61kN, about 6-tonnes. This was chosen because the whole weight of the antenna has to be lifted through a radius of 400mm by the wishbone arms attaching the centre hub of the dish to the primary elevation shaft. If the chain should break, a severe amount of damage would result. The chain slack is adjusted by slotted holes in the plummer block bearings supporting the secondary shaft. The mass of the antenna and the pendulum effect of the feed-horn cause it to try to fall towards the zero elevation state. Hence, the top run of the chain is always in tension and the bottom of the run is the slack side.

Provision is made to manually decline the antenna below 0° to allow easier access to the feed horn whilst commissioning the system or during maintenance. The elevation wishbones will then rest on the elevator platform stop bars so preventing the antenna going below -10°, which would foul the supporting tower.

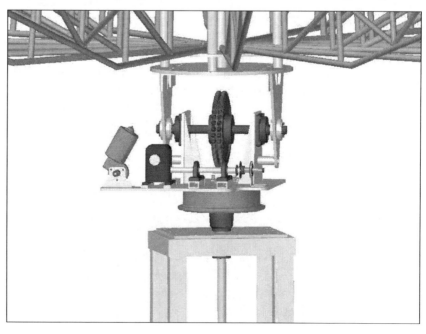

Fig 14.21: 3D CAD drawing of the elevation assembly. The final drive primary sprocket and chain are not shown in this view. The bottoms of the wishbones have holes lining up with hollow sleeves welded to the bearing support brackets to accept the stowing pins. The secondary shaft and gearbox are mounted at the rear of the elevation assembly. The input drive to the worm gearbox is via a toothed belt, not shown in this view

The elevation shaft is supported near the outer ends with two self-aligning flange bearings. The final drive sprocket sits midway between the bearings. Two Y shaped wishbones connect to the outer ends of the 30mm shaft. The elevation motion is provided by a 60:1 worm gearbox driven by a single-speed 12V wiper motor via a 12mm wide XL tooth belt and pulleys with a step-down ratio of 2.4:1.

Fig 14.22: Elevation worm gearbox with toothed belt pulley on the input shaft

Antenna Mounting to Central Hub

64 x 8mm bolts attach the 16 fabricated ribs to two circular steel plates spaced apart by 200mm by four 38mm diameter thick wall tubes and a 50mm tube in the centre. This is arc welded at all points to make a very stiff structure. Four 16mm bolts connect this hub assembly to the elevation plate in order that the completed rib and mesh assembly may be lifted and placed in position on site with a crane. The general arrangement of the complete azimuth and elevation show the rib to hub mounting arrangement. The three circular steel plates are 10mm thick. The rib hub plates are 400m diameter and the elevator plate is 500mm diameter. (The 50mm tube serves as a cable passageway for the various cabling between the control unit and the feedhorn electronics).

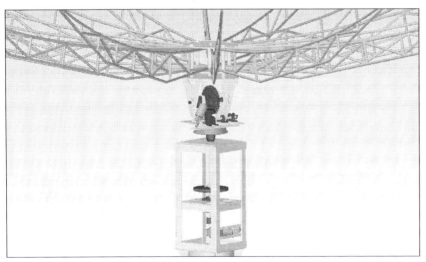

Fig 14.23: General arrangement of antenna mounting

POWER SUPPLY DETAILS

The 12V DC motors can draw up to 6A per motor and these current needs to be supplied with minimum voltage drop in the wiring. The main 12V supply is derived from a sealed lead-acid battery mounted near the top of the tower in a box and fed with a charging circuit consisting of several ICs connected in parallel. The raw unstabilised supply is fed up the tower via a two-core cable rated at 10A to

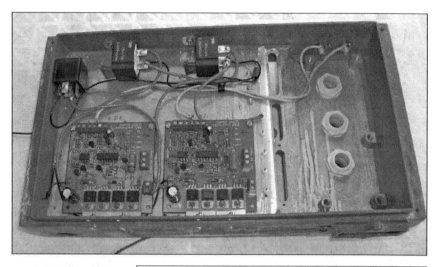

(above) Fig 14.24: Servo box showing the servo boards and associated control relays

(right) Fig 14.25: Battery charger schematic

(below) Fig 14.26: Battery charger portion of operator's console

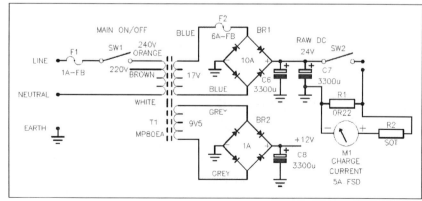

the servo box enclosure that contains the charging circuit as well as the servo boards and associated control relays. This raw DC supply is provided by a transformer, bridge rectifier, smoothing capacitors and is nominally 24V.

Fig 14.27: Modified Storno trunk mount radio die-cast box showing charger PCB details. The relays below switch the focussing drive motor between forward and reverse

This same supply is used in the operator console to power the noise source for calibration purposes. The noise source is situated in the receiver box on the rear of the feedhorn and connected to one of the monopoles in the feedhorn, the second monopole is the normal receive antenna with circular polarisation.

SERVO BOARDS

The servo boards are also contained in the waterproof aluminium die-cast box with O-ring seals. This box was modified from an old Storno trunk-mount VHF radio by removing all the modules and then machining off some heat sink fins to provide a flat surface to allow cable glands to be fitted.

The servo boards each have a 30A relay between the battery positive terminal and the servo board. These relays are operated via the umbilical cable between the servo box and the operators console. Hence, switching via the operator console can inhibit one or both servo boards. The elevation axis uses a single speed motor whereas the azimuth motor is a two speed version. The gear ratio is such that the

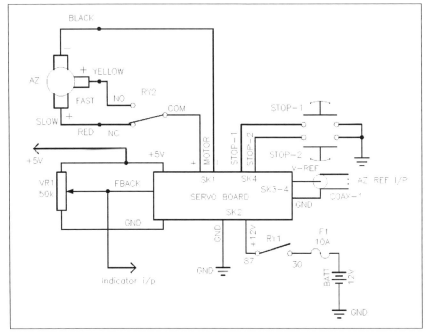

Fig 14.28: Azimouth servo board connection details

elevation shaft moves at about 30° per minute. For the azimuth axis under normal tracking mode the lower speed brush gear is selected. For rapid slewing the high-speed brush gear is selected by a changeover relay controlled from the operator console.

The two D-A converter signals are fed from the operator console via two RG-58/U coaxial cables and enter the servo box via BNC connectors. This keeps switching transients and other interfering signals from upsetting the servo board comparator circuits. The original 34-way connector used on the Storno radio is used for connecting various low power signals from the servo box to the operator console for control and monitoring purposes.

The operators console contains the battery charger raw DC supply as well as a dual comparator circuit to monitor the battery voltage. If the battery voltage is above 13.0V the "BATT OK" LED is lit, should the voltage fall below 12.8V the "LOW BATT" LED will be lit.

The charge current is measured by sensing the voltage drop across a low value 5W wire-wound resistor in series with the negative return line, accessed via two banana sockets on the operators console front panel. A DVM is connected when charge current needs to be measured.

ADDITIONAL METERING

Two additional moving coil meters show the current position of the antenna in azimuth and elevation. These are not intended to be very accurate, they are simply used as a confidence check that things are working as they should. The DC signals for these two meters are derived from the feedback pots and buffered by voltage follower operational amplifiers before being fed via the 34-way connector to the console. In the console scaling resistors on the D-A board set the full-scale deflection.

The azimuth moving coil meter was removed from an old rotator control box and it was suitably scaled with North at mid-scale. The elevation meter was salvaged from a redundant elevator system made by the writer many years ago for 2m EME. This features a square meter with a 90° needle movement and scaled 0 to 100, so it was suitable.

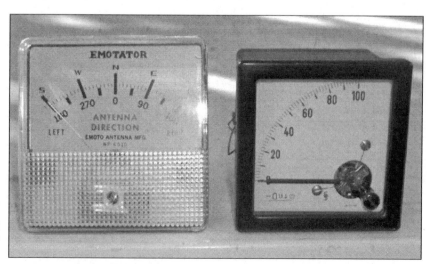

Fig 14.29: Azimuth and elevation indicator meters

FEED HORN SUPPORTING STRUTS

One of the decisions that need to be made is the number of struts that are used to support the feed horn in front of the dish. Common logic tells us that a three-legged stool, although the legs may be of unequal lengths, will always be stable. A four-legged stool with different length legs will rock. Richard Turrin, W2IMU in the Crawford Hill VHF Club newsletters recommends the use of three struts. Other large telescopes use four struts. If the dish is viewed face on and the three-strut system is used then the strut at 12-oclock will be in tension and the other two struts in compression when the dish is moved from the zenith to 0° elevation. When the dish is pointed to the zenith all the struts are in compression. The use of four struts gives a better system. In this method the struts are placed at approximately 10-o'clock, 2-o'clock, 4-o'clock and 8-o'clock and the two lower struts will be in compression with the two upper struts in tension. Which method is the better one depends on how many ribs are used. A common choice when constructing a ribbed dish is to work in multiples of eight and 16 ribs is a good choice. Since this is not equally divisible by three but is by four means that the four legged strut method is preferable. If the number of ribs is increased to 24, a tri-strut method can be chosen. The reason being that it is not a good idea to feed in tension or compression loads between the ribs, but rather attach the struts directly to the ribs. The portion of the dish structure between the ribs only has to support the reflecting mesh and not direct loads.

The struts cause some feed blocking if they are of substantial size comparable to the wavelength being used. Smaller diameter struts cause less feed blocking and hence four struts are preferable, as they can be a smaller diameter to support the same feed horn load. The point where the struts attach to the ribs is

Fig 14.30: Meerkats. (left) An indigenous animal belonging to the mongoose family that stands on its hind legs to see the surrounding area; (right) Prototype South African KAT (Karoo Array Telescope) 15 metre diameter radio telescope showing the quadripod prime feed mount. This telescope is one of seven being built for the MeerKat array as a demonstrator for the SKA project. In the Afrikaans language "meer" means more so the MeerKAT array literally means "more KAT arrays"

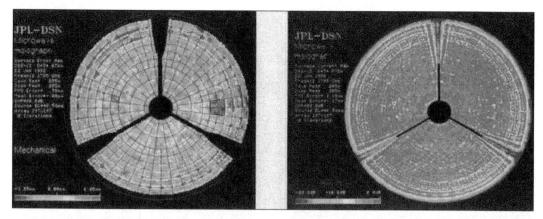

Fig 14.31: Holographic images of the aperture blocking which occurred on the JPL Deep Space Network dish due to the Cassegrain feed sub-reflector and support struts at 12GHz. The dark areas are the shadows caused by the blocking. The picture on the left is the original 64m dish with the bigger and longer struts attached to the edge of the dish. The picture on the right is after extending the dish to 70m diameter with a more perfect profile and the feed struts moved towards the centre of the dish allowing smaller struts. This modification increased the efficiency from 60% to nearer 70%. The sub-reflector remained the same diameter at 6.4m. The modification increased the gain by almost 2dB

also important. If the struts attach to the outer rim of the dish the rim needs to be more substantial and hence requires more material and bracing to prevent deflection. A good compromise is to attach the struts about two-thirds out from the centre of the dish at which point the ribs are quite stiff and can support the additional loading. The holographic images of the JPL dish (Fig 14.31) illustrate this problem.

ADJUSTING THE FOCAL POINT

Provision needs to be made to adjust the position of the feed so the focusing is optimised. This means we have to be able to move the feed towards and away

Fig 14.32: Indlebe original radio telescope Kumar feed showing the slide bars for adjusting the focal length

from the dish vertex in some way to place the feed phase centre in the correct place. If the phase centre of the feed is not aligned correctly with the dish focal point then some loss of gain occurs. Minor deviations are not too serious, but if the error exceeds about $\lambda/10$ the loss of gain starts to become greater.

It is a good idea to allow at least a movement of $\lambda/2$ either side of the predicted focal

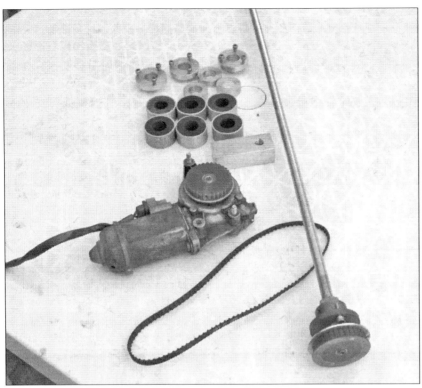

Fig 14.33: Component parts for the focus mechanism. The leadscrew is shown with bearing housing, toothed belt pulley, the nut and drive motor. The six slide bushes and the end stop collars are also shown. The slide bars are 19mm OD thick-wall aluminium tube. The 12V DC motor is an automotive window winder with a toothed pulley fitted to the output shaft

point to allow for any errors that may exist. Once the correct position has been established the feed can be locked in place.

In the new Durban telescope the feed horn will be supported in a square framework consisting of two 'picture-frames' with three slide bars running between them and a leadscrew driven by a small DC motor. The feed horn fits inside the square hole and is attached to six slide bushes (two per slide bar) by a pair of circular clamps around the small portion of the feed horn. The slide bushes are short lengths of 38mm aluminium tube with inserted bushes of a low friction nature eg Vesconite or lignum vitea, which material is inherently self-lubricating. This allows the feed horn to move with little friction and the nut on the leadscrew pushes or pulls the feed horn along the slide bars in or out from the dish vertex. This allows the adjustment from the operator console to confirm the correct focal point. It was included as the students can then see the effect of defocusing on the observed signal.

ADDITIONAL SAFETY FEATURES

As well as the already mentioned emergency limit switches and operator override switches, thought needs to be given of how best to protect our investment in time and money in extreme conditions. One of the greatest concerns is wind of higher than normal velocity. A large dish antenna has a substantial wind loading if pointing into the wind, even with a mesh reflector. The norm for a large dish used for a radio telescope is to stow it pointing directly upwards towards the zenith. In this attitude the wind-loading surface is greatly reduced. To ensure the elevation mechanics are not unduly stressed when the dish is stowed it is

Fig 14.34: Azimuth shaft with lower bearing and potentiometer drive toothed pulley fitted. The shaft is 800mm in length

common practice to fit two or more locking pins or bolts that prevent the dish rocking. These can either be manually fitted or some form of remote actuation is often used.

The azimuth similarly needs a locking mechanism. For the new Durban telescope the azimuth main shaft is a side-shaft from a Ford commercial vehicle rear axle and this has the end of the differential casing with the hub bearing cut off. The original drum brake and back-plate carries the normal brake shoes and an extended hand-brake cable and hand-brake lever mounted close to ground level allowing positive braking in severe weather conditions. Limit switches (E-stop) on both the elevation stowing pins and the hand-brake lever feed abort grounding signals to the servo boards to prevent operation when the antenna is stowed in that axis.

The azimuth shaft consists of the Ford F150 commercial vehicle side-shaft and portion of the original differential casing. The shaft is 32mm in diameter and made from a very tough type of alloy steel (V-155) that can withstand high torque and shock loads. A secondary sleeve bearing has been machined up from cast-iron and inserted below the main taper needle roller bearing to restrict the sideways movement. This also contains a grease seal to prevent the loss of lubricant. The central plate attaches to the flywheel with ring-gear that turns the shaft. The bottom bearing is a self-aligning flange bearing that prevents the bottom end of the shaft from whipping.

The brake drum bolts onto the hub with its associated back-plate and brake shoes. In the picture the wheel studs have been removed to allow machining work on the shaft in a lathe between centres. The original shaft was 35mm in

Fig 14.35: Azimuth sensor drive mechanism

diameter. It was a hot forged part and was not exactly round and also the shaft had a slight bend, and to correct this it had to be reduced in diameter to get it to run true. The short section of the hub casing is welded into the centre of a 10mm thick 450mm square steel plate that forms the top plate of the tower section.

A 12mm wide XL style toothed belt attached to the

bottom of the azimuth shaft drives the azimuth feedback potentiometer. A dual ball bearing housing supports the smaller pulley and this with slotted mounting holes takes up the slack to ensure zero backlash exists. The 10-turn precision linear potentiometer is enclosed in a waterproof die-cast box to keep out the moisture.

Further Mechanical Aspects

In a rotator or elevator system the need often arises to attach a sprocket or gear to a shaft with positive locking. For light loads a method is to use a screw tapped into the collar or bush on the sprocket or gear that bears on the shaft to prevent movement. Often a hole is drilled a little in the shaft for the screw to engage with or a flat machined making the shaft D shaped. For high torque loads the screw point is in shear and if the torque generated is high enough the material can be severely stressed and the screw end can be broken off. Shock loads can be many times the static loads and if the shear stress is high enough it can leave the two parts disconnected. This is an unsafe situation.

For high torque interfaces one choice is a form of keyway. This can also be used as a 'weak-link' to prevent damage. Common types of keys are feather keys, gib-head keys and Woodruffe keys. For the feather and gibhead key a square slot is machined in the shaft and a corresponding slot in the sprocket or bush. (For the feather key a slot drill makes the rounded ends so the key seats correctly). The square space is filled with a piece of key material that is a close fit between the two. The feather key can also use a screw in the collar bearing on it to give extra security. The gib-head key has a slight taper and it is driven

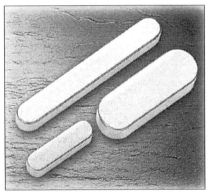

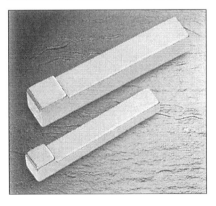

Fig 14.36: (top left) Feather key; (top right) Gib head key and (bottom left) Woodruffe key. [www.hkais.com]

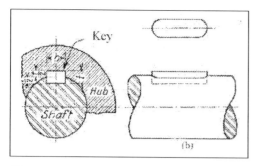

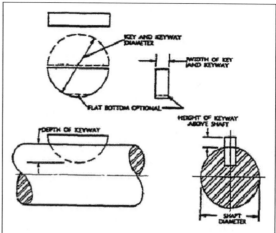

Fig 14.37: (left) Feather key application and (right) Woodruffe key application

into the square hole formed between the shaft and collar. For Woodruffe keys the shaft has a semi-circular slot machined into it and a Woodruffe key inserted to fill the space fitting into the square slot machined in the sprocket or bush.

Formula to Calculate Safe Torque Load

Where a feather key is used to interface between a shaft and collar the following formula can be used to calculate the approximate safe torque load (dimensions in mm).

Torque (Nm) = 0.065 x Key Length x Key Width x Shaft Diameter

For an 8mm square key 25mm long in a shaft of 30mm diameter the safe torque load is 390 Nm (39.75 kgf-m = 287.4 ft-lb).Note: Half the key height is in the shaft and slightly less than half is in the collar allowing a small clearance for the top of the key. For a 8mm wide key the shaft depth is 4mm and the hub keyway is typically 3.3mm deep, so a 8mm x 7mm key is used, giving 0.3mm clearance. These dimensions are standardised in either an ANSI standard for imperial keys or in a DIN standard for metric keys.

Cutting the keyway in a shaft is relatively easy using a milling machine and a slot drill or other types of cutters. However, cutting the corresponding keyway in the hub or sprocket requires special slotting machinery or a broach made to the exact size, which is an expensive item and incurs considerable expense in setting up a machine to make a one off.

14.38: TaperLock™ weld on hub

An alternative method is to utilise 'Taper-Lock™' hubs. Several manufacturers make them, (typically Fenner) and these can be purchased as 'bolt-on' hubs or 'weld-on' hubs for sprockets etc. (If only one or two hubs need slotting then the cost of labour and machine set up costs often greatly exceeds the cost of buying these off the shelf, they are made to very close tolerances and are not expensive). They have the internal keyway already machined to close tolerances as well as the split taper collet that is drawn up tight by grub screws. They are available in imperial and metric versions to suit common shaft diameters. The combination of the key and the taper collet, which grips the shaft tightly, is a simple method of providing an adequate high torque interface. (To release the taper collet the two grub screws are removed and placed in the two unused holes where they serve to jack the collet out of the hub). The advantage of the taper lock hub is that the key does not have to transmit all the torque, the collet grips the shaft tightly and the key only comes into play once the torque is sufficient to cause the hub to slip on the shaft. Hence, a smaller key than normal can often be used.

Shear-Pin drive

A common method of coupling two tubes together is to have an overlap with the smaller tube inside the larger tube and then one or more holes are drilled through the tubes and a bolt inserted to transmit the torque. This is a simple and low cost solution, but some thought needs to be given to the shear stress on the bolt. The pin is in 'double-shear' where it passes through the walls of the tube. Any slackness aggravates the problem and the pin is liable to failure. Stainless steel bolts, although they might seem to be attractive from a corrosion point of view, are less able to withstand high shear loads than high-tensile steel bolts. The common stainless steel bolts are only some 40% of the safe shear stress of a high-tensile bolt of the same diameter.

A better solution than a bolt is to utilise 'Roll-Pins' (also known as Spring-Pins or Split Dowel Pins). These are split tubes made from high tensile material that are sprung slightly open so they are a little larger in diameter than the hole they are fitted to.

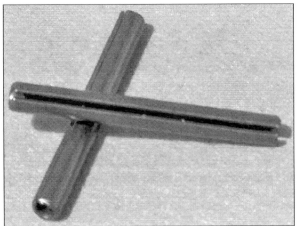

Fig14.39: Roll pins

By pressing the pin into the hole the springy material grips the hole tightly eliminating any slop. They are available in imperial and metric sizes in various lengths and the hole

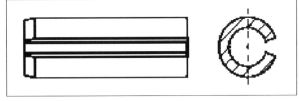

Fig 14.40: Detailed drawings of roll pins

required can be simply drilled with the correct size drill.

An alternative to a roll-pin is a taper dowel pin, this requires a hole to be drilled across the hub and shaft and then reamed to an exact taper. The pin is then pressed or driven into the hole. The taper pin is a high tensile material similar to 'silver steel'.

System Calculations

To show the importance of investigating the potential limiting factors we will now run through a typical set of calculations for the elevation main cross-shaft and wishbones for the proposed Indlebe-2 radio telescope. Firstly, we need an accurate estimate of the mass to be elevated through an arc. For the 7.5m diameter parabola with aluminium welded ribs and a wire mesh reflector we can deduce the following.

The mass of the ribs was calculated from the manufacturer's data of the aluminium tubing per metre length, the lengths being obtained from the drawing, the various tube lengths being added together and an extra 15% added for the welding filler.

Ribs = 5kg each x 16 = 80kg
Mesh = 40kg (approx)
Other mass = 20kg (feed horn, focussing mechanism and struts, receiver plus mounting hardware)

This is a total of ≈140kg and to allow for the various nuts, bolts, cabling etc we will round it up to 150kg.

The effective length of the Y shaped wishbones is 200mm between the shaft centre and the hub back plate. The front hub plate is spaced 200mm above the first so the effective radius is increased to 400mm.

The torque applied to the elevation shaft by the 150kg mass acting through a radius of 400mm is 150 x 0.4 = 60kgf-m. (To convert to Newton-metres we multiply by 9.81 = 588.6Nm). Since the two wishbones - shaft interfaces equally share the load then each has a load of ≈294Nm acting on them.

The 30mm elevation shaft, which is V-155 alloy steel, has a yield-strength of 900N/mm2 and a tensile strength of 1100 to 1400N/mm^2. (1N/m^2 = 1Pa and 1N/mm^2 = 1Mpa).

From the manufacturers data on the taper-lock bush (without a keyway) the slip-torque (to make the bush slip on the shaft) is 193Nm. (This is equivalent to a mass of 19.6kgf acting through a lever of 1m in length). For our effective lever of 400mm this rises to 49kgf per bush or a total of 98kgf, and since the total static load is 60kgf divided between the two bushes (30kgf per bush) this should be adequate. For the selected taper-lock bush it has an 8mm wide keyway. The data to calculate the torque to make the bush slip so that the key takes the full load is given by the formula:

Slip Torque with key =
Bush major diameter / shaft diameter x Average slip torque without a key.

The Fenner 1210 taper-lock bush has a major diameter of 47.5mm, so the torque to slip is increased to 305Nm. Since this is slightly more than the 294Nm calculated earlier the bush should not require the key to come into play. However, transient shock loads can exceed this value and the key will be required for an adequate safety factor.

The key is in shear and to calculate this effect we need to know the yield strength of the key material. C45 is a standard key material (alloy steel) with yield strength of about 900Mpa. Since this is the same as the shaft material both are equally loaded. A normal maximum safe load is generally taken to be 45% (0.45) of the yield strength, so the key and shaft are safe to 405MPa.

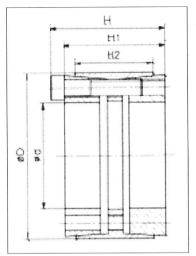

Fig 14.41: Fenlock 400 dimensions

The interface between the elevation shaft and the 38-tooth sprocket however carries the full torque load of 588Nm and a more substantial type of taper-lock device is required. The Fenner FenLock™ is a suitable choice. This is a self-centring type similar to the taper-lock hub but has two tapered interfaces, one expanding outwards to grip the bore of a hole and the other contracting inwards to grip the shaft. The 38-tooth sprocket chosen has a substantial hub and this can be bored out for the required depth to accommodate the FenLock™ device.

A suitable device is the FLK 400 series, for a 30mm diameter shaft it requires a 55mm bore in the sprocket (dimension D in the diagram) of a minimum of 40mm deep (dimension H1). This locking device requires no keyway and in this size it is rated to 891Nm of torque. The cones are closed by a ring of high tensile cap screws (six in the FLK 400 of M6 thread). It would also be a suitable device for the two wishbones if it were wished to standardise on a locking device, but would require suitable thick wall hollow tubes to be welded onto each wishbone. The advantage of the FenLock™ type is that no keyway is required in the shaft, saving a machining operation.

Indlebe-2 Proposed Radio Telescope Mechanics Design

The design of the azimuth and elevation was largely driven by what was to hand that could be utilised without having to purchase too many new components. (As the funding is limited and worm gear boxes are relatively expensive it was not possible to purchase all the parts new). Amongst the items the writer had collected over the years were two industrial worm gearboxes and several sprockets. The various windscreen wiper motors had been removed from scrap cars, donated or picked up for very little at mobile rallies and swap meets. The azimuth main-shaft and hub etc came from a friends scrap yard when he was breaking up an old Ford commercial vehicle that used a V8 engine.

Torque Measurement of the Motors

The specifications for the two Bosch wiper motors eluded all searching and so they were experimentally measured using a pulley and weight system to see if they were powerful enough. The average torque when run on 13.8V was found to be at least 10Nm on the low-speed winding and at least 25Nm on the high-speed winding. (This measurement without accurate torque gauges is a bit difficult and this figure being at the output shaft after the internal 60:1 worm drive. A second measurement, using a calibrated spring balance under locked-rotor condition, showed substantially more torque than the free-running measurements). Armed with this information the gear reduction to be used was largely easy to sort out.

Azimuth axis

Primary Gear Reduction: (131 tooth gear and 9 tooth pinion) = 14.555:1
Secondary Gear Reduction: 20:1 Crofts worm gearbox
Motor Gearbox: 60:1 worm gearbox
Motor Speed: 2-speed
Motor Type: Bosch 12V DC wiper motor Part No 0-390-346-138

Elevation axis

Primary Gear Reduction (38 tooth and 10 tooth sprockets): 3.8:1
Primary Drive: 20mm pitch duplex Renold chain, safe tension load = 61kN
Secondary Gear Reduction: 60:1 David Brown Radicon worm gearbox
Motor Gearbox: 60:1 worm gearbox plus 2.4:1 toothed belt pulleys
Motor Speed: 1-speed
Motor Type: Bosch 12V DC wiper motor Part No 0-390-692-054

Of the two worm gearboxes available one had a 20:1 step-down and the other 60:1, so it was logical to choose the second for the elevation portion as the mass to be lifted was a much greater effort than simply rotating the mass. Data on the 60:1 David Brown Radicon gearbox was obtained from the manufacturer that confirmed its suitability, the 20:1 gearbox manufacturer was no longer in business but by comparing the internals it was agreed that it was similarly rated. (The two gearboxes being almost exactly the same size was a good indication they were likely to be similar in performance). The 20:1 gearbox when opened showed severe wear to the output shaft ball bearings, it had been used for about 30 years driving an industrial concrete mixer with a 2HP motor (1.5kW) before being scrapped. Two new ball bearings and careful setting up of the gear meshing with the shims returned it to as new condition; the internal gearing showed very little signs of wear. The backlash on the output shaft was less than 2°. The final arrangement is listed in Table 14.1.

Output Torque

To calculate the torque available only requires the addition of the gear reduction and then to multiply by the motor torque measured. The elevation axis from the wiper motor to the final shaft has a reduction ratio of (2.4 x 60 x 3.8) = 547.2:1. Hence, with an input torque of 10Nm the final torque is 5,472Nm when free running. The torque under 'locked-rotor' condition can generally be taken to be about three to five-times the running torque, so the potential overload torque is 27,360Nm, which about 2,790kgf-m. Since the torque calculated earlier required to lift the 150kg mass of the antenna is ≈588 Nm, the gearing is quite under-rated for the task and has a generous safety factor.

The azimuth axis can be calculated in the same manner. The total reduction in the gearing is (20 x 14.555) = 291.1:1. For an input torque of 10Nm the output torque is 2,911Nm = 296kgf-m when free running and about 1,480kgf-m under locked-rotor condition.

The elevation axis is the most critical and the duplex chain used has a safe tension load of 61kN, which is about 6,200kgf (≈6-tonne). As this is about twice the locked-rotor torque the gearing can generate it should be very unlikely to break. The manufacturer's data gives a breaking figure of greater than 8,000kgf.

An alternative to Bosch wiper motors is the range of DC worm drive motors made by Transmotec Sweden AB. The nearest motor to the ones used is the WLD-70107, a motor with a 65:1 step-down worm gear that has an output torque of 138.1 kgf-cm.

Fig 14.42: WLD-7017 worm drive from Transmotec

To convert to Nm we divide the torque figure by 100, (as there are 100 centimetres in a metre), and then multiply by 9.81. The figure for this motor-gearbox is hence 13.5Nm, which agrees closely with the measured figures on the Bosch motors. This range is available in 12V and 24V versions.

CAD ANALYSIS OF THE STRUCTURE

The initial calculations took place before the mechanical engineering faculty at Durban University of Technology (DUT) performed a critical stress analysis of the major parts to confirm the soundness of the proposed design. Up to this point in the design the calculations had been based on first principles, however with the CAD analysis completed a slightly different picture was presented. The calculated mass of the parabola had neglected the central support hub, as it was an unknown at the time. The designed central hub is a heavy-duty steel plate construction. The pendulum effect of the feed horn also added extra torque to the elevation axis. (The estimated mass of the feed horn assembly with all the receiver components etc is about 8kg, the radius being about 4.2m, gives an additional torque loading of ≈33kgf-m = 323Nm).

Using the CAD software the 'mass balance point' of the antenna was found to be closer to 600mm rather than the assumed 400mm used in the initial calculations. This is due to the distributed mass in the ribs and mesh being a distance offset vertically from the central hub and acting through the radius of the ribs on the central hub. The additional mass and the feed horn pendulum effect increased the torque loading on the elevation shaft to ≈1,200Nm and required a rethink of the shaft-wishbone interface required. The effective total mass had increased to about 200kg and this acting at an effective length of 600mm gave the new figure for the torque, 200kg x 0.6m = 120kgf-m x 9.81 = 1177Nm. The load on each wishbone-shaft interface is hence now ≈600Nm as the load is shared equally between the two. The FLK 400 is safe to ≈900Nm so the load factor is about 66% per interface, which should be acceptable.

This exercise showed the importance of a careful analysis of the structure performed by a competent person, and someone re-checking the details! In the event the shaft–wishbone interface needed to be modified to utilise the FenLock™ FLK 400 locking devices and the 38-tooth sprocket would be arc welded on both sides to the elevation main shaft. Fortunately no parts had been made at this point so no material was scrapped and only minor details needed to be changed on the CAD drawing before the final manufacturing drawings were generated.

The available torque of the elevation gear reduction is about 5,000Nm, so it was still lightly loaded even with the new increased torque figure. The torque required by the secondary elevation shaft is hence about 320Nm, (1200Nm / 3.8 = 315.8Nm) which is a fraction of the capability of the Radicon worm gearbox of ≈1,500Nm.

Bottom Support Assembly

One other design change was made to the round supporting tube. The tube if made in one piece would have a total mass of about 375kg. As this may be a problem to assemble on site the decision was made to make this item in two pieces of 2.8m in length with circular flanges with gusset plates welded to each piece, these will then be bolted together on site. The bottom section with the base plate can then be fitted onto the concrete foundation base and adjusted with the jacking nuts on the holding down bolts to ensure it was truly vertical. The eight holding down bolts cast in the concrete foundation block will be 24mm diameter high tensile hook bolts with a nut and washer placed on each bolt. Thereafter the bottom section can be placed and further washers and nuts fitted. To adjust the bottom section to be truly vertical the nuts are adjusted to level the structure and finally tightened to the required torque. This leaves the bottom flange about 40mm clear of the concrete block so reducing corrosion potential from water. The picture of the Hart RAO 6m antenna (Fig 14.2) shows the method used. Thereafter the top section can be lifted into place and attached. The square tower section containing all the azimuth and elevation mechanics is finally lifted and bolted in place. Provision was made to erect a temporary gin-pole structure so that the top tower section and then the finished parabolic antenna could be lifted with a block and tackle hoist and fitted onto the mounting plate. It was important to plan carefully how the structure would be be assembled on site with limited lifting apparatus.

Fabrication of Piece Parts

In the design of the new DUT radio telescope extensive use will be made of laser cut pieces from standard steel plate. This is a cost-effective method to generate accurate complex shapes, however some wastage of material occurs if the shape to be cut is very complex. An alternative to laser cutting is water-jet cutting; this is offered by many engineering facilities and offers a cleaner cut that laser. Laser and water-jet cutting is currently limited to about 20mm thick plate but provides a far smoother cut surface than that of oxy-acetylene profile cutting, which however can cope with thicker sections. Oxy-acetylene cut surfaces often need much fettling to provide a clean surface and some distortion is possible due to the high temperatures involved. Oxy-acetylene and laser cutting can cause a change in the material property making for a weaker final product, water-jet cutting as it is performed with the material immersed in a tank of water causes no distortion. For profiled parts that will be later arc-welded together the rough surface of oxy-acetylene cutting can however be a benefit as some clearance is needed between parts to be welded together to allow adequate penetration of the weld fillet from the filler rod.

One nice feature of laser cutting is that holes that are too small to cut accurately do not have to be cut, a small dimple, similar to a centre-pop punch mark can be formed for later drilling. The accuracy of laser 'spotting' of holes can be held to better than 0.1mm, which is far better than marking out by hand from a drawing.

Facts About Fasteners

A fastener is an item that serves to attach two pieces together, such as two over-lapped plates. Common fasteners are rivets, self-tapping screws and nuts and bolts. Nuts and bolts for attaching various items together are common items used by amateurs. Most amateurs have little knowledge of the correct types to use for some applications. There is a standard marking method that identifies the tensile strength of bolts and nuts. For non-critical applications a common bolt and nut purchased at the local hardware store will normally suffice, but what about critical applications?

A typical critical application is antenna towers; antenna mounting and hold-ing down bolts set in the concrete base. If the wrong type is used there is a potential disaster waiting to happen!

The material it is made from determines the ultimate tensile strength of a bolt. For a bolt and nut to hold two items firmly together the bolt needs to be stressed so that it elongates slightly, like a spring. Modern automobile design uses spe-cial 'stretch-bolts' to attain the necessary clamping pressure for the cylinder head to block interface. It is the stretching of the fastener that causes the clamp-ing pressure to the items to be secured. With sufficient clamping pressure the friction generated when you try to turn one part relative to another resists the turning effort.

Common or garden bolts bought from the local hardware store usually have no marking on them but most professional isometric bolt manufacturers use a num-bering system to identify the bolt material. The lowest grade bolt will have a code stamped on the head such as 4.6 or 4.8. The first digit gives the tensile strength of the material in hundreds of Mega-Pascals (MPa). The second digit after the decimal point gives the maximum safe elongation relative to the tensile strength. Hence, a bolt stamped 4.8 means 400 MPa and a safe tensile load of 80% or 320 MPa. These are the lowest grade bolts marked. The manufacturer's name or logo is shown in the picture and the grade below. These are normally raised lettering and not recessed. *Note that American bolts use a different marking system than isometric bolts, which will not be considered here.*

For critical applications a higher tensile strength bolt is required. For exam-ple, seat belt attachment bolts are required to be a minimum of 8.8 grade. This is a maximum tensile strength of 800 MPa and safe up to 640 MPa when torqued up. Critical items, such as suspension and brake caliper attachments, require much higher tensile strength bolts. For example, connecting rod cap bolts are often 12.9 grade. Aircraft grade bolts start at 10.9 and go up to 12.9. Tower holding down bolts should be a minimum of 10.9 grade and adequately sized for the intended stress under tension.

As well as the tensile strength the shear strength rating need to be carefully considered. Shear is what happens when you use a pair of scissors to cut paper, the blades press into the paper and generate a weakened area. In some applications shear strength is more important than tensile strength. A pair of pipes connected with a bolt passing through both pipes as in an antenna rotator system places the bolt in shear.

> Note that a bolt and a screw are different. A bolt has a plain un-threaded portion between the head and the threaded portion. A screw is threaded all the way up to the head.

14.43: Some unscrupulous sell-ers of bolts stamp the blank bolt head with punches, which produces an indented type. These bolts are hence suspect as they may be lower tensile strength passed off as high-er grade types, so beware when you purchase this type

A common mistake is to utilise stainless steel bolts because they are resistant to corrosion. This can be a dangerous assumption as there are several different stainless steel grades used for bolts and nuts. EN302 is a corrosion resistant material and EN316 is a material resistant to acids and alkali. EN316 was developed for things like attaching lugs to battery terminals that require little tensile strength. A bolt made from EN302 is marked A2 and one made from EN316 is marked A6. The problem with stainless steel is that the tensile strength is lower than normal steel bolts. A2 bolts are about 60% of the tensile strength of 4.8 grade and A6 bolts are only about 40% of a 4.8 grade bolt.

If you must use stainless steel in critical applications it is essential to increase the bolt diameter by at least 25%.

Hence, if the normal bolt is 8mm then an A2 bolt will need to be 10mm or larger to be comparable. It is the carbon content in normal steel bolts that gives it greater tensile strength, stainless steel fasteners have little or no carbon and hence have inferior tensile strength.

Another problem with stainless steel fasteners is that the material does not slide easily on another piece of stainless steel and often the threads "pick-up" or seize. This is known as 'galling' and is a serious problem as once the bolt and nut have seized they are impossible to undo without snapping the bolt. When trying a nut on a stainless steel bolt by hand it often feels as if there is a gritty substance between them and they are stiff to turn. In such a case it is advisable to run a tap through the nut and a die along the bolt to clean up any whiskers formed when the parts were made. Many modern bolts are not cut with a threading die as in the older days; the thread is formed under immense pressure by a thread rolling process. Although rolled threads have superior tensile strength to die cut threads this leaves the bolt thread slightly tri-lobular and hence not perfectly round which aggravates the galling problem. The mass production of bolts and screws today uses a process known as 'cold heading'; the bar stock used is the same as the finished diameter of the bolt. Squeezing the end into a die, the material flows under the immense pressure to form the head. This gives greater strength and reduces the wastage of machining it from hexagonal bar stock.

Another problem with stainless steel fasteners is that to obtain the same tensile load when tightening the bolt or nut requires about twice the torque as a conventional high tensile bolt. Stainless steel bolts and nuts must be used with an anti-seize compound (Copper-Slip compound) or oil or grease to reduce the torque required to achieve the same tension. Common black high tensile bolts and nuts are heat treated and then quenched in oil, this produces the black surface finish and the bolt and nut is naturally oily and requires less torque to obtain the required tension. No matter what grade of bolt is used it should never be torqued up dry, always use oil or anti-seize compound. Another important consideration is the use of flat washers under the bolt head and the nut to reduce friction when torqueing up the joint.

Cap screws (known as Allen screws) are normally grade 10.9 or 12.9 and are normally black. Other types made in stainless steel are shiny and have the marking A2 or A6 depending on the material used.

Common surface treatment of lower grade bolts is zinc plating, often done by electroplating or cadmium plating which has a golden colour. These reduce the safe tensile load rating by about 2 to 5 %.

Hart RAO KAT Demonstrator Antenna

T he Hartebeesthoek Radio Astronomy (Hart RAO) facility is the base for the South African bid for the Square Kilometre Array (SKA). The design and construction of the first prototype array (XDM – experimental development model) commenced in 2007. This design is a radical new method to manufacture radio telescope parabolic antennas using mass production techniques and a considerable cost saving to conventional methods. The diameter of the parabola is 15m and eventually about 100 antennas will be sited in the Western Cape Karoo near Carnavon. At present (April 2010) 7 systems have been assembled at the SKA site and four have been commissioned and coupled as an interferometer. The mould for the KAT dishes has been assembled on site to make the dishes, which have been reduced in size to 12m diameter.

Although the method is probably not applicable to amateurs it could be scaled in size for a smaller antenna.

The parabola manufacture starts with a mould made up from carbon fibre segments with a high accuracy. This was assembled at Hart RAO adjacent to the site of the support tower.

After the mould has been assembled and checked for accuracy the outer surface is coated with a release agent to prevent the subsequent layers from adhering to it. The second phase is the spraying of primer paint to the mould. This will eventually be the surface of the finished dish.

> Note that all the pictures presented in this chapter are copyright of Hart RAO and are used with their permission.

Fig A1.1: Assembly of the dish mould from segments

Fig A1.2: The mould is sprayed with the primer coat

The joints between the segments are covered with masking tape to prevent ingress of paint. The platform runs on rollers on the edge of the mould and the operator's assistants move the platform in a circular path to allow consistent coating. The pivot point is the centre of the dish mould.

The next phase is the reflecting coating. This is aluminium sprayed on using a plasma metal spraying technique. The aluminium wire is fed into the gun and a thin coating applied to the surface.

The bulk of the dish is a resin and glass-fibre composite with honeycomb material to give high strength but low weight. When this has cured, the backing structure is attached. The backing structure is a fabricated steel structure that attaches to the rear of the antenna. This is an X shaped structure that also carries the declination (elevation) gear rack. The curve fits the back of the dish exactly. The studs visible below the declination rack are for the counterweights to balance the antenna. Visible below the studs are the two mounting pads that bolt to the declination shaft assembly.

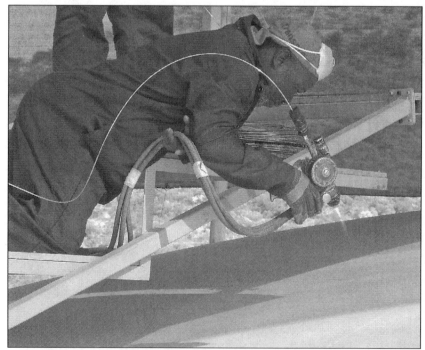

Fig A1.3: Applying the aluminium coating to the surface

Fig A1.4: Backing structure with declination rack

Fig A1.5: Placing the backing structure onto the finished dish

Fig A1.6: Lifting the finished dish from the mould. The support tower and yoke are seen in the foreground

When the backing structure has been correctly positioned on the dish it is bonded in place with a high strength industrial epoxy adhesive. The holes visible near the end of the strut accept bolts that pass through the dish and attach to the feed horn quadripod legs.

The next operation is to attach the dish to the support tower elevation shaft yoke. This is a tricky operation and required great care to prevent damage.

Fig A1.7: Lifting the finished dish ready for mounting on the support tower. The person in the foreground is Dr Justin Jonas, Director of Hart RAO

Fig A1.8: The finished dish with the backing support ready for attachment to the support tower

Fig A1.9: The antenna in position and the yoke attached. One of the bearings for the shaft that the antenna pivots on is visible. The declination rack engages with the pinion below for elevation

Fig A1.10: Drawing showing the attachment of the antenna to the declination shaft. The antenna can be elevated through 180° with the quadrant gear rack.

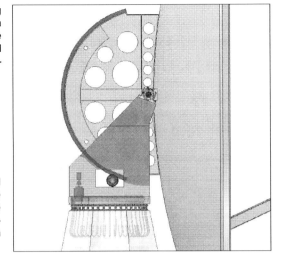

(below) Fig A1.11: KAT XDM with the ex NASA Space Tracking 26m antenna in the background. The counterweights have not been fitted in this picture

Fig A1.12: Close up view of the 12GHz 7 feed horn assembly. In this view only two feed horns are in place, the other positions have protective covers fitted. The centre horn is on the dish central axis giving an 'on-sky' beam and the second is offset for 'off-sky' calibration tests. The feed is rotated with a motor for exploring the dish surface for any errors in profile. The quadripod feed mount is fabricated from aluminium sections welded together to reduce the weight.

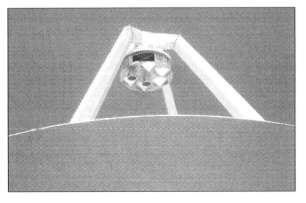

(above) Fig A1.13: Attaching the feed horn to the quadripod support arms. Visible next to the declination rack are the counterweight blocks

(above) Fig A1.14: Celebrations after the first object was acquired with the XDM ('first-light'). The marks on the dish surface are calibration pads for checking the surface accuracy optically

(below) Fig A1.16: The South African SKA site with seven MeerKats completed

(above) Fig A1.15: Artist's impression of what the proposed SKA array will look like when completed. The parabolic antennas encircle the large flat plate phased array for the lower frequencies

Further Information

BOOKS

The Evolution of Radio Astronomy, **James Stanley Hey.**

Science History Publications, New York, 1973, ISBN 0 88202 027 7
This book is now out of print, but second hand copies can often be often
obtained via the usual specialist booksellers on the Internet, although they are
expensive due to the very limited publication.

Radio Astronomy, **Dr John D Kraus, W8JK**

McGraw-Hill, 1966 ISBN 0 07035392 1
This book is now out of print, but early edition second hand copies can be often
obtained via the usual specialist booksellers on the Internet. Again not inexpensive for a well cared for copy but worth buying if possible. Current secondhand
price about $70-00.

Astronomer by Chance, **Dr A C B Lovell**

Oxford University Press 1992, ISBN 0 19 282949 1
An excellent read covering not only the history of Jodrell Bank in considerable
detail but also Lovell's wartime work on radar systems. Of the various books by
Lovell probably the best one to purchase as it contains the first two books information, albeit in a shortened form. Unfortunately the paperback version does
not contain any pictures.

The History of Jodrell Bank, **Dr A C B Lovell**

Lovell's first book tracing the early history and the dramas surrounding the
building of the Mk1 antenna.

Out of the Zenith, **Dr A C B Lovell**

Oxford University Press, 1973. ISBN 0 1927624 2
Lovell's second book covering the period between the Mk1 completion and the
later years.

Radar Handbook, **Merrill I Skolnik**

McGraw-Hill, 2nd Edition 1990. ISBN 0 07057913 X
The definitive textbook on radar. Although quite heavy in places with complex
formulae the section on radio astronomy is a must read. The earlier editions are
the best to look for as the later versions omit much of the historical details. Also
by the same author is a student soft back version that contains an abridged version of much of the original book.

Antenna Engineering Handbook, Henry Jasik

McGraw-Hill. No ISBN available.
The definitive textbook on all types of antennas. Also contains a complete chapter by Dr John D Kraus, W8JK, on Radio Astronomy which is a must read. The best edition is the first, published in 1961 although these are now very scarce and expensive. The second edition was edited by Richard C Johnson in 1993 and omits some of the earlier historical details.

Comet, Carl Sagan & Ann Druyan

Random House, 1st edition 1985. ISBN 0 39454908 2
A very comprehensive book on comets, meteors and asteroids. Amply illustrated and in an easy to read format. Aimed more at the younger reader but containing a host of information for amateurs interested in meteor scatter and meteor radar experiments.

International Microwave Handbook, edited by Andy Barter, G8ATD

RSGB, 2002. ISBN 9781 9050 8644 3
A lot of useful information although not specifically intended for radio astronomy.

VHF/UHF Handbook, edited by Andy Barter, G8ATD

RSGB, 2007. ISBN 9781 9050 8631 3
A host of constructional details for equipment that can be adapted for radio astronomy purposes.

Planets, Stars and Galaxies, A E Fanning

Dover Publications, INC, New York, 1966. ISBN 0 486 21680 2
An excellent primer in basic astronomy details.

WEBSITES

There are so many that it is impossible to list every one, but the ones shown are good starting points.

Radio Astronomy Observatories

Jodrell Bank - *http://www.jb.man.ac.uk*
The home page contains the normal navigation tools to find the section you require. Of particular interest is the 'Jodrell Bank Live' section where you can look at the various telescope details in real time. The seven telescopes making up the MERLIN system are shown with the current antenna positions and front end amplifier status.

Parkes Radio Telescope, Sydney, Australia - *http://www.parkes.atnf.csiro.au*
Another interesting website with a lot of good information. If you can, download the animated videos and also look at the real time streaming video camera shots taken from the dish. Watch out for the kangaroos!
Max Planck Observatory, Bonn, Germany - *http://www.mpifr-bonn.mpg.de*
Some excellent diagrams of how radio telescope receivers work.

National Radio Astronomy Observatory (NRAO) USA - *http://www.nrao.edu*
There are several remote sites linked to the main one at Greenbank, Virginia.

The VLA (Very Large Array) in Socorro, New Mexico was featured in the film 'Contact' and consists of 27 dishes each of 25m diameter.

Arecibo Observatory, Peurto Rico - *http://www.naic.edu*
The very large fixed dish operated by Cornell University pioneered much of the recent work on meteors and deep space objects. Also featured in the film "Contact".

Hart RAO, South Africa - *http://www.hartrao.ac.za*
My local radio astronomy observatory situated at Hartebeesthoek, near Johannesburg. Originally built by NASA as a space tracking station for the Apollo moon program today it is operated under the National Research Foundation (NRF). Although only a small dish the work is of international importance.

British Astronomical Association Radio Astronomy Group (BAARAG) - *http://www.britastro.org/radio/*
This is mainly radio amateurs who have an interest in the practical side of the science.

Related Topics

Antennas - *http://www.w1ghz.org*
The website by Paul Wade, W1GHZ, is an excellent source of information on parabolic antennas and feed horns. W1GHZ is probably the leading amateur authority on dishes and feeds; if you can't find it here it probably hasn't been invented yet! Many of the articles are reprints from ARRL publications written by Paul Wade. See the sad story of Dr John D Kraus's, W8JK, big telescope which was demolished in 1997 to build a golf course!

Magazines - *http://www.vhfcomm.co.uk*
The popular English version of *UKW-Berichte* is *VHF Communications* edited by Andy Barter, G8ATD. Lots of good stuff for VHF, UHF and microwave amateurs.

SETI League - *http://www.setileague.org*
There seems to be as many websites for SETI as most other topics, but this is the best place to start. There is a wealth of information on equipment and software for controlling radios.

Software - *http://www.radiosky.com*
Computer software to track objects are few and far between. One of the best I have come across is Radio-Eyes written by Jim Sky. You can download a free 30-day trial version here. If you wish to purchase a licensed copy it can be done online.

Index